SUPER GREAT

BRAIN BOOSTERS

Richard Manchester

BRISTOL
PARK
BOOKS

Visit www.pennydellpuzzles.com for more great puzzles

Originally published as *Colossal Grab A Pencil Book of
Brain Boosters*

First Bristol Park Books edition published in 2015

Bristol Park Books
252 W. 38th Street
NYC, NY 10018

Bristol Park Books is a registered trademark of Bristol Park
Books, Inc.

Published by arrangement with Penny Publications LLC

ISBN: 978-0-88486-652-7

Printed in the United States of America

Contents

PUZZLES

IN THE ABSTRACT

VISUAL ♦ SPATIAL

Fill in each section with one of the four symbols so no sections containing the same symbol touch. Four sections are already complete.

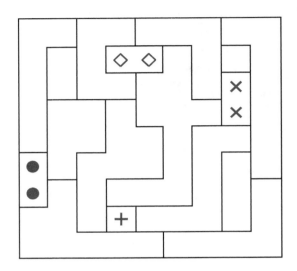

● ✚ ✕ ◇

CODE WORD

DECODING

Decipher a quip and the Code Word's ten letters, represented by the numbers 1 through 10. For example, if the Code Word were "FORMULATES," 1 in the quip would be F, 2 would be O, etc.

$$\overline{1}\ \overline{2}\ \overline{3}\ \overline{4}\ \overline{5}\ \overline{6}\ \overline{7}\ \overline{8}\ \overline{9}\ \overline{10}$$

4 6 L 6 V 3 8 3 9 10   1 3 L L   10 6 V 6 7

C 9 M 5 L 6 4 6 L Y   7 6 5 L 2 C 6   4 H 6

10 6 1 8 5 2 5 6 7   8 3 10 C 6   10 9   9 10 6

C 2 10   8 1 2 4   2   F L Y   1 3 4 H   3 4.

8

WHAT'S YOUR NUMBER?

WEEK 1

Can you figure out the relationship of the numbers in the first three rectangles and, based on that, what missing number goes into the space with the question mark?

2
18

20
54

7
28

?
34

RELATIONSHIPS QUIZ

KENNEL is to DOG as STY is to PIG because a DOG lives in a kennel and a PIG lives in a STY. Each of these statements is a relationship of some kind. Can you select the right word from the four following each?

1. EGG is to CARTON as SODA is to _____ .
   (a) cola   (b) straw   (c) bottle   (d) lunch

2. LOOK is to LEEK as FOOL is to _____ .
   (a) lake   (b) file   (c) lock   (d) feel

3. FEBRUARY is to AUGUST as APRIL is to _____ .
   (a) September   (b) October   (c) November   (d) December

4. OLD is to YOUNG as GOOD is to _____ .
   (a) bad   (b) satisfactory   (c) best   (d) ancient

5. GEORGE is to LAURA as DWIGHT is to _____ .
   (a) Laura   (b) Mamie   (c) Martha   (d) Hillary

6. CLOCK is to MINUTE as ODOMETER is to _____ .
   (a) car   (b) gas   (c) mile   (d) speed

MAGNIFIND

Figure out which areas of the drawing have been enlarged.

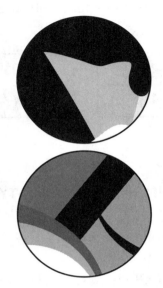

EASY PICKINGS

To solve, simply cross out one letter in each pair. When the puzzle is completed correctly, the remaining letters will spell out a fact.

"FT HV RE   AS GU NA   NA LG SI OR

RL VI SN CE XS"   LW NA SW

WT RH EI TN AT TE HN   BG YK

DE RG EN AE NS TA

EH RE MG VI NX GQ WI DA BY.

VISUAL ◆ SPATIAL

To solve this puzzle, write down the three letters that describe each triangle (a figure with three sides) here. We found 13 triangles; how many can you locate?

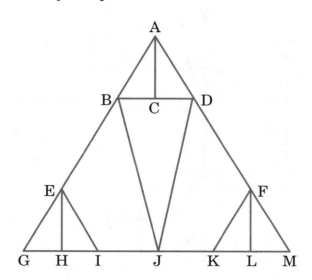

LANGUAGE

ANTONYMS QUIZ

An antonym is a word that is opposite in meaning to another word; for example, "cold" is the antonym of "hot." One of the words following each capitalized word is the antonym of that word.

1. SPURN   a. split   b. welcome   c. scorch

2. CAUSTIC   a. soothing   b. lofty   c. obsolete

3. IMPETUS   a. hindrance   b. conjecture   c. foundation

4. MELANGE   a. duration   b. industry   c. singularity

5. INFIRM   a. basic   b. healthy   c. stagnant

6. CONVIVIAL   a. solemn   b. exhausted   c. prying

7. DIFFIDENT   a. sturdy   b. innocent   c. bold

8. OBSCURE   a. clear   b. persuade   c. sustain

SUDOKU

LOGIC

Place a number into each box so each row across, column down, and small 9-box square within the larger square (there are 9 of these) contains 1 through 9.

			7	4				
8		2	1		6	7		
3	4					6	9	1
6			8		7	1	3	
5								7
	3	9	6		2			5
4	5	1					7	6
		3	5		1	9		8
				7	4			

TRI, TRI AGAIN

LANGUAGE ◆ SPATIAL

Fit the nine triangles into the big one so six everyday words are spelled out reading across the arrows. Do not rotate the triangles.

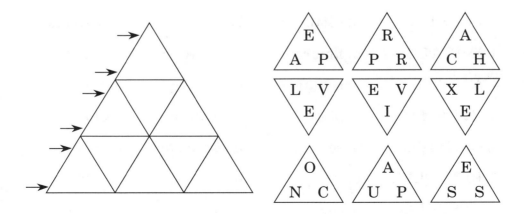

TIPS OF THE ICEBERG

WEEK 1

The chart shows the gratuities each waiter or waitress earned on a recent breakfast shift at the Iceberg Diner. All you have to do is some careful addition and then answer the following questions:

1. Who made the most in total tips?
2. Who made the least?
3. Which two waitpersons made exactly the same amount?

EMPLOYEE	TIP 1	TIP 2	TIP 3	TIP 4	TIP 5
Al	$1.00	$1.10	$1.35	$0.95	$1.05
Brenda	$0.75	$2.70	$0.10	$0.90	$1.55
Charlie	$1.65	$1.10	$1.40	$1.00	$0.70
Dena	$1.00	$0.10	$0.65	$2.20	$1.00
Ed	$0.75	$0.10	$0.90	$0.90	$0.90
Flora	$1.00	$1.40	$0.90	$0.65	$1.00
Greta	$0.75	$0.05	$0.95	$0.90	$0.75

COUNTDOWN

VISUAL

Following the connecting lines, find the only route in this grid that passes through the numbers backward from 9 to 1 consecutively.

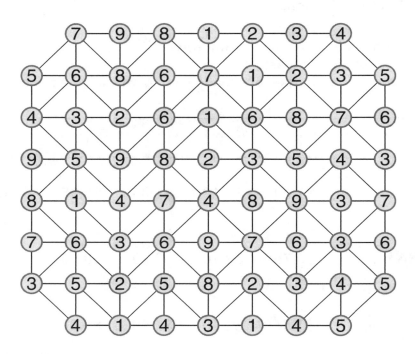

SYMBOL-ISM

DECODING

This is simply a Cryptogram that uses symbols instead of letters to spell out a truism. Each symbol stands for the same letter throughout. For this puzzle, we've already indicated that ✪ = T and 🎲 = P.

ROUND TRIP

When this puzzle has been completed correctly, you will have made a round trip through its set of dots. You must visit every dot exactly once, make no diagonal moves, and return to your starting point. Parts of the right path are shown; can you find the rest?

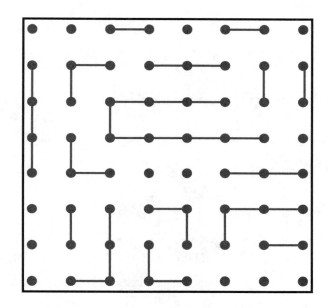

MATH

FUN WITH FACTS AND FIGURES

This puzzle tests you on several little facts and figures. Solve the quiz in the order given since each answer is used in the next statement. There are no fractions used here.

1. Take the number of fingers on the human body and multiply by the value of the Roman numeral VI. _____

2. Next, divide by the number of months in the year. _____

3. Now, add the number of singers in six quartets. _____

4. Subtract the number of letters in the name of the state that contains El Paso and Dallas. _____

5. Add the number that sounds like the past tense of the verb "win." _____

Our answer is the number of cents in five nickels. *Is yours?*

ANAGRAM MAZE

LANGUAGE ◆ VISUAL

The diagram contains 36 words, 19 of which are anagrams of other everyday words. Start at the top arrow and anagram HEAR. While solving, move up, down, right, or left to the only adjacent word that can be anagrammed. Continue until you arrive at the bottom arrow. There is only one path through the maze.

1 HEAR	2 KNOW	3 FLEE	4 LACY	5 PEAT	6 UNDO
7 RIFE	8 COLA	9 SWAP	10 TINY	11 FATS	12 MICE
13 TERM	14 CELL	15 FOUL	16 BUSH	17 MILE	18 PIGS
19 WISH	20 BEAK	21 VEIN	22 LAST	23 CLAP	24 FULL
25 CLIP	26 BRAN	27 MILL	28 BANG	29 LOOK	30 BODY
31 AFAR	32 ABLE	33 RIPE	34 LIFE	35 EGOS	36 OWLS

ALL IN A ROW

MATH

Which row contains the most groups of consecutive numbers adding up to 11? Look carefully, because some groups may overlap. We've underlined an example of a group in each row to start you off.

A. 7 3 1 3 3 4 8 2 2 2 2 2 1 7 7 3 2 <u>1 5 5</u> 5 9 6 2

B. 5 1 1 1 1 6 <u>2 2 5 2</u> 8 6 2 1 3 1 2 1 9 1 7 7 9 2

C. 6 1 1 1 8 5 4 4 2 1 7 <u>7 1 3</u> 9 5 6 2 2 1 3 7 5 1

16

JACK IN THE BOX

Circle every letter in the box that is directly under a J, A, C, or K. When completed correctly, the circled letters, when read from top to bottom, will spell out a 7-letter word.

V	B	X	J	I	V	P	E	S	L	S	B
O	G	T	D	O	G	I	S	K	P	V	E
W	I	Q	F	A	E	T	R	R	O	H	T
N	L	O	U	I	K	R	E	D	N	U	U
E	M	P	L	S	Z	W	O	B	C	W	L
H	N	L	N	V	U	X	O	T	Z	A	O
O	J	M	O	Q	O	D	V	D	D	L	E
Z	E	E	P	S	Z	F	P	U	W	U	B

THE LINEUP

While scrutinizing this lineup of letters, can you answer the questions correctly in five minutes or less?

IJFPEXAMLOBEMARGUMENTVSQUEEZEHYKNOWD

1. Which letter of the alphabet does not appear in the lineup? _____

2. What 7-letter word — with its letters in correct order and appearing together — can you find in the lineup? _____

3. Which letter of the alphabet appears exactly three times in the lineup? _____

4. What 8-letter word — with its letters in correct order and appearing together — can you find in the lineup? _____

5. Other than the answers to Questions 2 and 4, how many everyday words — with their letters in correct order and appearing together — of four or more letters can you find in the lineup? _____

COUNT TO TEN

VISUAL ◆ MATH

Examine the items and then answer these questions: 1. Which row contains the most gloves? 2. Which row contains the most boots? 3. Which row contains an equal number of gloves and boots?

1.
2.
3.
4.
5.
6.
7.
8.
9.
10.

WAYWORDS

LANGUAGE

An 8-word thought can be found beginning with the word THE. Then, move to any adjacent box up, down, or diagonally for each following word.

QUEST	VANITY	SHINING	PRICE
TREATMENT	BY	THE	ON
NOTHING	SUN	WISEST	ALL
LOSES	PEOPLE	APPEAR	JUSTICE

18

GRAND TOUR

WEEK 2

Form a continuous chain of 5-letter words moving through the maze from START to FINISH. The second part of one word becomes the first part of the next word. This puzzle starts with MO-LAR-VA (molar, larva).

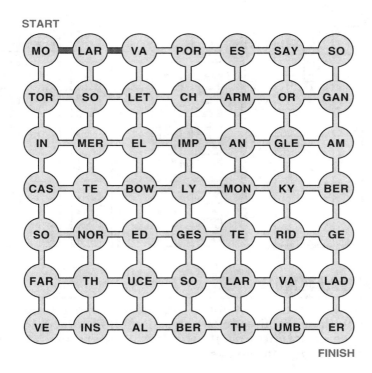

START

FINISH

BLOCK PARTY

Study the different views of the block, and draw what should appear on the face that has a question mark.

  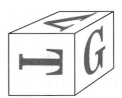 

LOOSE TILE

VISUAL ◆ SPATIAL

The tray on the left seemed the ideal place to store the set of loose dominoes. Unfortunately, when the tray was full, one domino was left over. Determine the arrangement of the dominoes in the tray and which is the Loose Tile.

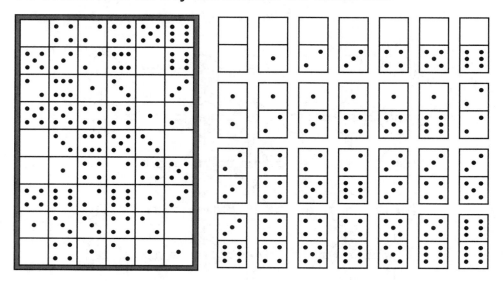

ASSOCIATIONS

LANGUAGE

You'll find eight groups of three words that can be associated in some way with each other (example: mantel, fireplace, logs). Cross out each group as you find it. The initial letters of the remaining words will spell out the answer to the riddle:

WHAT DID THE ICE CREAM SAY TO THE NUTS?

AGITATE HEROIC BLUE ENGINE CAKE ROMANCE

CARDINAL DARK ELEVATE DISTURB CANOPY

ENERGY RED OVAL BISHOP GLOOMY MATH COOKIE

ELEPHANT FIELD FORCE SANITY TRACT TART

TRUCE FINLAND HAPPY PRIEST ENVELOPE VIGOR

FALSE SHAKE UPSTAGE SWEDEN DESTINY GREEN

GALVANIZE PLOT NORWAY ENCHILADA SOMBER

HEXAGON HUNT

In this diagram of six-sided figures, there are ten "special" hexagons. These ten are special because the six numbers around each one are all different from each other and the center. We've circled one of the ten. Can you find the other nine?

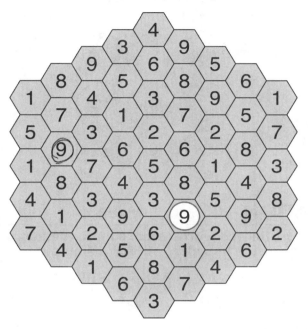

SLIDE RULE

Slide each column of letters up or down in the box and form as many everyday 3-letter words as you can in the windows where SAT is now. We formed 34 words, including SAT.

Your list of words:

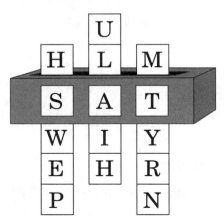

21

CIRCLE SEARCH
LANGUAGE

Move from circle to adjoining circle, horizontally and vertically only, to form 13 common, everyday words of at least three letters. Don't change the order of the letters in the circles that contain more than one letter. Proper names are not allowed.

ELIMINATION
LANGUAGE

Cross off the capitalized words according to the instructions given. The remaining words, in order, will form a quip.

SHY BULL A DRAGON PAINT BROTH PRY CLOSED
LOVE THE MOUTH PARADISE CONSOMME WILL
RADICAL STOP NIGH GATHER SIGHT TOWN EYE
NO BOUILLON FALL FEET ADROIT RED

Eliminate…

1. the three words that are types of soups.

2. the two words that complete the following to form a phrase:
   — at first —

3. the three words that can follow "pit."

4. the word that sounds like two gambling cubes.

5. the four words that form a phrase that means "employ an oil- or water-based vermilion pigment to a locality."

6. the four words that rhyme with each other.

7. the three words that begin with the same three letters (in any order).

WORD WHEEL

WEEK 3

Starting with the "M" at the arrow, see how many everyday words of three or more letters you can find going clockwise. Don't skip over any letters. For example, if you saw the letters C, A, R, E, D, you would form five words: CAR, CARE, CARED, ARE, and RED. We found 30 words.

KEEP ON MOVING

The goal is to move from the shaded square to the asterisk. Since the shaded square contains the number 3, you must move three squares up, down, left, or right, but not diagonally. In the new square will be another number; move that number of squares up, down, left, or right, continuing in this way until you reach the asterisk. It's okay to cross your own path.

4	5	3	3	1	2
1	2	2	*	4	2
2	2	3	3	3	5
4	3	2	1	2	3
2	4	4	1	4	3
5	2	1	5	1	2

TARGET SHOOT

LANGUAGE

Find the two letters which, when entered into the center circle of each target, will form three 6-letter words reading across.

1.

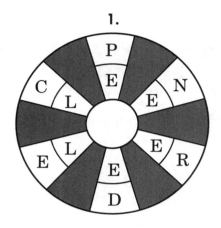

2.

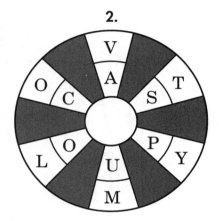

DOVETAILED WORDS

LANGUAGE

Two related words, with their letters in the correct order, are combined in each row of letters. Can you find both words? In a line like POTEORDRLEIER, or POteOrDrLEier, you can see the two words POODLE and TERRIER.

1. A B R D I O B E C K _____ _____

2. S C I Q U A R R C L E E _____ _____

3. L S A U T G C G H A G E E L _____ _____

4. S W H H I O S U P E T R _____ _____

5. H S O O C C C K E E R Y _____ _____

6. F O F I R F T T Y Y _____ _____

24

NEXT TO NOTHING

In the first row below, the A is next to the number zero, and the W is next to the letter O. First, circle all of the letters next to zeroes. Next, scramble the circled letters to spell out the name of a creature.

A0	WO	HO	SO
L0	YO	VO	E0
FO	BO	I0	DO
ZO	P0	RO	MO
KO	QO	UO	GO
XO	C0	N0	JO

MATH

SQUARE ROUTE

Travel from Start to Finish by moving from one square to an adjacent one if the two answers to the arithmetic problems are equal OR if the two operations (addition, subtraction, multiplication, or division) are the same. For example, from $56 \div 8$, you could move next to $9 \div 3$ because division is involved twice, or to $1 + 6$ because both answers are 7. Do not make diagonal moves, use the same square twice, or cross your own path.

START

5×6	$40 - 10$	$28 + 2$	4×8	2×6	10×10
$15 + 15$	$3 + 2$	$6 - 1$	$1 + 1$	5×20	$20 + 80$
$14 + 10$	$12 \div 3$	$10 - 2$	$5 + 3$	$4 \div 2$	12×5
$48 \div 2$	$10 + 10$	2×4	$4 - 2$	$7 + 8$	$4 + 6$
$5 \div 5$	$6 + 3$	$16 \div 2$	$9 \div 3$	$1 + 2$	$20 \div 2$
$4 + 7$	$4 - 4$	5×7	$15 + 20$	$2 - 2$	$12 \div 3$

FINISH

ARROW MAZE

VISUAL

Starting at the S and following the arrow to the right, see if you can find your way to F. When you reach an arrow, you MUST follow its direction and continue in that direction until you come to the next arrow. When you reach a two-headed arrow, you can choose either direction. It's okay to cross your own path.

WORD VISIBILITY

LANGUAGE

Here are six 5-letter words. The first letter of the answer is found in the first pair of letters, and it is either the top or the bottom letter. Continue across each pair.

For example, the word GIRL would be found thus: G A R L
                                                   L I T X

1. Q R E N N
   S U A E K

2. W O X H E
   B I M E R

3. R O E L H
   T A O T D

4. L E G I C
   F Y R E P

5. S L E C T
   H A I G K

6. P L Y M N
   T H A O E

ONLINE NETWORK

In each two-column group, take the letters in the left-hand column along the paths (indicated by the lines) and place them in their proper boxes in the right-hand column. When done, for each puzzle you'll find three related words reading down the right-hand column.

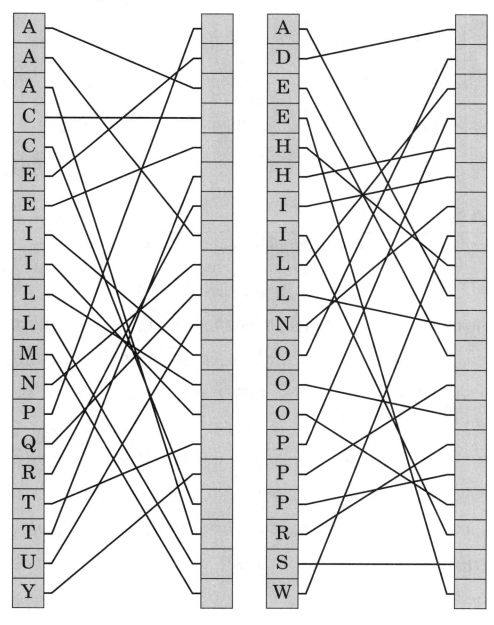

LICENSE PLATES

LANGUAGE

Each box contains six letters of the first and last name of an early rock-and-roll star. The top three are a part of the first name and the bottom three are a part of the last name, in order.

1.
```
L V I
R E S
```

2.
```
D D Y
L L Y
```

3.
```
A R L
E R K
```

4.
```
H U C
E R R
```

5.
```
I T T
R I C
```

6.
```
B I L
A L E
```

ASSOCIATIONS

LANGUAGE

Directions for solving are on page 20.

WHAT DID CINDERELLA SAY WHEN HER PHOTOGRAPHS DIDN'T ARRIVE?

SOCIAL DRY OBVIOUS MELODY FACE GARNET

EACH GUATEMALA DANGLE ARID APTITUDE INERT

YELL MYSTERY CONFRONT LEAK YEAST OPAL

POETRY HONDURAS RAPTURE MARSH INSTINCT

STATIC SEEP NERVOUS TAPESTRY SWAMP

SIMPLE TOPAZ WISDOM CHALLENGE ITCH DRIP

LAUGHTER LABEL DORMANT CRIME PONY MOOR

ORGAN WATERLESS HORSE MISSISSIPPI BELIZE

ENTRANT STEED

SUDOKU

Directions for solving are on page 12.

9		8			6			1
3		4		1			8	
					3	2	4	9
		2	6	4		5	3	
				9				
	1	7		2	8	9		
6	8	1	2					
	4			6		1		3
2			1			6		8

DISC MEMORY

Here are six discs with different designs. Study them carefully for exactly 30 seconds, and then cover them up with a sheet of paper and try to draw them in proper order in the empty discs on the right. Getting four correct is average, five is good, and six is excellent. Good luck, and no peeking!

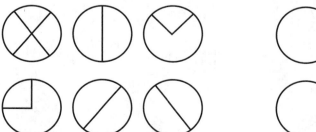

SQUARE LINKS

LANGUAGE

Write one letter in each empty box so that an everyday 8-letter word is spelled out around each purple box. Each word may read either clockwise or counterclockwise, and may start at any of its letters.

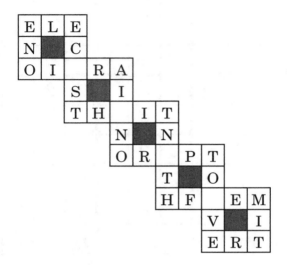

RINGERS

LANGUAGE ◆ SPATIAL

Each Ringer is composed of five rings. Use your imagination to rotate the rings so that you spell out four 5-letter words reading from the outside to the inside when all five rings are aligned correctly.

1.

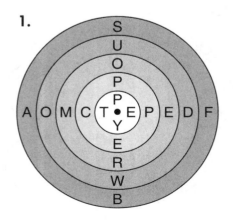

2.

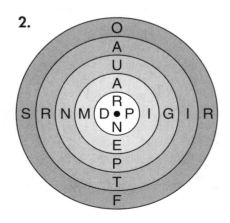

STAR WORDS

Only five of the eight words given will fit together in the diagram. Place them in the directions indicated by the arrows.

BEND   LEND

BULL   LIES

DULL   SEND

GLIB   SNUG

CIRCLE MATH

Each overlapping circle is identified by a letter having a different number value from 1 to 9. Where some circles overlap, there is a number: It is the SUM of the values of the letters in those overlapping circles. Can you figure out the correct values for the letters? As a starting help, A = 5.

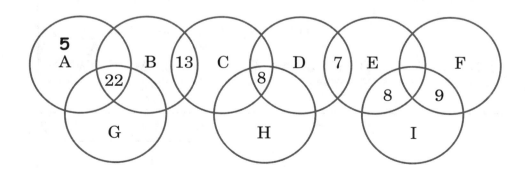

BULL'S-EYE LETTER

LANGUAGE

Add the SAME single letter to each group of three letters, then rearrange the letters to form six everyday 4-letter words.

— — — —

— — — —

— — — —

— — — —

— — — —

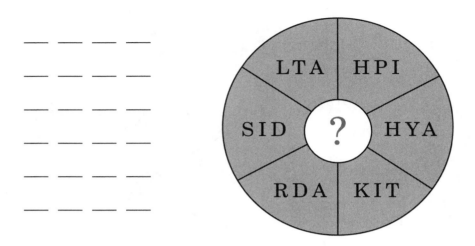

ALPHABET SOUP

LANGUAGE ◆ VISUAL

Cross off each letter from the alphabet list that appears in the larger group of letters. Then rearrange the letters not crossed out to form the name of a color.

V	K	L	A	V	L	W	K	V	W	L	K	A	K	V	W
O	C	W	F	M	X	T	O	M	K	O	C	X	M	A	V
H	X	Q	M	U	Z	H	C	Q	I	U	W	H	Y	U	Z
N	Q	S	G	B	N	J	M	G	B	N	S	M	G	W	P

A B C D E F G H I J K L M N O P Q R S T U V W X Y Z

Color: _____

GOING IN CIRCLES

In each circle, insert one letter into each empty space to form an 8-letter word. Words may read either clockwise or counterclockwise and may begin with any letter in the circle.

1.

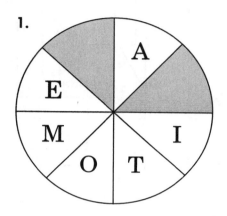

2.

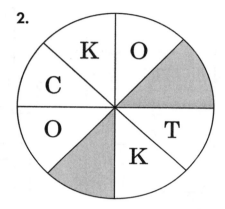

CODED STATES

In this list of U.S. states, we've replaced each consonant with an X and each vowel (including Y) with an O. Can you decode each state's name?

1. X O X X O X X X O X

2. X O X   X O X O X O

3. X O X X O X X O

4. O O X O

5. O X O X O

6. O X X O X X O X

7. X O X O X

8. X O X X X   X O X O X O

OVERLAY

When you overlay the three diagrams in the top row, which of the three lettered diagrams, A, B, or C, will be formed?

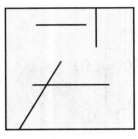 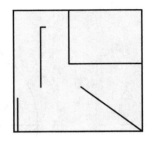 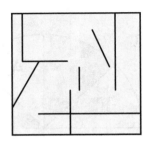

A. 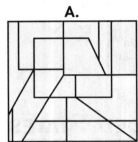   **B.** 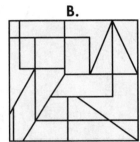   **C.**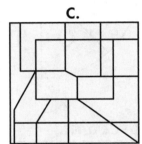

COMPOUND IT

LANGUAGE

Starting at #1, pick a word that will form a compound word with a word chosen in #2. Then with the word you've selected in #2, pick one from #3 to form another compound word. Continue in this manner to #10, so that you've formed nine compound words. In some instances more than one compound word can be formed, but there is only one path to get you to #10.

1. hand, ginger, night, land

2. bread, shade, mark, snap

3. basket, dragon, powder, down

4. fly, hollow, ball, stream

5. game, paper, line, park

6. way, blind, girl, backer

7. quest, hood, side, trap

8. juice, arm, wink, tribe

9. band, earth, bath, pit

10. robe, fall, wagon, shaking

MISSING DOMINOES

WEEK
5

In this game you use all 28 dominoes that are in a standard set. Each one has a different combination from 0-0, 0-1, 0-2, to 6-6. Domino halves with the same number of dots lie next to each other. To avoid confusion we have used an open circle to indicate a zero. Can you fill in the missing white dominoes to complete the board?

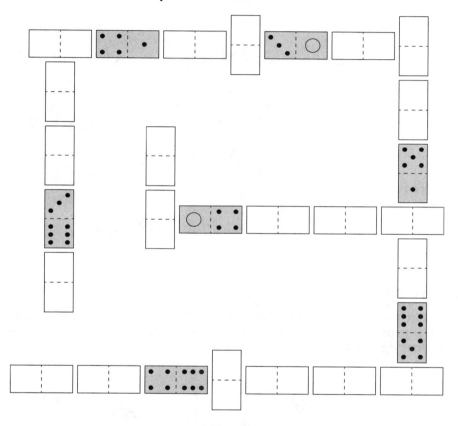

DOMINOES

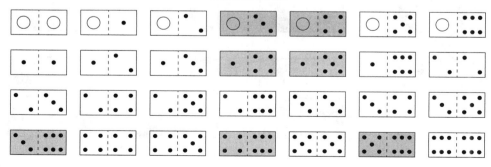

SEVEN WORD ZINGER   LANGUAGE

Using each letter once, form seven everyday 3-letter words with the first letter coming from the center, the second from the middle, and the third from the outer circle. Your words may differ from ours.

— — —

— — —

— — —

— — —

— — —

— — —

— — —

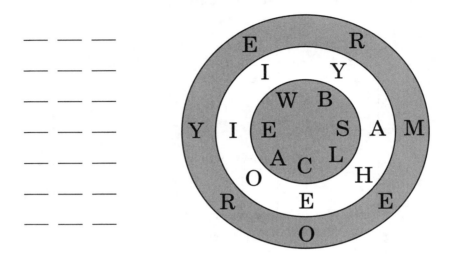

STACKED UP   VISUAL ◆ SPATIAL

The box on the left can be formed by three of the numbered boxes superimposed on top of each other; do not turn them in any way. Can you figure out which three work?

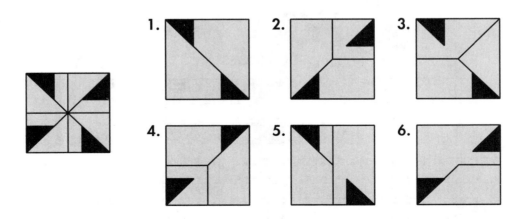

36

VISION QUEST

Find the row or column that contains five DIFFERENT dogs.

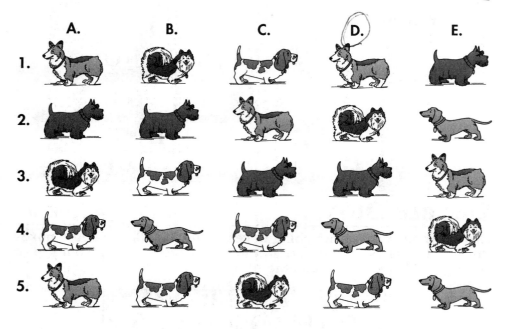

PRESIDENTIAL RHYMES

Replace each word here with a rhyming word to form the full name of a U.S. President. For example, if you saw "SPILL HINTIN'," you would answer "BILL CLINTON."

1. CON MADAMS

2. AIMS JOKE

3. SHIMMY BARTER

4. FORGE PUSH

5. SPARTAN MAN TURIN

6. PRAIRIE CUMIN

7. WAN FILER

8. FOREIGN GUARDING

9. HERALD BOARD

10. DAIQUIRI SAILOR

SLIDE RULE

Directions for solving are on page 21. Here, you're to form 4-letter words. We found 47 words, including TALL.

Your list of words:

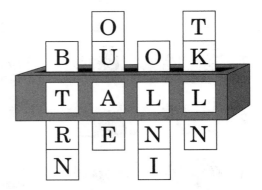

DOUBLE DUTY

Cross off each set of matching boxes, and you will see some boxes don't have mates. The letters in the unmatched boxes, from top to bottom, will spell out the name of a famous man.

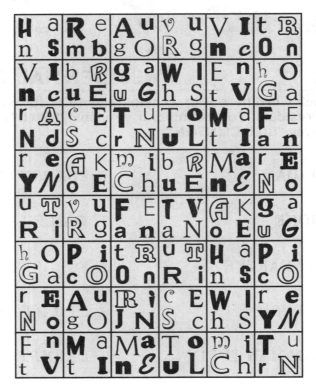

WORD CHARADE

Find each letter in the diagram according to the instructions, and write each letter on its dash to spell out a 6-letter word.

My first letter is the only consonant in one of the corners.

My second letter is the only letter in one of the rows that does not appear in the word ROUTINE.

My third letter is the only letter in one of the columns that appears in the word PRODUCTIVE.

My fourth letter appears to the immediate left of a J and directly above a T.

I	M	E	G	P	Q	L	O
N	A	U	A	J	I	W	B
P	C	P	Z	C	S	Y	D
G	R	V	F	Q	N	J	F
I	N	O	U	A	T	R	E
U	K	X	J	W	L	K	S
X	D	R	M	T	B	Z	M
E	G	C	Q	M	I	P	L

My fifth letter appears in the bottom row but not in the top row.

My sixth letter does not appear in the diagram.

—— —— —— —— —— ——

EASY PICKINGS

To solve, simply cross out one letter in each pair. When the puzzle is completed correctly, the remaining letters will spell out a truism.

YB EU   PU HR KE WP AW RN SE DS,

BM OE   OA EB US RE BR VE IA NG MT,

AV NX CD   BF EA

IH ED KL PZ FE KU LG.

WORD HUNT

LANGUAGE ◆ SPATIAL

Find words by moving from one letter to any adjoining letter. You may start a word with any letter in the diagram.

In forming a word you may return to a letter as often as you wish, but do not stand on a letter using it twice in direct succession. In this Word Hunt, you are searching for 4-letter words that end with M. We found 22 words, including SLIM.

Your list of words:

E	K	S	H	C
H	L	I	U	P
B	F	M	R	A
E	A	O	D	F
T	N	L	O	Z

ROUND TRIP

VISUAL ◆ LOGIC

Directions for solving are on page 15.

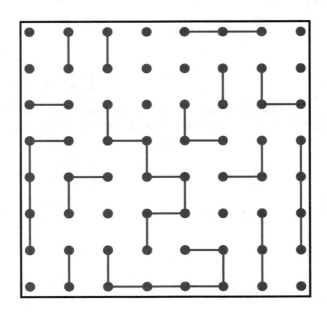

ANAGRAM MAZE

Directions for solving are on page 16. This time, there are 19 words to anagram and the first word you'll be anagramming is DOSE.

1 OXEN	2 MALT	3 DOSE	4 LANE	5 NEON	6 CHUM
— — — —	— — — —	— — — —	— — — —	— — — —	— — — —
7 MINK	8 LESS	9 HAVE	10 MAKE	11 BANK	12 STUB
— — — —	— — — —	— — — —	— — — —	— — — —	— — — —
13 CHIN	14 TEAM	15 CASK	16 IDLE	17 WOOL	18 CALM
— — — —	— — — —	— — — —	— — — —	— — — —	— — — —
19 HEAT	20 BEAU	21 TINY	22 STEP	23 EVIL	24 DONE
— — — —	— — — —	— — — —	— — — —	— — — —	— — — —
25 OURS	26 RENT	27 FANG	28 HOOT	29 GRIT	30 FERN
— — — —	— — — —	— — — —	— — — —	— — — —	— — — —
31 MAZE	32 LIPS	33 DIRE	34 CURE	35 LILY	36 QUIT
— — — —	— — — —	— — — —	— — — —	— — — —	— — — —

SKILLS TEST

There are eight everyday, uncapitalized 5-letter words that begin with T and end with K. Can you determine all of them?

T __ __ __ K   T __ __ __ K

T __ __ __ K   T __ __ __ K

T __ __ __ K   T __ __ __ K

T __ __ __ K   T __ __ __ K

SUDOKU

Directions for solving are on page 12.

		8					5	
6	2		4	1				8
	1			2		4	6	
5	9	7	3					
8			9	4	2			3
				5	6	1	9	
	8	4		3			9	
7				8	9		4	6
	3					8		

LICENSE PLATES

Each box contains six letters of a capital city and its island country. The top three are a part of the capital and the bottom three are a part of the nation, in order.

1.
```
A V A
U B A
```

2.
```
J A K
D O N
```

3.
```
K Y O
A P A
```

4.
```
B L I
E L A
```

5.
```
I L A
H I L
```

6.
```
S T O
A M A
```

THE LINEUP

Directions for solving are on page 17.

APJSKIMCOFFEEWZDIMEBTRELIEVINGQFOXYH

1. Which letter of the alphabet does not appear in the lineup? _____

2. What 6-letter word — with its letters in correct order and appearing together — can you find in the lineup? _____

3. Which letter of the alphabet appears exactly three times in the lineup? _____

4. What 9-letter word — with its letters in correct order and appearing together — can you find in the lineup? _____

5. Other than the answers to Questions 2 and 4, how many everyday words — with their letters in correct order and appearing together — of four or more letters can you find in the lineup? _____

VISUAL ◆ SPATIAL # MAGNIFIND

Figure out which area of the drawing has been enlarged.

CODE WORD

DECODING

Directions for solving are on page 8. Here, you are to determine an 11-letter Code Word.

$$\overline{1}\ \overline{2}\ \overline{3}\ \overline{4}\ \overline{5}\ \overline{6}\ \overline{7}\ \overline{8}\ \overline{9}\ \overline{10}\ \overline{11}$$

9 10 2   3 1 2 6 7   6 D V 6 10 7 6 3 2   9 F   M 6 10 Y

P 6 1 K 8 10 3   5 9 7 11   8 11   7 H 6 7   7 H 2 Y   3 8 V 2

4 11   11 9 M 2 7 H 8 10 3   7 9   B 5 6 M 2   7 H 2

B 4 M P 2 D   F 2 10 D 2 1 11   9 10 .

ALPHABET SOUP

LANGUAGE ◆ VISUAL

Cross off each letter from the alphabet list that appears in the larger group of letters. Then rearrange the letters not crossed out to form the name of a fabric.

```
G  Z  A  E  Z  G  A  M  U  Z  A  M  G  Z  E  M

H  P  X  W  H  P  C  J  H  X  C  W  H  P  C  J

Q  D  N  F  U  D  N  F  Q  E  N  F  T  D  X  F

R  J  B  Y  R  O  U  Y  O  R  B  X  R  O  V  Y
```

A B C D E F G H I J K L M N O P Q R S T U V W X Y Z

Fabric: _____

"We think in generalities, but we live in detail."
— Alfred North Whitehead

TRI, TRI AGAIN

WEEK 6

Directions for solving are on page 12.

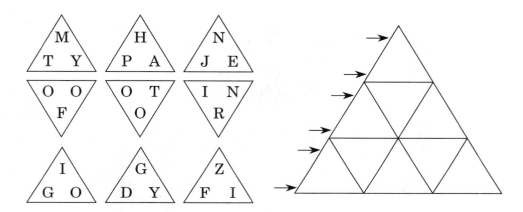

LANGUAGE

ANIMAL CHARADES

Each line contains a clue to a letter of the alphabet. These letters, in the given order, will spell out the name of an animal. The animal's identity is also hinted at in the last sentence of the Charade.

My FIRST is in PIGEON and in GROWN;   _____

My SECOND is in SHREW and in THROWN;   _____

My THIRD is in SARDINE but not in DRAPE;   _____

My FOURTH is in GOAT but not in GRAPE;   _____

My FIFTH is in FALCON and in LEAK;   _____

My SIXTH is in TURTLE and in TEAK.   _____

My WHOLE is a critter chiefly yellow and black,
In Baltimore this avian folks do not lack.

_____

GRAND TOUR

LANGUAGE ◆ VISUAL

Directions for solving are on page 19. This time, you'll be looking for a chain of 5-letter words starting with GI-ANT-IC (giant, antic).

START

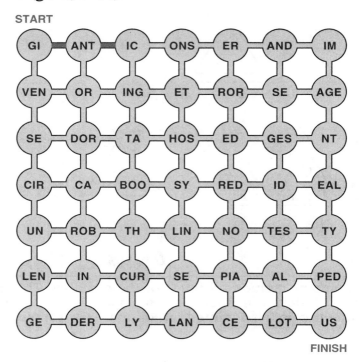

FINISH

FUN WITH FACTS AND FIGURES

MATH

Directions for solving are on page 15.

1. Take the number of consonants in the word UNCOORDINATED and subtract the number of vowels in the word. _____

2. Next, multiply by the number opposite the six on a standard clock dial. _____

3. Now, divide by the number of U.S. states with names that start with the letter "O." _____

4. Add the number of quarts in ten gallons. _____

5. Subtract the number of years in half of a decade. _____

Our answer, when spelled out, can be scrambled to form the phrase "I TRY THE INN." *Can yours?*

MARCHING ORDERS

WEEK 6

Using a different two-step sequence of addition and subtraction, can you make your way from Start to Finish in each puzzle by moving up, down, or diagonally? We've started the first one for you using the sequence +6 and −2; continue this sequence to reach Finish. You will not cross your own path or pass through any square twice.

1.   FINISH ↑

30	34	32	38	34	40
24	28	30	26	36	42
20	14	24	30	22	16
10	28	26	20	24	18
4	2	8	16	14	12
0	6	4	10	8	16

↑ START

2.   FINISH ↑

8	12	16	20	24	22
6	10	8	12	22	26
8	4	14	10	20	18
10	6	12	14	12	20
4	2	2	10	16	16
0	6	8	12	14	18

↑ START

SKILLS TEST

Complete the two quotes by author Mark Twain by writing A, E, I, O, or U on each dash.

1. "L __ T   __ S   B __   TH __ NKF __ L   F __ R

TH __   F __ __ LS .   B __ T   F __ R   TH __ M

TH __   R __ ST   __ F   __ S   C __ __ LD

N __ T   S __ CC __ __ D ."

2. " __ N   H __ S   PR __ V __ T __   H __ __ RT

N __   M __ N   M __ CH   R __ SP __ CTS

H __ MS __ LF ."

47

COUNTDOWN

VISUAL

Directions for solving are on page 14.

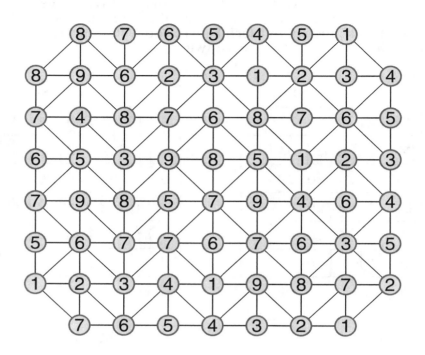

WAYWORDS

LANGUAGE

Directions for solving are on page 18. This time, you'll be looking for a 9-word thought beginning with A.

MAN'S	SHEET	ZENITH	GOOD
ONLY	LAZY	VERY	TWIST
EXERCISE	A	REGRET	HIS
PLEASURE	IS	PUSHING	LUCK

QUOTATION MARKS

Enter the capital letters in the diagram as indicated by the number-letter combinations to form a quote by Mark Twain. For example, one of the C's should be placed in the box where column 10 and row k intersect.

	1	2	3	4	5	6	7	8	9	10	11	12	13
a													
b													
c													
d													
e													
f													
g													
h													
i													
j													
k													
l													

A: 6a, 8a, 5b, 2e, 1f, 12f, 2g, 11g, 11h, 6i, 10i, 12j, 11k, 11l

B: 1d, 4e, 1h, 1l

C: 10k, 3l

D: 6g

E: 2a, 3a, 10b, 1c, 2d, 8d, 6f, 10f, 7h, 10h, 5i, 12i, 6j, 7j, 2l, 6l, 10l

F: 11a, 5j

G: 3i, 8l

H: 4c, 10g, 6h, 11j

I: 4d, 5e, 7e

K: 1a, 11i

L: 6b, 7b, 13b, 3d, 7d, 2f, 3f, 9f, 13f, 12h, 13h, 8j

M: 1b, 4b, 3e, 13e, 9i, 5l

N: 9e, 12k

O: 13a, 11b, 5c, 12c, 11d, 8e, 7f, 7g, 2j, 3k, 7k, 8k, 4l

P: 4a, 9b, 12b, 5f, 8f

R: 12a, 8c, 13d, 9h, 4i, 9l

S: 3b, 10e, 12e, 4g

T: 7c, 11c, 5d, 6d, 6e, 9g, 12g, 3h, 5h, 7i, 10j, 13j, 6k, 12l

U: 12d, 2h, 3j, 4k

W: 7a, 3c, 1g

Y: 9a, 9c, 10d, 3g, 1i, 1j, 2k

ANAGRAM MAZE

LANGUAGE ◆ VISUAL

Directions for solving are on page 16. This time, there are 19 words to anagram and the first word you'll be anagramming is FAST.

1 BUDS	2 CHAR	3 LOIN	4 DUMB	5 ZINC	6 FAST
7 ICON	8 HIGH	9 TOGA	10 NAIL	11 HOWL	12 KALE
13 BARE	14 NEWT	15 CURL	16 GAPE	17 DUST	18 FACE
19 MEMO	20 ACTS	21 SNOW	22 JOLT	23 COMA	24 FORK
25 BUFF	26 PRAY	27 ACRE	28 FOOT	29 WAGE	30 KIWI
31 JETS	32 RATS	33 NOEL	34 BEET	35 CAVE	36 FURY

ALL IN A ROW

MATH

Directions for solving are on page 16. This time, look for the most groups of consecutive numbers adding up to 14.

A. 8 3 4 1 6 5 6 2 8 4 3 5 2 6 8 9 1 2 3 4 6 1 5 8

B. 2 6 4 9 3 7 4 1 8 3 6 2 4 2 7 3 5 1 2 3 6 9 4 1

C. 7 6 3 2 1 2 5 6 9 3 8 4 1 5 2 8 3 3 6 2 4 1 7 5

"Every good thought you think is contributing its share to the ultimate result of your life." — Grenville Kleiser

50

LETTER, PLEASE

The numbers here stand for certain letters on the telephone dial. You will see that one number may stand for more than one letter — for example, 3 may be D, E, or F. By finding the correct letter for each number in each puzzle below, you will have spelled out a quote by politician Adlai Stevenson.

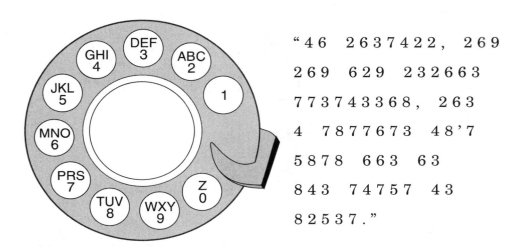

"46 2637422, 269

269 629 232663

773743368, 263

4 7877673 48'7

5878 663 63

843 74757 43

82537."

U COUNT

Here's an eye exam that's also a U exam! First, read the sentence here. Next, go back and read it again, but this time count all of the U's. How many are there?

LULU SUNUNU MURMURED, "UNUSUAL,

FLUFFY CUMULUS CLOUDS DULY

OBSTRUCTED FOUR FUTURISTIC,

TUBULAR TUNNELS OUTSIDE OUR

URBAN BOROUGH THROUGH AUGUST."

IN THE ABSTRACT

VISUAL ◆ SPATIAL

Directions for solving are on page 8.

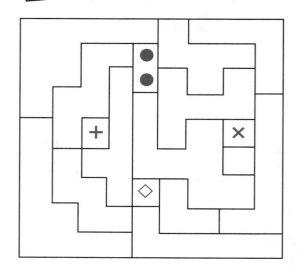

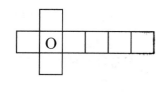

CROSS-UPS

LANGUAGE

Using only the letters given above each diagram, fill in the boxes in such a way that an everyday compound word is formed, one part reading across and the other part reading down. The letter already in the diagram is a letter shared by both parts of the word. Note: Each part of the compound word is an entire word on its own.

1. A L M N O R T W
2. A B D F L O R R
3. C E E F F P T

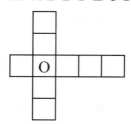

"Remember happiness doesn't depend upon who you are or what you have; it depends solely on what you think."
— Dale Carnegie

FILLING STATION

Place the given consonants on the dashes to form words. The vowels have already been placed for you, and as an additional help, each entry lists its category beside its given consonants.

1. D H H L L P P (U.S. city)

   _ _ I _ A _ E _ _ _ I A

2. D H H R S S W (household sight)

   _ I _ _ _ A _ _ E _

3. M N P R T T W (movie)

   " _ _ E _ _ Y   _ O _ A _ "

4. C C D F H K N R (food)

   _ _ I E _   _ _ I _ _ E _

5. L M P R R S T (actress)

   _ E _ Y _   _ _ _ E E _

6. F G G G L M N N S S (tool on a desk)

   _ A _ _ I _ Y I _ _   _ _ A _ _

MATH ◆ LOGIC # SKILLS TEST

Christopher is a clothing-store clerk who last week racked up a different sales total each day, Monday through Friday. Monday's sales were $100 lower than Tuesday's, which were $200 higher than Wednesday's, which were $250 lower than Thursday's, which were $300 higher than Friday's.

If on Christopher's worst day he brought in $400, what were his sales totals on each day?

LOOSE TILE

VISUAL ◆ SPATIAL

The tray on the left seemed the ideal place to store the set of loose dominoes. Unfortunately, when the tray was full, one domino was left over. Determine the arrangement of the dominoes in the tray and which is the Loose Tile.

CIRCLE SEARCH

LANGUAGE

Directions for solving are on page 22. Here you're looking to form 17 words of at least three letters.

VISION QUEST

Find the row or column that contains five DIFFERENT fireplace tools.

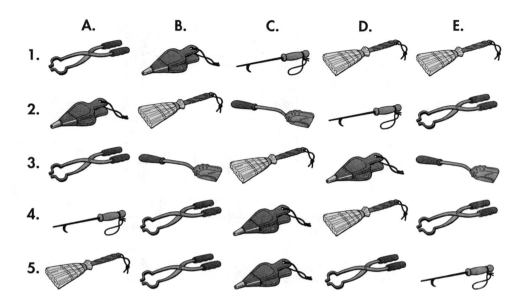

SEVEN WORD ZINGER

Directions for solving are on page 36.

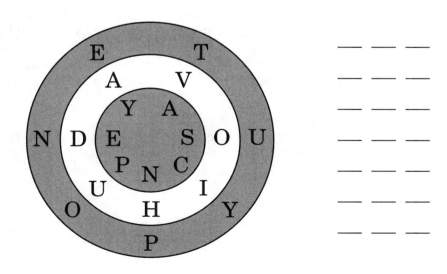

ARROW MAZE

VISUAL

Directions for solving are on page 26. This time, you'll begin by moving to the right from the starting box.

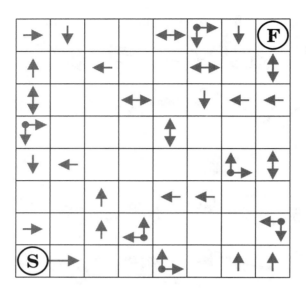

DEDUCTION PROBLEM

LOGIC

Mr. Black, Mr. White, Mr. Brown, and Mr. Green are coworkers who regularly enjoy eating lunch together. When the four left the restaurant today, though, they all made a number of big clothing mistakes. You see, each man inadvertently took the hat belonging to another man as well as the coat belonging to still another man. For example, the guy who grabbed Mr. Green's hat erroneously put on Mr. Brown's coat, and Mr. Black wrongfully appropriated Mr. White's hat.

From this information, can you correctly determine who took whose hat and whose coat?

CHANGELINGS

WEEK
8

Can you change the first word into the second word by changing only one letter at a time? Do not rearrange the order of the letters with each change. Each change must result in an everyday word, and words beginning with a capital letter, slang, or obsolete words aren't allowed.

1. FINE

_____

_____

_____

WORD
(4 changes)

2. GOES

_____

_____

_____

HOME
(4 changes)

3. LOSE

_____

_____

_____

GAME
(4 changes)

CODED STATES

In this list of U.S. states, we've replaced each consonant with an X and each vowel (including Y) with an O. Can you decode each state's name?

1. XOXX   XOXXOXOO

2. OXXOXOOX

3. XOXOXOXXOO

4. XXOXO   OXXOXX

5. XOXOXOXX

6. XOXXOXXOXOXXX

7. OXOXOX

8. XOXXOXXOXXO

"Thought makes the whole dignity of man."
— Blaise Pascal

WORD HUNT

LANGUAGE ◆ SPATIAL

Directions for solving are on page 40. This time, you'll be searching for 4- and 5-letter words that end with SS (such as BASS). We found 12 4-letter words, including BASS, and 16 5-letter words.

Your list of words:

G	U	T	R	D
H	I	E	P	U
K	L	S	S	M
F	O	B	A	I
T	C	R	G	L

CIRCLE MATH

MATH

Directions for solving are on page 31. We've started you off by telling you that B = 7.

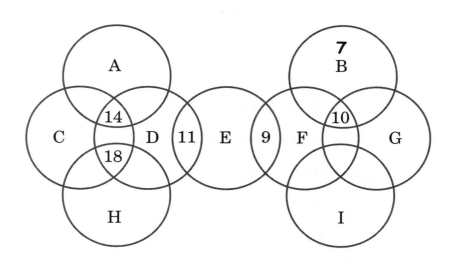

GOING IN CIRCLES

WEEK
8

Directions for solving are on page 33.

1.
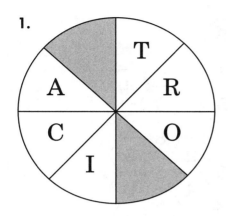

2.
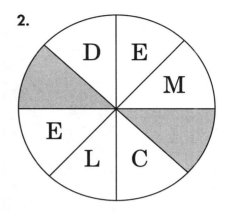

LETTER, PLEASE

Directions for solving are on page 51. In this puzzle, the answer will be a quote by writer Oscar Wilde.

"2   5 4 8 8 5 3

7 4 6 2 3 7 4 8 9   4 7

2   3 2 6 4 3 7 6 8 7

8 4 4 6 4 ,   2 6 3   2

4 7 3 2 8   3 3 2 5

6 3   4 8   4 7

2 2 7 6 5 8 8 3 5 9

3 2 8 2 5."

HEXAGON HUNT   VISUAL

Directions for solving are on page 21.

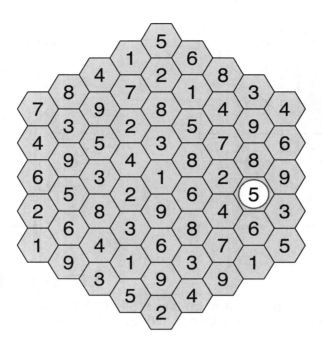

WORD EQUATIONS   LANGUAGE

Determine the three defined words in each equation. The third word is formed when the second is written directly after the first; for example, for "for each + shape = act in a play," you would respond "per + form = perform."

1. little kid + wartime friend = in every way

2. arc of facial hair + croon a tune = customer's store activity

3. black goo on a road + receive = archery-competition need

4. be the victor + Wall Street index, for short = place for a screen

5. opposite of con + metric unit of weight = TV show

6. short dresses + attempt = preacher's service to the community

MISSING DOMINOES

In this game you use all 28 dominoes that are in a standard set. Each one has a different combination from 0-0, 0-1, 0-2, to 6-6. Domino halves with the same number of dots lie next to each other. To avoid confusion we have used an open circle to indicate a zero. Can you fill in the missing white dominoes to complete the board?

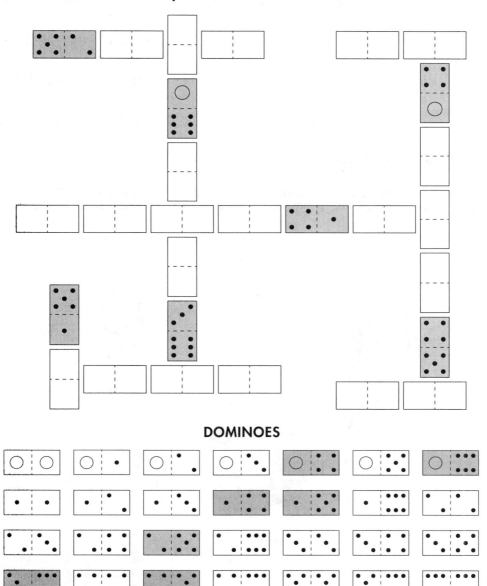

DOMINOES

COMPOUND IT

LANGUAGE

Directions for solving are on page 34.

1. wood, tender, free, cook

2. way, book, chuck, foot

3. store, bridge, side, top

4. work, flower, front, show

5. line, brain, pot, boat

6. storm, home, yard, up

7. date, hold, mother, stick

8. final, land, over, ball

9. law, coat, fruit, mark

10. suit, cake, tail, bought

WORD WHEEL

LANGUAGE

Directions for solving are on page 23. Beginning with the "F" at the top of the wheel, we formed 34 words of three or more letters.

"People should think things out fresh and not just accept conventional terms and the conventional way of doing things."
— *Buckminster Fuller*

BULL'S-EYE LETTER

Directions for solving are on page 32.

WEEK 9

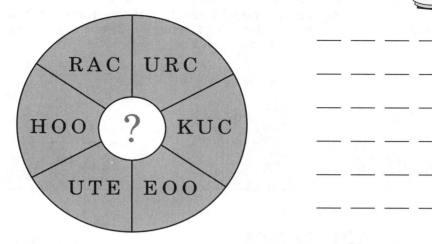

RAC URC
HOO ? KUC
UTE EOO

— — — —
— — — —
— — — —
— — — —
— — — —
— — — —

LANGUAGE

WHIRLIGIG

In each numbered section are five letters. Rearrange each group of letters so that when you add "BE" from the middle of the diagram to the front of each group, you will form 12 common 7-letter words.

1. _____
2. _____
3. _____
4. _____
5. _____
6. _____
7. _____
8. _____
9. _____
10. _____
11. _____
12. _____

63

WHAT'S YOUR NUMBER?

MATH ◆ LOGIC

Can you figure out the relationship of the numbers in the first two triangles and, based on that, what missing number goes into the space with the question mark?

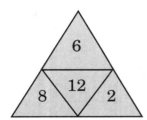 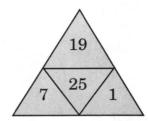 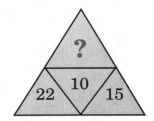

ANIMAL CHARADES

LANGUAGE

Directions for solving are on page 45.

My FIRST is in BULLDOG and in GRAB;   _____

My SECOND is in COBRA and in DRAB;   _____

My THIRD is in BLUEBIRD but not in BLEND;   _____

My FOURTH is in LEMUR but not in MEND;   _____

My FIFTH is in IGUANA and in BLANK;   _____

My SIXTH is in COUGAR and in CRANK;   _____

My SEVENTH is in BURRO but not in ROPE;   _____

My EIGHTH is in CONDOR but not in COPE;   _____

My NINTH is in TERRAPIN and in PLEASE.   _____

My WHOLE is a fierce fish of tropical seas.

_____

COUNT ON IT!

Use the given letters to fill in the familiar saying, one letter per dash. All the letters following 1 are the first letters of each word, the letters following 2 are the second letters of each word, etc. It is up to you to determine which letter goes where.

1. B L L Y   2. E E O O   3. A F O U

4. K O P   5. R   6. E

$\overline{}\ \overline{}\ \overline{}\ \overline{}$ $\overline{}\ \overline{}\ \overline{}\ \overline{}\ \overline{}\ \overline{}$
1 2 3 4   1 2 3 4 5 6

$\overline{}\ \overline{}\ \overline{}$ $\overline{}\ \overline{}\ \overline{}\ \overline{}$.
1 2 3   1 2 3 4

WORD CHARADE

Directions for solving are on page 39.

My first letter appears in the words MONASTIC and RESONANT and is in a column that only has letters from those words.

My second letter is the sixth letter in the row with letters in alphabetical order.

My third letter is the middle letter of a word that reads right to left for its first four letters then turns down for its last three letters.

V	F	M	A	Q	T	X	D
B	G	I	K	N	P	S	W
R	H	C	P	L	C	W	N
M	E	R	T	U	E	F	G
I	L	C	E	T	P	V	K
P	T	E	S	G	B	L	A
S	Z	S	Y	H	I	O	J
E	B	I	J	I	C	E	M

My fourth letter appears in three different groups of three letters (two groups reading down and one group reading left to right) that are in alphabetical and successive order.

My fifth letter is surrounded by eight letters from the first half of the alphabet.

My sixth letter appears to the immediate left or right or directly above or below wherever my second letter appears.

— — — — —

QUICK FILL

LANGUAGE

Determine the 10-letter word from the clues. All the letters in the word are listed.

A C C E I L O P R R

1. Letter 3 appears elsewhere in the word.

2. Letter 1 is the third letter of the name of Montpelier's state.

3. Letter 10 can be added to the beginning of "end," "ash," and "ore" to form new words.

4. Letter 7 is from the second half of the alphabet.

5. Letter 5 can be added to the end of "clam," "slur," and "plum" to form new words.

6. In the alphabet, letter 2 is somewhere before letter 4.

7. Letter 6 appears in the word CRUSTACEAN but not in EVACUATION.

8. Letter 8 is a consonant.

9. Letter 9 appears in VULNERABLE and CONSOLATION.

$$\overline{1} \ \ \overline{2} \ \ \overline{3} \ \ \overline{4} \ \ \overline{5} \ \ \overline{6} \ \ \overline{7} \ \ \overline{8} \ \ \overline{9} \ \ \overline{10}$$

TARGET SHOOT

LANGUAGE

Directions for solving are on page 24.

1.

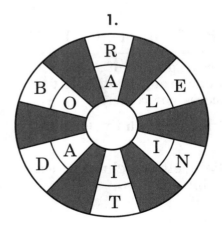

2.

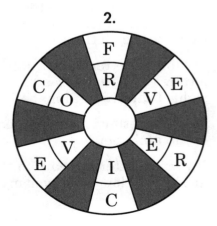

ALL IN A ROW

Directions for solving are on page 16. This time, look for the most groups of consecutive numbers adding up to 16.

A. 7 2 6 1 8 5 4 6 3 1 2 9 3 2 5 7 6 8 3 4 4 7 8 1

B. 2 9 3 5 3 6 7 9 3 7 2 1 4 8 3 9 5 4 1 3 3 5 7 1

C. 8 5 2 3 1 5 4 9 6 2 7 7 3 5 8 4 2 6 9 1 5 3 8 3

FILLING STATION

See page 53 for solving directions.

1. B C C J K K L (game)

   __ __ A __ __ __ A __ __

2. C C N P R R S T (actor)

   __ __ E __ __ E __   __ __ A __ Y

3. C D L M N R (TV show)

   "A __ E __ I __ A __   I __ O __ "

4. B D L N N N S T V (home accessories)

   __ E __ E __ I A __   __ __ I __ __ __

5. B C H N P T (fictional character)

   __ A __ __ A I __   A __ A __

6. G G H K N N S T V (event)

   __ __ A __ __ __ __ I __ I __ __

STACKED UP

VISUAL ◆ SPATIAL

Directions for solving are on page 36.

 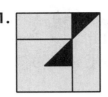 

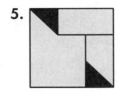 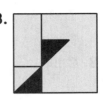 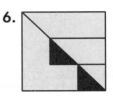

MINUS ONE

LANGUAGE ◆ VISUAL

Determine the letter missing from each alphabet. The five missing letters, reading downward, will spell out a woman's first name.

1. C W J M N O X P B K Y E L I Q D R G S Z F T H U V

2. S T N J A M Z R D I Y Q E P B X O K W G C H V U F

3. W H L A J K X B V T C N O D P Y Q E F R S G M U Z

4. L W M Z N F Y B V Q A P R H D S G T E I J K U O X

5. X H Q I P W A O V D N B U M F Z L T C K G J R Y S

68

WORD LINK

Place the words in parentheses after each capitalized word in the diagram so that they cross or connect with the capitalized word. ZESTY has been placed in the diagram; SALTINE and ELEMENT cross or connect with ZESTY.

ANT (green, throne)

ASSETS (consider, element, jilt, pleases, salary, saltine)

CONSIDER (assets, elderly, ire, looking, sail, stem)

EDGE (egg, green)

EGG (edge, grew, looking)

EGO (feat, ogre, throne)

ELDERLY (consider, element, pleases, salary, saltine)

ELEMENT (assets, elderly, ire, sail, stem, zesty)

FEAT (ego, for, tee, yearn)

FOR (feat, ogre, throne)

GREEN (ant, edge, grew)

GREW (egg, green)

IRE (consider, element, saltine)

JILT (assets, looking)

LOOKING (consider, egg, jilt, pleases)

OGRE (ego, for, tee, yearn)

PLEASES (assets, elderly, looking, sail, stem)

SAIL (consider, element, pleases, saltine)

SALARY (assets, elderly, yearn)

SALTINE (assets, elderly, ire, sail, stem, zesty)

STEM (consider, element, pleases, saltine)

TEE (feat, ogre, throne)

THRONE (ant, ego, for, tee, yearn)

YEARN (feat, ogre, salary, throne)

ZESTY (element, saltine)

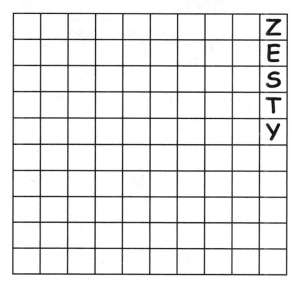

HEXAGON HUNT

VISUAL

In this diagram of six-sided figures, there are 10 "special" hexagons. These 10 are special because the six numbers around each one are all different from each other and the center. We've circled one of the 10. Can you find the other 9?

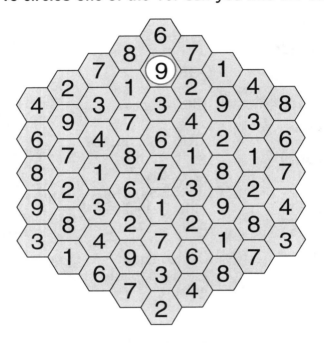

T COUNT

VISUAL

Here's an eye exam that's also a T exam! First, read the sentence below. Next, go back and read the sentence again, but this time count all of the T's. How many are there?

THERE'S THE STATE'S TOW TRUCK

THAT THEY DON'T TRUST; THEY THINK

THAT IT MIGHT JUST TIP, TILT, OR

TEETER THEIR THIRTY-TWO AUTOS

TOO TREACHEROUSLY.

SUDOKU

Place a number into each box so each row across, column down, and small 9-box square within the larger square (there are 9 of these) contains 1 through 9.

	8		5	9		7	2	
		7					3	6
		1		6	7			4
		9			5	6		
2			6		4			7
		3	7			2		
1			4	3		5		
5	3					4		
	9	6		5	8		7	

LANGUAGE

QUICK FILL

Determine the 10-letter word from the clues. All the letters in the word are listed.

A E E L M N O R T W

1. In the alphabet, letter 7 is somewhere before letter 5, which is somewhere before letter 1.

2. Letter 2 is the first letter of a word that means "uncle's mate."

3. In the alphabet, letter 10 is immediately before letter 9.

4. Letters 6, 4, 8, and 3, in order, spell out a word meaning "thaw."

$$\overline{1} \ \overline{2} \ \overline{3} \ \overline{4} \ \overline{5} \ \overline{6} \ \overline{7} \ \overline{8} \ \overline{9} \ \overline{10}$$

ONLINE NETWORK

WEEK 10

VISUAL

In each two-column group, take the letters in the left-hand column along the paths (indicated by the lines) and place them in their proper boxes in the right-hand column. When done, for each puzzle you'll find three related words reading down the right-hand column.

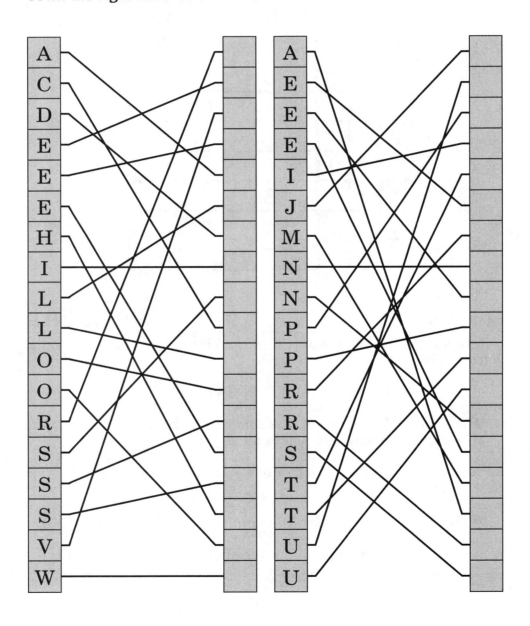

To solve this puzzle, write down the four letters that describe each rectangle in this figure. We found 14 rectangles; how many can you locate?

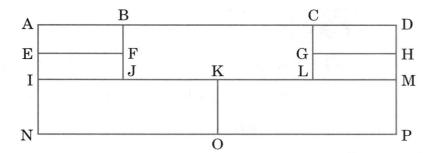

ELIMINATION

Cross off the capitalized words below according to the instructions given. The remaining words, in order, will form a thought.

NEW RESPONSE TRANQUIL SOLUTIONS FACTORY SERENE LIGHT MAY IRRITATES GENERATE CALM MINUTE NEW QUIET PROBLEMS ADORATION

Eliminate...

1. the word that can precede "house," "year," "headed," and "weight."

2. the word that spells out a dance when its final two letters are reversed.

3. the word that has three consecutive letters of the alphabet grouped together, in some order.

4. the word that can be split into two words, one meaning "fuss" and the other meaning "allowance."

5. the word that can be anagrammed into a body of water after the three pairs of duplicated letters are removed.

6. the four words that mean "peaceful."

7. the word with more than one syllable that forms another word when both end letters are removed.

ASSOCIATIONS

You'll find eight groups of three words that can be associated in some way with each other (example: mantel, fireplace, logs). Cross out each group as you find it. The initial letters of the remaining words will spell out the answer to the riddle:

WHAT DO YOU CALL SOMEONE WHO PRETENDS TO BE A GANGSTER?

ANACONDA FEMUR ADVENTURE BONBON DEPART

FRANKFURT FAMOUS PEP APPLE CARDINAL

PANTS LOUDNESS TIBIA PYTHON LEAVE SCIENCE

VITALITY MUNICH EMPIRE RATTLESNAKE SLACKS

HARNESS ROBIN GUMDROP OVATION GO BERLIN

TROUSERS OXYGEN SPARROW ULNA LOLLIPOP

DRAMA ANIMATION

CODE WORD

Decipher a quote and the Code Word's eleven letters, represented by the numbers 1 through 11. So, if the Code Word were "THUNDERCLAP," 1 in the quote would be T, 2 would be H, etc.

$$\overline{1}\ \overline{2}\ \overline{3}\ \overline{4}\ \overline{5}\ \overline{6}\ \overline{7}\ \overline{8}\ \overline{9}\ \overline{10}\ \overline{11}$$

D U R 5 10 G   8 5 D D 4 9   1 G 9   8 1 10 Y   P 9 3 P 4 9

C 3 8 8 9 10 11   1 2 3 U 11   7 3 W   6 4 5 8   11 7 9 Y

U 6 9 D   11 3   2 9   W 7 5 4 9   3 11 7 9 R 6   G 3

3 10   1 2 3 U 11   7 3 W   6 4 5 8   11 7 9 Y ' R 9

G 3 5 10 G   11 3   2 9 .

COUNT TO TEN

Examine the pails and umbrellas and then answer these questions: 1. Which row contains the most pails? 2. Which row contains the most umbrellas? 3. Which row contains an equal number of pails and umbrellas?

1.

2.

3.

4.

5.

6.

7.

8.

9.

10.

ALL IN A ROW

Which row below contains the most groups of consecutive numbers adding up to 9? Look carefully, because some groups may overlap. We've underlined an example of a group in each row to start you off.

A. 2 3 8 6 4 <u>1 1 5 2</u> 4 1 4 7 1 2 3 1 2 6 5 2 8 4 5

B. 7 <u>3 6</u> 1 7 1 4 2 1 1 6 4 3 5 1 2 3 3 7 2 5 2 1 1

C. 8 1 2 3 5 1 6 4 7 1 3 2 1 2 5 6 2 8 4 1 3 <u>4 2 3</u>

IN THE ABSTRACT

VISUAL ◆ SPATIAL

Fill in each section with one of the four symbols so no sections containing the same symbol touch. Four sections are already complete.

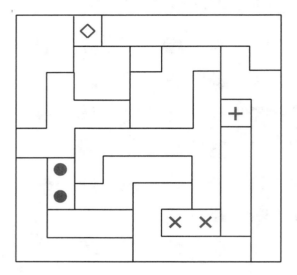

● + ✕ ◇

THE LINEUP

LANGUAGE

While scrutinizing the lineup of letters, can you answer the five questions correctly in five minutes or less?

SDGFOXYJUMPWRHODODENDRONVCKUMQUATHILLZ

1. Which letter of the alphabet does not appear in the lineup? _____

2. What 12-letter word — with its letters in correct order and appearing together — can you find in the lineup? _____

3. Which letter of the alphabet appears exactly three times in the lineup? _____

4. What 7-letter word — with its letters in correct order and appearing together — can you find in the lineup? _____

5. Other than the answers to Questions 2 and 4, how many everyday words — with their letters in correct order and appearing together — of four or more letters can you find in the lineup? _____

76

ARROW MAZE

Starting at the S and following the arrow to the right, see if you can find your way to F. When you reach an arrow, you MUST follow its direction and continue in that direction until you come to the next arrow. When you reach a two-headed arrow, you can choose either direction. It's okay to cross your own path.

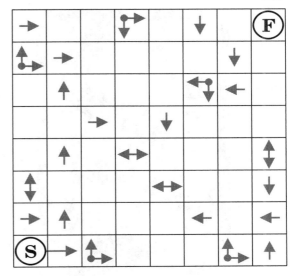

LANGUAGE

ANIMAL CHARADES

Each line contains a clue to a letter of the alphabet. These letters, in the given order, will spell out the name of an animal. The animal's identity is also hinted at in the last sentence of the Charade.

My FIRST is in PANTHER and in SHARE; _____

My SECOND is in EAGLE and in PEAR; _____

My THIRD is in CARDINAL but not in NAIL; _____

My FOURTH is in ZEBRA but not in BAIL; _____

My FIFTH is in IGUANA and in GRIN; _____

My SIXTH is in PORCUPINE and in SPIN; _____

My SEVENTH is in STURGEON but not in SCREEN. _____

My WHOLE is a fish akin to a sardine.

_____

MAGNIFIND

Figure out which areas of the drawing have been enlarged.

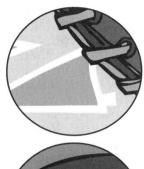

CARD SENSE

LOGIC

Five playing cards were shuffled and put in a pile, one on top of another. Using the clues, can you identify each card's position in the pile?

1. The queens are not adjacent.

2. Neither the top card nor the bottom one is black.

3. The ace is somewhere above the club and somewhere below the diamond.

ANAGRAM MAZE

WEEK
11

The diagram contains 36 words, 21 of which are anagrams of other everyday words. Start at the top arrow and anagram TRAM. While solving, move up, down, right, or left to the only adjacent word that can be anagrammed. Continue until you arrive at the bottom arrow. There is only one path through the maze.

1 TRAM	2 LIFE	3 GEAR	4 PEST	5 CORK	6 LILY
7 CELL	8 GROW	9 MALT	10 BEAU	11 CHAR	12 LESS
13 TINY	14 MINK	15 VETO	16 COIN	17 IDLE	18 FANG
19 PROD	20 DUES	21 RIOT	22 HAVE	23 AFAR	24 MAZE
25 SIRE	26 WOOL	27 HOOT	28 MUCH	29 BURY	30 DUBS
31 FACE	32 COED	33 BEAN	34 FEAT	35 MAKE	36 CARS

EASY PICKINGS

To solve, simply cross out one letter in each pair below. When the puzzle is completed correctly, the remaining letters will spell out a fact.

OT HN YE   BZ GI GP NG DE VS TY

MO MA TM MT IA DL   IN AS

CT HE EG   DW HG AT AL NE.

SEVEN WORD ZINGER   LANGUAGE

Using each letter once, form seven everyday 3-letter words with the first letter coming from the center, the second from the middle, and the third from the outer circle. Your words may differ from ours.

— — —

— — —

— — —

— — —

— — —

— — —

— — —

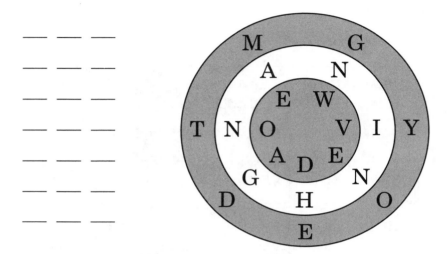

FUN WITH FACTS AND FIGURES   MATH

This puzzle tests you on a lot of little facts and figures. Solve the quiz in the order given since each answer is used in the next statement. There are no fractions used here.

1. Take the number of sides on a rectangle and add the number of dimes in one dollar. _____

2. Next, subtract the number of letters in the name of the country that contains Warsaw and Krakow. _____

3. Now, multiply by the number of seasons in the year. _____

4. Divide by the number of musicians in two quartets. _____

5. Add the value of the Roman numeral VI. _____

Our answer is the number of Commandments in the Bible. *Is yours?*

GRAND TOUR

Form a continuous chain of 5-letter words moving through the maze from START to FINISH. The second part of one word becomes the first part of the next word. This puzzle starts with EX-TRA-DE (extra, trade).

START

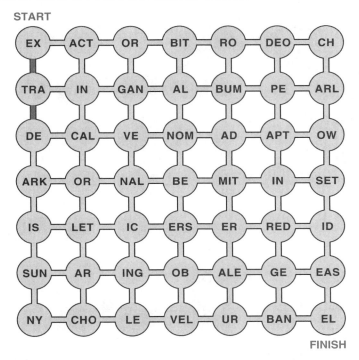

FINISH

LANGUAGE

COUNT ON IT!

Use the given letters to form a thought by placing them on the dashes in this manner: All the letters following 1 are the first letters of each word, the letters following 2 are the second letters of each word, etc. It is up to you to determine which letter goes where.

1. T G C H A T I A   2. O R H A S E   3. R A I U
      4. V R N D   5. Y G Y G   6. E

$\overline{1}$ $\overline{1}\ \overline{2}\ \overline{3}\ \overline{4}\ \overline{5}\ \overline{6}$ $\overline{1}\ \overline{2}$ $\overline{1}$

$\overline{1}\ \overline{2}\ \overline{3}\ \overline{4}\ \overline{5}$ $\overline{1}\ \overline{2}\ \overline{3}\ \overline{4}\ \overline{5}$ $\overline{1}\ \overline{2}$

$\overline{1}\ \overline{2}\ \overline{3}\ \overline{4}\ \overline{5}$.

FILLING STATION

LANGUAGE

Place the given consonants on the dashes to form words. The vowels have already been placed for you, and as an additional help, each entry lists its category beside its given consonants.

1. N R T T (animal)

   A __ __ E A __ E __

2. D G H L N R S T T V Y (television program)

   "__ A __ U __ __ A __   __ I __ __ __   __ I __ E"

3. C D G G N R R T (thing)

   __ __ E E __ I __ __   __ A __ __

4. H K R S T (country)

   __ O U __ __   __ O __ E A

5. C D L N S T T W (person)

   __ __ I __ __   E A __ __ __ O O __

TARGET SHOOT

LANGUAGE

Find the two letters which, when entered into the center circle of each target, will form three 6-letter words reading across.

1.

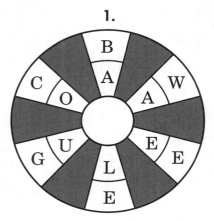

2.

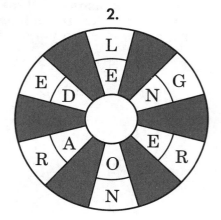

COUNTDOWN

Following the connecting lines, find the only route in this grid that passes through the numbers backward from 9 to 1 consecutively.

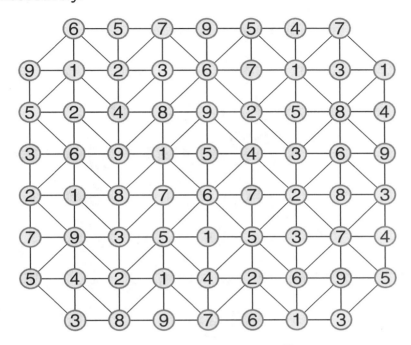

LANGUAGE

COMPOUND IT

Starting at #1, pick a word that will form a compound word with a word chosen in #2. Then with the word you've selected in #2, pick one from #3 to form another compound word. Continue in this manner to #10, so that you've formed nine compound words. In some instances more than one compound word can be formed, but there is only one path to get you to #10.

1. word, child, needle, stand

2. work, play, bearing, still

3. ground, force, pen, table

4. hog, top, spoon, breaking

5. sail, wash, tie, coat

6. fish, cloth, boat, freeze

7. bowl, field, ribbon, yard

8. earth, stick, under, learn

9. bound, sell, stand, ball

10. room, less, out, blue

83

WHIRLIGIG

LANGUAGE

In each numbered section are five letters. Rearrange each group of letters so that when you add "BACK" from the middle of the diagram to the front of each group, you will form 12 common 9-letter words.

1. _____
2. _____
3. _____
4. _____
5. _____
6. _____
7. _____
8. _____
9. _____
10. _____
11. _____
12. _____

BLOCK PARTY

VISUAL ◆ SPATIAL

Study the different views of the block, and draw what should appear on the face that has a question mark.

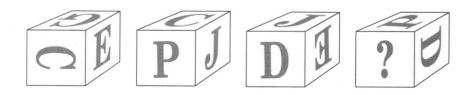

84

LETTER, PLEASE

The numbers below stand for certain letters on the telephone dial. You will see that one number may stand for more than one letter — for example, 3 may be D, E, or F. By finding the correct letter for each number, you will have spelled out a thought.

4 6 6 3   8 4 4 6 4 7

2 6 6 3   9 4 3 6

9 6 8   5 3 2 7 8

3 9 7 3 2 8   8 4 3 6 .

GOING IN CIRCLES

In each circle, insert one letter into each empty space to form an 8-letter word. Words may read either clockwise or counter-clockwise and may begin with any letter in the circle.

1.

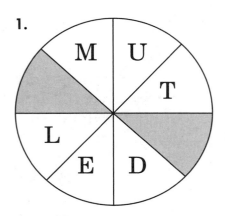

2.

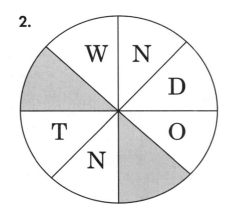

MISSING DOMINOES

VISUAL ◆ LOGIC

WEEK 12

In this game you use all 28 dominoes that are in a standard set. Each one has a different combination from 0-0, 0-1, 0-2, to 6-6. Domino halves with the same number of dots lie next to each other. To avoid confusion we have used an open circle to indicate a zero. Can you fill in the missing white dominoes to complete the board?

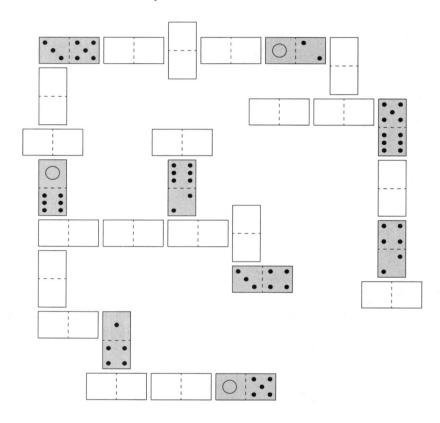

DOMINOES

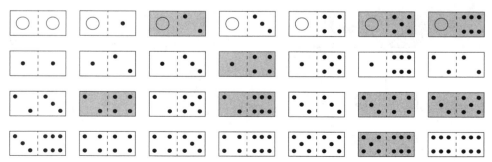

86

LICENSE PLATES

Each box contains six letters of a summer Olympics locale. The top three are a part of the city and the bottom three are a part of the country, in order.

1.
```
L O N
P A I
```

2.
```
K Y O
A P A
```

3.
```
P A R
N C E
```

4.
```
H E N
R E E
```

5.
```
Y D N
T R A
```

6.
```
J I N
I N A
```

LOGIC

SUDOKU

Directions for solving are on page 71.

7							8	
	6	8	2		3		1	
		5		6	8			9
4				5	6	2		8
				9				
3		9	1	2				5
8			7	4		6		
	7		6		5	9	4	
	5							1

MARCHING ORDERS

MATH ◆ LOGIC

Using a different two-step sequence of addition and/or subtraction, can you make your way from Start to Finish in each puzzle by moving up, down, or diagonally? We've started the first one for you using the sequence +4 and -1; continue this sequence to reach Finish. You will not cross your own path or pass through any square twice.

1. FINISH ⬆

13	15	22	21	25	28
9	12	18	19	24	20
5	6	8	9	15	16
3	1	6	10	11	12
2	3	7	9	13	14
0	4	5	8	16	12

⬆ START

2. FINISH ⬆

7	9	11	12	14	15
5	6	8	9	10	16
8	4	9	7	13	12
3	7	5	10	8	11
6	2	6	11	12	9
1	0	4	7	6	7

⬆ START

SYMBOL-ISM

DECODING

This is simply a Cryptogram that uses symbols instead of letters to spell out a truism. Each symbol stands for the same letter throughout. For this puzzle, we've already indicated that ▶ = T and 🐦 = R.

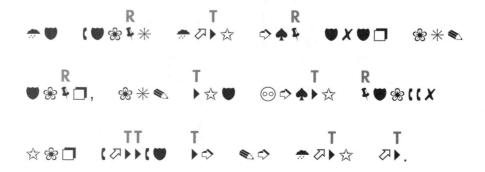

ALPHABET SOUP

WEEK 12

Cross off each letter from the alphabet list that appears in the larger group of letters. Then rearrange the letters not crossed out to form the name of an animal.

K	R	W	E	K	A	R	K	E	W	J	R	A	K	E	S
D	N	U	D	Y	N	V	Y	D	N	Y	J	Y	N	D	V
T	K	D	Z	R	Y	T	L	A	Y	C	N	S	Z	H	Q
B	Y	L	X	V	Z	F	A	J	O	M	L	F	Q	E	T

A B C D E F G H I J K L M N O P Q R S T U V W X Y Z

Animal: _____

CHANGELINGS

Can you change the first word into the second word (in each set) by changing only one letter at a time? Do not rearrange the order of the letters with each change. Each change must result in an everyday word, and words beginning with a capital letter, slang, or obsolete words aren't allowed. The number in parentheses indicates the number of changes we used for that Changeling.

1. BAND

_____

_____

_____

TUNE
(4 changes)

2. BEAR

_____

_____

_____

PAWS
(4 changes)

3. MOSS

_____

_____

_____

BEDS
(4 changes)

89

VISION QUEST

VISUAL

Find the row or column that contains five DIFFERENT pool toys.

A. B. C. D. E.

1.

2.

3.

4.

5.

WHAT'S YOUR NUMBER?

MATH ◆ LOGIC

Can you figure out the relationship of the numbers in the first two grids and, based on that, what missing number goes into the space with the question mark?

16	40	4
10	4	6

13	57	8
14	15	7

1	?	4
9	11	12

"Don't judge each day by the harvest you reap but by the seeds that you plant."
— Robert Louis Stevenson

90

RELATIONSHIPS QUIZ

KENNEL is to DOG as STY is to PIG because a DOG lives in a KENNEL and a PIG lives in a STY. Each of the statements below is a relationship of some kind. Can you select the right word from the four following each?

1. SOIL is to DIRT as SEA is to _____.
   (a) ocean   (b) land   (c) blue   (d) fish

2. VITAMIN C is to ORANGE as VITAMIN A is to _____.
   (a) peanut   (b) eye   (c) pill   (d) carrot

3. DOZEN is to GROSS as INCHES is to _____.
   (a) foot   (b) mile   (c) ruler   (d) yard

4. BASKETBALL is to JORDAN as TENNIS is to _____.
   (a) Ali   (b) Williams   (c) Love   (d) Elway

5. HOUSE is to ROOM as BOOK is to _____.
   (a) title   (b) cover   (c) chapter   (d) index

SQUARE LINKS

Write one letter in each empty box so that an everyday 8-letter word is spelled out around each black box. Each word may read either clockwise or counterclockwise, and may start at any of its letters.

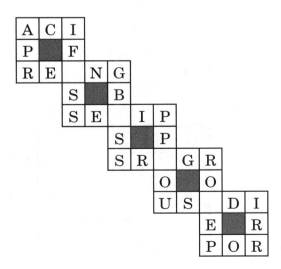

WORD VISIBILITY

LANGUAGE

There are six 5-letter words below. The first letter of the answer is found in the first pair of letters, and it is either the top or the bottom letter. Continue across each pair.

For example, the word GIRL would be found thus: <u>G</u> A <u>R</u> <u>L</u>
                                                     L <u>I</u> T X

1. S E T N D
    W U N I Y

2. D O R G K
    H A D L E

3. P O U S P
    Y E C T H

4. C A G E N
    S I M I L

5. F Y I N M
    M A H D T

6. G E R N E
    P H A C R

OVERLAY

VISUAL ◆ SPATIAL

When you overlay the three diagrams in the top row, which of the three lettered diagrams, A, B, or C, will be formed?

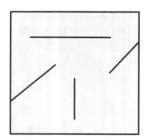 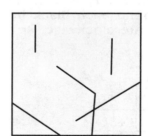 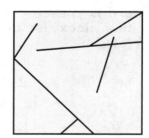

A.	B.	C.
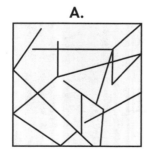	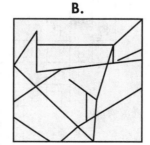	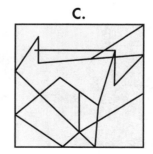

92

ANTONYMS QUIZ

An antonym is a word that is opposite in meaning to another word; for example, "cold" is the antonym of "hot." One of the words following each capitalized word is the antonym of that word.

1. FACILITATE   a. revere   b. designate   c. hinder

2. ESTEEM   a. ridicule   b. abridge   c. gauge

3. SAGACIOUS   a. savage   b. dank   c. ignorant

4. ROBUST   a. weak   b. arrogant   c. progressive

5. TAUT   a. procure   b. slack   c. fraternal

6. BEFUDDLE   a. clarify   b. buoyant   c. wheedle

7. DISHEVELED   a. glib   b. verbatim   c. orderly

8. HEINOUS   a. pleasant   b. obstinate   c. contemptible

GOING IN CIRCLES

Directions for solving are on page 85.

1.
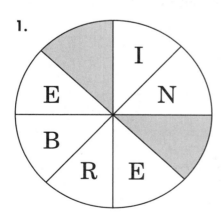

2.
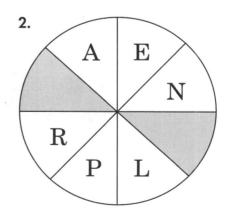

LOOSE TILE

VISUAL ◆ SPATIAL

The tray on the left seemed the ideal place to store the set of loose dominoes. Unfortunately, when the tray was full, one domino was left over. Determine the arrangement of the dominoes in the tray and which is the Loose Tile.

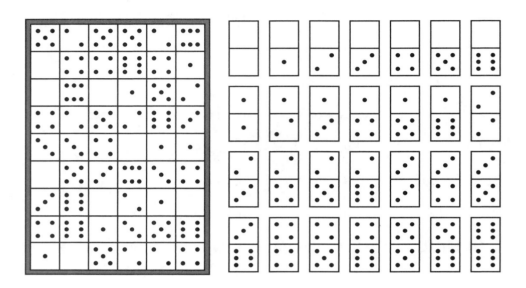

SKILLS TEST

LANGUAGE

Rearrange each group of letters to spell out the name of an animal you might see on a safari.

1. LARGIOL _____

2. FERIFGA _____

3. ATHECEH _____

4. HOERIRCSNO _____

5. STILEEBEWD _____

STATE LIMITS

WEEK
13

The list below consists of the names of seven U.S. states, but we've removed all of the letters between the first and last ones. Can you complete the names?

1. U _____ H

2. N _____ K

3. V _____ T

4. C _____ T

5. M _____ A

6. W _____ A

7. C _____ A

LANGUAGE **WAYWORDS**

A 7-word thought can be found beginning with the word GOOD. Then, move to any adjacent box up, down, or diagonally for each following word.

PURCHASE	FRIENDS	OFTEN	RIDDANCE
REACT	DESSERTS	GOOD	LOVE
BOOKS	ARE	THE	PLEASE
SOOTHING	SAME	JUSTICE	ROMANCE

"Let us be grateful to people who make us happy, they are the charming gardeners who make our souls blossom."
— *Marcel Proust*

TIPS OF THE ICEBERG

WEEK 13

MATH

The chart shows the gratuities each waiter or waitress earned on a recent breakfast shift at the Iceberg Diner. All you have to do is some addition and then answer the following questions:

1. Who made the most in total tips?
2. Who made the least?
3. Which two waitpersons made exactly the same amount?

EMPLOYEE	TIP 1	TIP 2	TIP 3	TIP 4	TIP 5
Al	$0.70	$1.20	$1.20	$1.70	$1.05
Brenda	$1.10	$1.80	$1.25	$1.05	$1.00
Charlie	$1.10	$1.10	$1.00	$1.10	$1.90
Dena	$2.10	$2.85	$2.05	$3.00	$2.80
Ed	$1.05	$2.90	$1.00	$1.00	$2.75
Flora	$1.25	$2.40	$4.80	$0.55	$1.70
Greta	$0.30	$0.95	$2.35	$2.60	$1.00
	660	1320	1345	1100	1220

KEEP ON MOVING

The goal is to move from the shaded square to the asterisk. Since the shaded square has the number 2 in it, you must move two squares up, down, left, or right, but not diagonally. In the new square will be another number; move that number of squares up, down, left, or right, continuing in this way until you reach the asterisk. It's okay to cross your own path.

1	3	5	4	4	2
5	4	4	2	4	2
3	3	2	4	*	5
5	3	1	3	3	2
2	2	3	2	1	1
4	5	1	3	2	5

DOVETAILED WORDS

Two related words, with their letters in the correct order, are combined in each row of letters. Can you find both words? In a line like POBOOXDELER, or POboOxDeLEr, you can see the two words POODLE and BOXER.

1. C T A A L B I C B O Y   _____   _____

2. F S U U N D D A G E E   _____   _____

3. Q R O U E Y E A N L   _____   _____

4. S P L K I N U N M Y P   _____   _____

5. R C O O M M A E N D C E Y   _____   _____

CIRCLE SEARCH
LANGUAGE

Move from circle to adjoining circle, horizontally and vertically only, to form ten common, everyday words of at least three letters. Don't change the order of the letters in the circles that contain more than one letter. Proper names are not allowed.

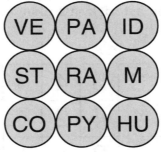

WORD CHARADE
LANGUAGE ◆ VISUAL

Find each letter in the diagram according to the instructions, and write each letter on its dash to spell out a 6-letter word.

My first letter appears directly below a Y and directly above an N.

My second letter appears only in the first four columns and last four rows.

My third letter is the only letter that both starts and ends a column or row.

Z	J	E	O	K	C	I	B
L	P	F	R	M	O	V	H
D	H	B	V	L	R	S	D
C	Q	G	J	E	N	P	O
N	J	Y	V	C	F	H	Q
L	H	G	I	K	I	Y	M
P	F	N	O	Z	E	C	R
I	V	A	M	Y	D	S	G

My fourth letter is in the diagram, but it does not appear in the top or bottom rows or in the first or eighth columns.

My fifth letter, when inserted somewhere in the eight letters in one of the columns, forms a 9-letter compound word that means "an area for growing a particular crop."

My sixth letter is the only letter from the second half of the alphabet in one of the rows.

— — — — — —

MISSING LINKS

Using only the letters below, fill the diagram with real, everyday words. Be careful — this puzzle isn't as easy as it may look, so a little extra thought will be needed.

	A	C		I	N	E			R	A		K		T	
A			E				O			R		M			
	E	A		O	U			S			R	O		F	E
O		I			B		T	R		C			L		E
	F		S	A						C		I	O		N
	C	M			I		H	T			I	O		E	
S				M		R	O				N				E
	U	R		A			O	G					A		
A			A			W		A				U		
T		R			A		Y		R	A		E		
I			I				E					E		E
	H			A			B				N		C
G		L		E	V		U					N	
	R	A	N		D		M		E		L	
		T		L		M		U	E			
	A	R		K	E		U		U			A
E			R			A		N		E		I
	W	A				A	L			A	P	E

AA BB CC DD EEEEEEE F GG HH III
JJ KK LLLLL M NNN OOOO PP Q RRR
SSSS TTT UU V W X Y Z

99

WORD WHEEL

LANGUAGE

Starting with the "A" at the arrow, see how many everyday words of three or more letters you can find going clockwise. Don't skip over any letters. For example, if you saw the letters C, A, R, E, D, you would form five words: CAR, CARE, CARED, ARE, RED. We found 31 words.

QUICK FILL

LANGUAGE

Directions for solving are on page 71.

A A I I L P R T T Y

1. Letter 7 is from the first half of the alphabet and letter 3 is from the second half.

2. Letter 9 appears elsewhere in the word.

3. Letters 2 and 5, in order, are the middle letters of a 4-letter word that can come before "box," "order," and "room."

4. Letter 10 is the last letter of the fifth month of the year.

5. Letter 6 is a vowel.

6. Letters 4, 8, and 1, in order, spell out a word that is a waiter's gratuity.

$$\overline{1} \ \overline{2} \ \overline{3} \ \overline{4} \ \overline{5} \ \overline{6} \ \overline{7} \ \overline{8} \ \overline{9} \ \overline{10}$$

SUDOKU

Directions for solving are on page 71.

		1	9		7		
				7		5	2	9
7	3		2			8		
	9		5			1	7	
	2		9	1	4		5	
	6	5			3		4	
		4			9		1	7
9	1	6		2				
		2		3		4		

DECODING

CODED PRESIDENTS

In this list of U.S. Presidents, we've replaced each consonant with an X and each vowel (including Y) with an O. Can you decode each Chief Executive's name?

1. XOOXXO   XOXX

2. XOXOX   XOXXOO

3. XOOXXOX   XOXXOX

4. XXOXOX   XXOXOXOXX

5. XOXXOXO   XOOXOX

6. XOXXO   XOXXOX

7. XOXXOOX   XXXOXXOO

8. XXOXXXOX   XOOXXO

9. XOXXOXOX   XOXXOXOX

10. XOXX   XOXOX

101

CIRCLE MATH

MATH

Each overlapping circle is identified by a letter having a different number value from 1 to 9. Where some circles overlap, there is a number: It is the SUM of the values of the letters in those overlapping circles. Can you figure out the correct values for the letters? As a starting help, G = 5.

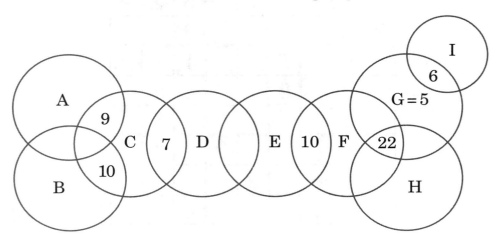

ASSOCIATIONS

LANGUAGE

Directions for solving are on page 74.

WHAT DID THE SIGN IN THE POTTERY SHOP READ?

OPERATE   ROTATE   FLAME   OINTMENT

MEDITERRANEAN ENVY PHYSICS ASPIRATION

POPULATION BALM TAMBOURINE RUN SCARLET

TURN SANCTITY SPOON CASPIAN ORDINARY

RESIDENTS WORK FANTASTIC CRIMSON BIOLOGY

CANVAS KNIFE BALTIC LISTEN REVOLVE ROSE

AVENUE SALVE COMMUNITY YESTERDAY FORK

CHEMISTRY

102

WAYWORDS

Directions for solving are on page 95. This time, you'll be looking for an 8-word thought beginning with IT.

TO	BEAR	WANDER	FEAST
BECOMES	EASY	ANOTHER	DEFEATED
NATURAL	MEAN	IS	PERSON'S
QUICKLY	IT	DOESN'T	SORROW

CARD SENSE

Directions for solving are on page 78.

1. A four is somewhere above both hearts.

2. The spade is somewhere below the seven.

3. The club is somewhere below the nine.

4. The two black cards are not adjacent.

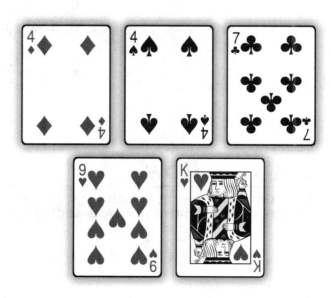

"If opportunity doesn't knock, build a door."
— *Milton Berle*

WEEK

GRAND TOUR

LANGUAGE ◆ VISUAL

Directions for solving are on page 81. This time, you'll be looking for a chain of 5-letter words, starting with AB-ASH-EN (abash, ashen).

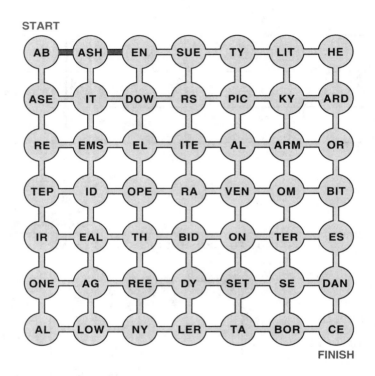

START

FINISH

ALL IN A ROW

MATH

Directions for solving are on page 75. This time, look for the most groups of consecutive numbers adding up to 11.

A. 5 7 1 1 2 6 4 3 1 2 1 6 3 1 1 9 7 3 2 5 1 4 1 9

B. 6 3 8 1 2 7 6 4 3 9 1 4 5 6 8 2 5 7 6 3 1 4 3 7

C. 1 2 4 6 3 7 4 1 2 8 5 5 3 9 1 7 2 2 6 3 4 1 5 1

STAR WORDS

Only five of the eight words given will fit together in the diagram. Place them in the directions indicated by the arrows.

DIRT   RANT

KNOT   TAKE

LEAK   TIER

LOAD   TOIL

HEXAGON HUNT

Directions for solving are on page 70.

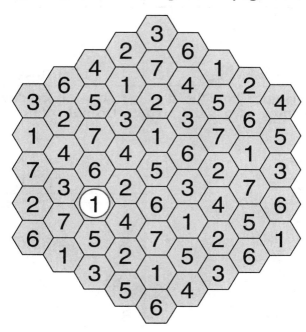

105

ROUND TRIP

VISUAL ◆ LOGIC

When this puzzle has been completed correctly, you will have made a round trip through its set of dots. You must visit every dot exactly once, make no diagonal moves, and return to your starting point. Parts of the right path are shown; can you find the rest?

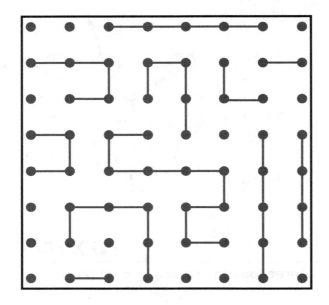

TRI, TRI AGAIN

LANGUAGE ◆ SPATIAL

Fit the nine triangles into the big one so six everyday words are spelled out reading across the arrows. Do not rotate the triangles.

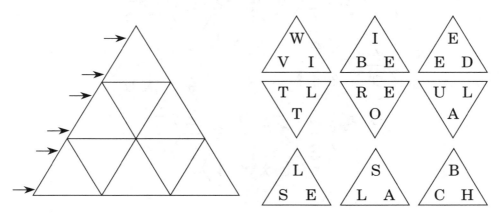

106

WORD EQUATIONS

Determine the three defined words in each equation. The third word is formed when the second is written directly after the first; for example, for "for each + shape = act in a play," you would respond "per + form = perform."

1. auto + cherished animal = wall-to-wall rug

2. country hotel + broke bread = existing since birth

3. golf standard + clip quickly = root veggie

4. made a lap + great fury = humorist's work

5. against + school exam = competitive game

RING LOGIC

Complete the diagram by drawing in the links between the rings using the statements. Assume that all the rings in the picture are locked rigidly into position and cannot be moved in any direction. Consider yourself a true ringmaster if you can find the solution in under six minutes!

1. The pattern looks the same even when it's rotated like a wheel.

2. Ring C is linked twice; its right side is to the front.

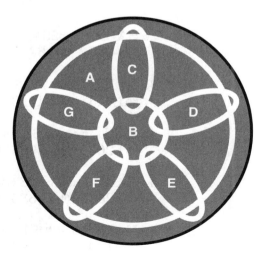

STACKED UP

VISUAL ◆ SPATIAL

The box on the left can be formed by three of the numbered boxes superimposed on top of each other; do not turn them in any way. Can you figure out which three work?

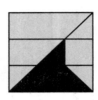

1. 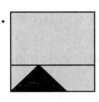 **2.** 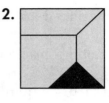 **3.**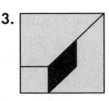

4. 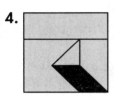 **5.** 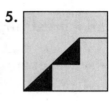 **6.**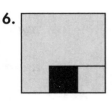

SWITCHEROO

DECODING

In each group, for the first word and its number equivalent given, determine what the number equivalent is for the second word.

1. LIME is to 9374 as MILE is to:
   (a) 7439 (b) 7943 (c) 7394 (d) 3479

2. SAIL is to 2648 as AILS is to:
   (a) 6482 (b) 6284 (c) 6428 (d) 6824

3. ACME is to 7143 as MACE is to:
   (a) 7431 (b) 4713 (c) 4317 (d) 4173

4. EVIL is to 5236 as VILE is to:
   (a) 2635 (b) 2653 (c) 2356 (d) 2365

5. PARE is to 6528 as REAP is to:
   (a) 2568 (b) 2685 (c) 2865 (d) 2856

6. NAIL is to 3981 as LAIN is to:
   (a) 1893 (b) 8193 (c) 1983 (d) 1938

SUDOKU

Directions for solving are on page 71.

	8				4			1
			3		8		2	
7		1						8
2	4				3	8		
	1			8			3	
		7	9				1	4
4						9		6
	6		7		5			
9			8				7	

LANGUAGE

SLIDE RULE

Slide each column of letters up or down in the box and form as many everyday 3-letter words as you can in the windows where BAY is now. We formed 33 words, including BAY.

Your list of words:

109

IN THE ABSTRACT

VISUAL ◆ SPATIAL

Directions for solving are on page 76.

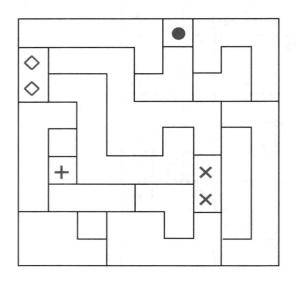

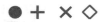

NEXT TO NOTHING

LANGUAGE ◆ VISUAL

In the first row, the H is next to the number zero and the Q is next to the letter O. Circle all of the letters next to zeroes then scramble the circled letters to spell out a man's name.

H0	QO	PO	S0
NO	E0	A0	YO
R0	WO	MO	JO
FO	BO	UO	L0
KO	XO	GO	ZO
DO	VO	C0	IO

MAGIC NUMBER SQUARES

Fill in the empty boxes so these groups add up to the number below each diagram: 1. each row; 2. each column; 3. each long diagonal; 4. the four center squares; 5. the four corner squares; and 6. each quarter of the diagram. A number will be used only once per diagram.

1.

18			
	5		10
7		8	
		11	

46

2.

10	11	13	
14			12
		8	

50

SKILLS TEST

The correct letters of each 3-letter unit will complete two 6-letter words, one which ends with the three missing letters, and one which begins with the three missing letters.

1. H A P __ __ __ C I L

2. B E C __ __ __ L E T

3. O R C __ __ __ D E N

4. H O N __ __ __ E E M

5. A T T __ __ __ U R E

6. B O T __ __ __ M I T

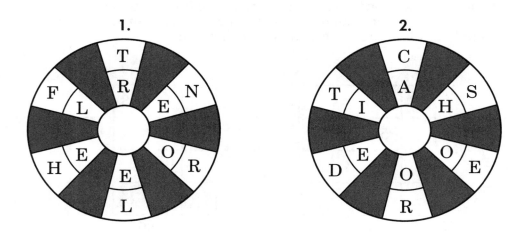

1.

2.

COUNT THE TRIANGLES

VISUAL ◆ SPATIAL

To solve this puzzle, write down the three letters that describe each triangle in this figure. We found 20 triangles; how many can you locate?

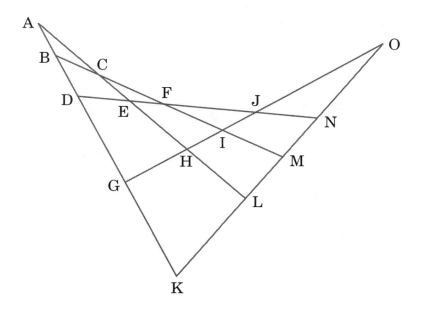

ELIMINATION

Directions for solving are on page 73. Once again, the remaining words will form a thought.

LINKS LIVE MINIMIZING YOUR
UNCOMPLIMENTARY LIFE MOTE AND
TRUDGE LET HEART OTHERS CAROUSEL
LIVE PLANKS THEIRS

Eliminate…

1. the word that contains all five vowels (a, e, i, o, and u) in reverse order.

2. the word that is a title of a Broadway musical.

3. the word that sounds like a wildcat.

4. the two words (one a verb and one a noun) that can mean "lumber."

5. the word with two vowels that forms a word no matter which vowel (a, e, i, o, or u) replaces its first one.

6. the word that contains the same letter four times.

7. the word that forms another word when its first letter is moved to the end.

VISUAL ◆ SPATIAL

BLOCK PARTY

See page 84 for solving directions.

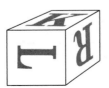   

FUN WITH FACTS AND FIGURES

MATH

Directions for solving are on page 80.

1. Take the number of vowels in the word COORDINATION and multiply by the number of consonants in the word. _____

2. Next, add the number of days in September. _____

3. Now, divide by the number of doughnuts in a half-dozen. _____

4. Subtract the number of sides on a coin. _____

5. Multiply by the number opposite the four on a standard clock dial. _____

Our answer is the number of degrees in a right angle. *Is yours?*

FILLING STATION

LANGUAGE

Directions for solving are on page 82.

1. D H L N W (Asian capital)

   __ E __   __ E __ __ I

2. B C L P P S S (artist)

   __ A __ __ O   __ I __ A __ __ O

3. D H R R R T Y Y (movie)

   "__ I __ __ __   __ A __ __ __"

4. B C F H K L N N R R Y (book character)

   __ U __ __ __ E __ E __ __ __   __ I __ __

5. F H K L N N R R T (singer)

   A __ E __ __ A   __ __ A __ __ __ I __

WHAT'S YOUR NUMBER?

Can you figure out the relationship of the numbers in the first two figures and, based on that, what missing number goes into the space with the question mark?

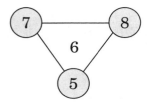 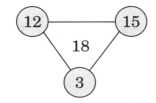 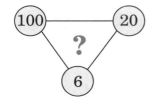

MATH

CIRCLE MATH

Directions for solving are on page 102. We've started you off by telling you that B = 4.

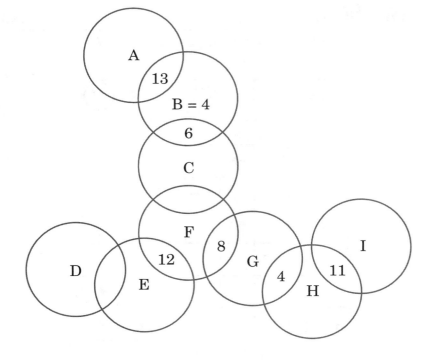

 **CROSS-UPS**

LANGUAGE

Using only the letters given above each diagram, fill in the boxes in such a way that an everyday compound word is formed, one part reading across and the other part reading down. The letter already in the diagram is a letter shared by both parts of the word. Note: Each part of the compound word is an entire word on its own.

1. A E E F H S T W

2. B B C E E L N S T

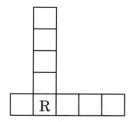

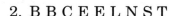
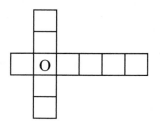

ARROW MAZE

VISUAL

Directions for solving are on page 77.

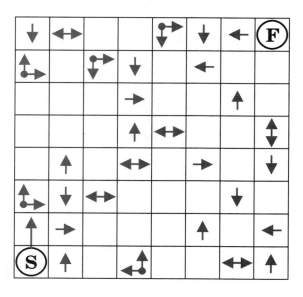

DOVETAILED WORDS

Directions for solving are on page 97.

1. J O R U A I N C G E E   _____   _____

2. N M U E D R I S E C   _____   _____

3. S D E T A P T I O O N T   _____   _____

4. W E L R B I S O W T   _____   _____

5. S T R A O N V G E E   _____   _____

LANGUAGE ◆ SPATIAL # WORD HUNT

Find words by moving from one letter to any adjoining letter. You may start a word with any letter in the diagram. In forming a word you may return to a letter as often as you wish, but do not stand on a letter using it twice in direct succession. In this Word Hunt, you'll be searching for 4-, 5-, and 6-letter words that end with OP, such as SWOOP. We found 12 4-letter words, 7 5-letter words (including SWOOP), and 7 6-letter words.

B	C	S	W	J	L
I	R	A	O	F	O
S	H	O	R	D	P
C	O	T	P	S	O
N	S	L	I	A	L
U	N	D	O	L	G

Your list of words:

VISION QUEST

VISUAL

Find the row or column that contains five DIFFERENT sandals.

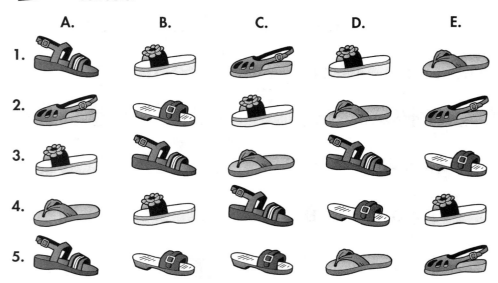

A.　　B.　　C.　　D.　　E.

1.
2.
3.
4.
5.

WORD WHEEL

LANGUAGE

Directions for solving are on page 100. Beginning with the "G" at the arrow, we formed 33 words of three or more letters.

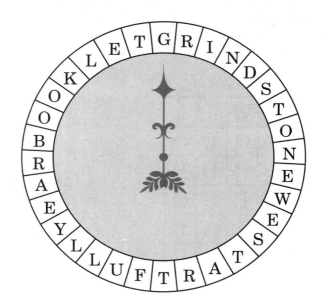

ANAGRAM MAZE

WEEK
17

Directions for solving are on page 79. This time, there are 19 words to anagram and the first word you'll be anagramming is EATS.

1 CULT	2 WAIT	3 EATS	4 TUBA	5 ACME	6 WHAT
7 WINE	8 HUNT	9 WHIM	10 DECK	11 PURR	12 DIET
13 COAL	14 DROP	15 NUTS	16 NEWT	17 OOZE	18 DOSE
19 RIPE	20 CUFF	21 PLUS	22 NEWS	23 LIST	24 FEET
25 VANE	26 KNEE	27 BODY	28 INTO	29 ALOE	30 FALL
31 FIVE	32 FAST	33 HARE	34 TACO	35 CREW	36 FOIL

LOGIC

SKILLS TEST

Can you determine the letter that goes into the space with the question mark?

A	L	K	J
B	M	P	I
C	?	O	H
D	E	F	G

119

CARD SENSE

LOGIC

Directions for solving are on page 78.

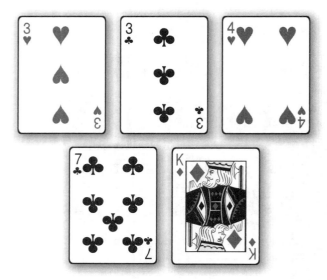

1. The diamond is neither on the bottom nor directly above a heart.

2. The four is somewhere between the threes.

3. The seven is somewhere above the king.

4. No two adjacent cards are the same suit.

BULL'S-EYE LETTER

LANGUAGE

Add the SAME single letter to each group of three letters, then rearrange the letters to form six everyday 4-letter words.

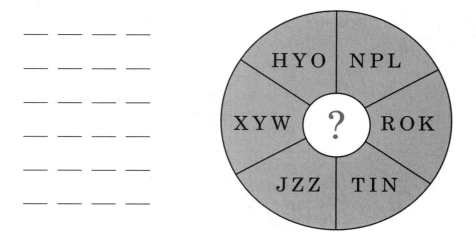

— — — —

— — — —

— — — —

— — — —

— — — —

— — — —

CIRCLE SEARCH

WEEK 17

Directions for solving are on page 98. Here you're looking to form 11 words of at least three letters, and proper names are not allowed.

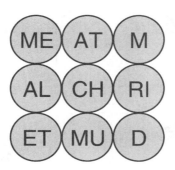

MAGNIFIND

Figure out which two areas of the drawing have been enlarged.

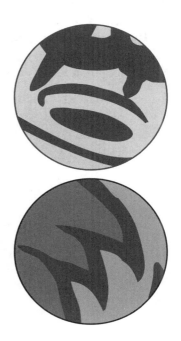

STACKED UP

WEEK 17

VISUAL ◆ SPATIAL

Directions for solving are on page 108.

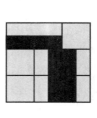

1.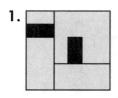

2.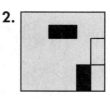

3.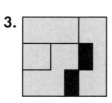

4.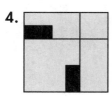

5.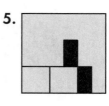

6.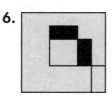

SLIDE RULE

LANGUAGE

Directions for solving are on page 109. Here, you're to form 4-letter words. We found 34 words, including APED.

Your list of words:

122

CODE WORD

Directions for solving are on page 74.

$$\overline{1} \ \overline{2} \ \overline{3} \ \overline{4} \ \overline{5} \ \overline{6} \ \overline{7} \ \overline{8} \ \overline{9} \ \overline{10} \ \overline{11}$$

A 10 5 4 7 8 3 4 6 V 6 1 11 7 N 6 2 N A 9 M A 10 10

5 7 W N K N 7 W 9 W 4 A 5 6 V 6 1 11 7 N 6 6 10 9 6 2 9

D 7 2 N 3, 5 4 6 11 9 5 2 10 10 4 A V 6 5 7 1 6 A D

5 4 6 N 6 W 9 P A P 6 1 5 7 F 2 N D 7 8 5 W 4 7 ' 9

B 6 6 N C A 8 3 4 5 A 5 2 5.

SQUARE LINKS

Directions for solving are on page 91.

WORD CHARADE   LANGUAGE ◆ VISUAL

Directions for solving are on page 98.

My first letter is directly between two vowels in one of the rows.

My second letter is the only letter in one of the rows that does not appear in the word PRUDENT.

R	J	E	Z	J	T	V	P
A	N	L	T	B	Z	U	I
X	M	I	E	V	U	T	L
F	S	T	B	Z	W	S	G
T	U	E	P	N	I	R	D
O	D	H	V	B	L	Q	T
U	T	L	J	P	K	P	B
C	Q	I	N	T	V	O	Q

My third letter is the first letter of a string of letters in consecutive alphabetical order reading up.

My fourth letter appears either directly above or directly below wherever my second letter appears.

My fifth letter appears in the fourth column but not in the fifth column.

My sixth letter appears once in each row and column.

— — — — — —

ALL IN A ROW   MATH

Directions for solving are on page 75. This time, look for the most groups of consecutive numbers adding up to 13.

A. 7 5 4 2 3 6 1 6 8 2 1 2 9 7 4 8 1 3 1 6 5 2 1 4

B. 9 3 1 8 6 5 7 2 1 4 5 1 8 3 9 4 2 5 3 7 4 2 1 1

C. 3 1 8 6 9 2 1 1 7 3 4 5 1 7 6 2 8 4 3 2 1 3 6 4

MISSING DOMINOES

Directions for solving are on page 86.

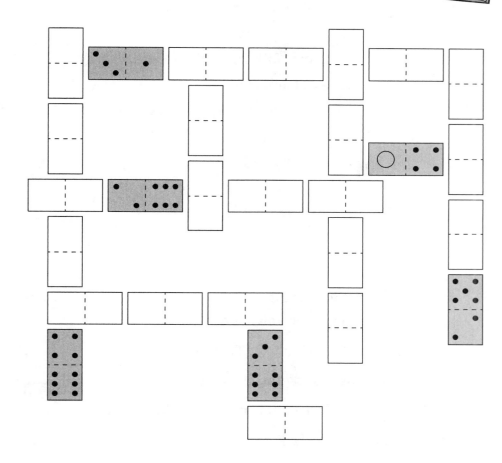

DOMINOES

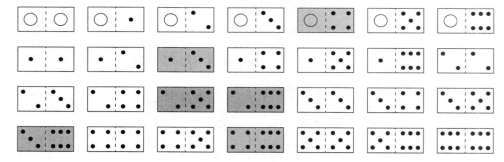

COMPOUND IT   LANGUAGE

Directions for solving are on page 83.

1. week, dish, dry, power
2. pan, cloth, night, wall
3. bound, fall, flower, handle
4. less, back, bar, pot
5. tender, room, splash, luck
6. mate, down, loin, foot
7. fox, bird, note, pack
8. book, tail, bath, horse
9. gate, grass, tub, shop
10. hopper, worn, way, fruit

ANIMAL CHARADES   LANGUAGE

Directions for solving are on page 77.

My FIRST is in MARTEN and in TRAIN;   _____

My SECOND is in RABBIT and in BRAIN;   _____

My THIRD is in GOLDFISH but not in FOIL;   _____

My FOURTH is in DOLPHIN but not in SPOIL;   _____

My FIFTH is in EGRET and in TAPE;   _____

My SIXTH is in THRUSH and in SHAPE;   _____

My SEVENTH is in WEASEL but not in LOOSE;   _____

My EIGHTH is in SHREW but not in TRUCE;   _____

My NINTH is in JACKAL but not in CRATE.   _____

My WHOLE is a bird, or one who stays up late.

_____

ROUND TRIP

Directions for solving are on page 106.

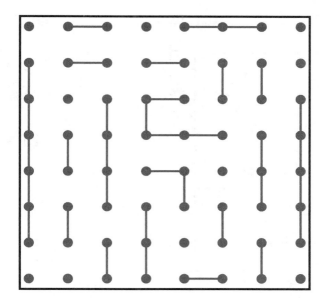

SEVEN WORD ZINGER

Directions for solving are on page 80.

127

IN THE ABSTRACT

VISUAL ◆ SPATIAL

Directions for solving are on page 76.

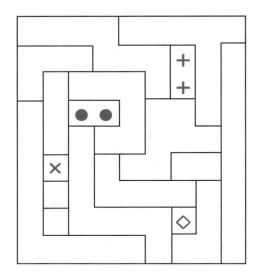

DEDUCTION PROBLEM

LOGIC

The vending machine in an office building has buttons for cocoa, coffee, tea, creamer, and sugar. The beverages are dispensed in cups and the latter two items in packets. However, something has gone awry with the machine, so that each button dispenses something different from what the label indicates, although no two buttons dispense the same item. Mary pushed the tea and sugar buttons but received coffee and a packet of creamer. Mike pushed the cocoa and creamer buttons but obtained tea and sugar. However, Ellen, who had brought a beverage to work, pushed the creamer and sugar buttons and received exactly those two items.

Can you figure out how the machine should be relabeled so that one may obtain just what is wanted?

VISUAL ◆ SPATIAL
LOOSE TILE

The tray on the right seemed the ideal place to store the set of loose dominoes. Unfortunately, when the tray was full, one domino was left over. Determine the arrangement of the dominoes in the tray and which is the Loose Tile.

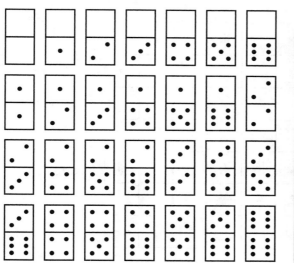 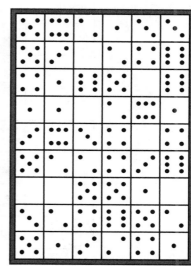

LANGUAGE

COUNT ON IT!

See page 81 for solving directions.

1. Y O M N W D F A   2. H O E A O N R

3. E N E U K E I   4. N D E T E   5. N   6. D

$$\overline{1}\ \overline{2}\ \overline{3}\ \overline{4} \qquad \overline{1} \qquad \overline{1}\ \overline{2}\ \overline{3}\ \overline{4}\ \overline{5}\ \overline{6} \qquad \overline{1}\ \overline{2}\ \overline{3}\ \overline{4}$$

$$\overline{1}\ \overline{2}\ \overline{3} \quad \overline{1}\ \overline{2}\ \overline{3}\ \overline{4}\text{,} \quad \overline{1}\ \overline{2}\ \overline{3}\ \overline{4} \quad \overline{1}\ \overline{2}\ \overline{3}\text{.}$$

ARROW MAZE

VISUAL

Starting at the S and following the arrow up, see if you can find your way to F. When you reach an arrow, you MUST follow its direction and continue in that direction until you come to the next arrow. When you reach a two-headed arrow, you can choose either direction. It's okay to cross your own path.

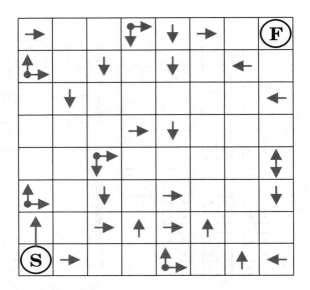

QUICK FILL

LANGUAGE

Determine the 10-letter word from the clues. All the letters in the word are listed.

A B D N O O R T U U

1. Letter 6 is from the first half of the alphabet.

2. Letter 2 does not appear in the word TURBAN.

3. Letters 4, 3, and 10, in order, spell out a pecan or acorn.

4. In the alphabet, letter 8 appears somewhere before letter 9.

5. In the alphabet, letter 7 appears somewhere before letter 5 and only one letter separates them.

6. Letter 1 is a consonant.

$$\overline{1}\ \overline{2}\ \overline{3}\ \overline{4}\ \overline{5}\ \overline{6}\ \overline{7}\ \overline{8}\ \overline{9}\ \overline{10}$$

SUDOKU

Place a number into each box so each row across, column down, and small 9-box square within the larger square (there are 9 of these) contains 1 through 9.

					8		2	
		1		6	4	8		7
	8	9				4		
4		7		1	3			6
8				4				1
3			7	5		2		4
		2				7	3	
6		8	1	3		9		
	4		2					

MATH

ALL IN A ROW

Which row below contains the most groups of consecutive numbers adding up to 9? Look carefully, because some groups may overlap. We've underlined an example of a group in each row to start you off.

A. 6 <u>1 8</u> 3 1 5 2 2 6 4 1 4 3 2 5 6 7 1 3 6 2 4 7 1

B. 7 3 5 4 4 <u>2 1 6</u> 8 5 7 4 3 2 6 5 3 2 1 3 8 3 7 4

C. 1 2 5 7 1 4 3 1 6 4 2 8 3 5 1 2 <u>6 3</u> 5 7 4 1 2 2

ONLINE NETWORK

WEEK 19

VISUAL

In each two-column group, take the letters in the left-hand column along the paths (indicated by the lines) and place them in their proper boxes in the right-hand column. When done, you'll find three related words reading down each of the two right-hand columns.

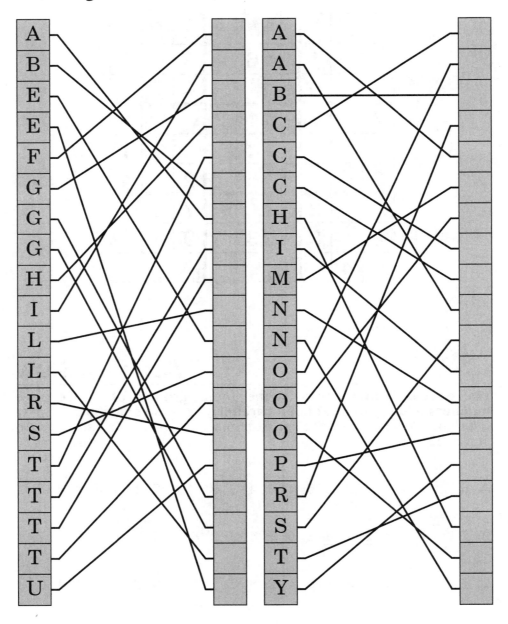

132

COUNT TO TEN

WEEK 19

Examine the gems and then answer these questions: 1. Which row contains the most opals? 2. Which row contains the most emeralds? 3. Which row contains an equal number of opals and emeralds?

1.
2.
3.
4.
5.
6.
7.
8.
9.
10.

EASY PICKINGS

To solve, simply cross out one letter in each pair below. When the puzzle is completed correctly, the remaining letters will spell out a thought.

NM AC OK EU   RS MU RT ET

ET OM   LC EA UL OG AH   AN ET

EL DE AM SU ST   NO EN CW BE

AE   RD TA YB.

ANIMAL CHARADES LANGUAGE

Each line contains a clue to a letter of the alphabet. These letters, in the given order, will spell out the name of an animal. The animal's identity is also hinted at in the last sentence of the Charade.

My FIRST is in GOPHER and in GRIP; ⸺⸺

My SECOND is in LION and in CLIP; ⸺⸺

My THIRD is in DINGO but not in FIND; ⸺⸺

My FOURTH is in EGRET but not in GRIND; ⸺⸺

My FIFTH is in PYTHON and in YOUNG; ⸺⸺

My SIXTH is in PORCUPINE and in TONGUE. ⸺⸺

My WHOLE is a bird with plump body and pointed wings;
   It murmurs and coos rather than warbles or sings.

CODE WORD DECODING

Decipher a quote and the Code Word's eleven letters, represented by the numbers 1 through 11. So, if the Code Word were "THUNDERCLAP," 1 in the quote would be T, 2 would be H, etc.

$$\overline{1}\ \overline{2}\ \overline{3}\ \overline{4}\ \overline{5}\ \overline{6}\ \overline{7}\ \overline{8}\ \overline{9}\ \overline{10}\ \overline{11}$$

3 10 3 5 7 Y 8 11 5 F 1 10 9 6 9 F 2 8 7 : 1 H 10

4 10 2 6 1 Y 5 F 2 7 5 11 10 F 2 D 10 11 8 9

1 8 3 10 , 4 6 1 1 H 10 11 1 8 9 G 5 F 1 H 10

1 H 5 7 9 7 10 3 2 8 9 11 .

ANAGRAM MAZE

WEEK
19

The diagram contains 36 words, 21 of which are anagrams of other everyday words. Start at the top arrow and anagram OWNS. While solving, move up, down, right, or left to the only adjacent word that can be anagrammed. Continue until you arrive at the bottom arrow. There is only one path through the maze.

1 HEAR	2 ARID	3 RIPE	4 VANE	5 MALT	6 OWNS
7 ACME	8 LILY	9 LESS	10 FAST	11 NUTS	12 NEWT
13 WHAT	14 DROP	15 MUCH	16 MINK	17 CELL	18 HOOT
19 SOME	20 BEAU	21 RELY	22 CAPE	23 RAPS	24 AFAR
25 HAVE	26 TINY	27 MAZE	28 MAKE	29 DIET	30 WOOL
31 CARS	32 DOES	33 NEWS	34 KNEE	35 COAL	36 KNOW

MATH ◆ LOGIC

WHAT'S YOUR NUMBER?

Can you figure out the relationship of the numbers in the first two groups of figures and, based on that, what missing number goes into the space with the question mark in the third group of figures?

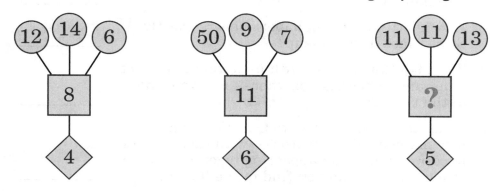

IN THE ABSTRACT

VISUAL ◆ SPATIAL

Fill in each section with one of the four symbols so no sections containing the same symbol touch. Four sections are already complete.

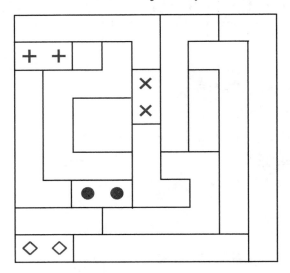

THE LINEUP

LANGUAGE

While scrutinizing the lineup of letters, can you answer the five questions correctly in five minutes or less?

TOBFSKIPEJARROGANTYZMINDRRECEIVINGQFLEWUX

1. Which letter of the alphabet does not appear in the lineup? _____

2. What 8-letter word — with its letters in correct order and appearing together — can you find in the lineup? _____

3. Which letter of the alphabet appears exactly three times in the lineup? _____

4. What 9-letter word — with its letters in correct order and appearing together — can you find in the lineup? _____

5. Other than the answers to Questions 2 and 4, how many everyday words — with their letters in correct order and appearing together — of four or more letters can you find in the lineup? _____

ELIMINATION

Cross off the capitalized words according to the given instructions. The remaining words, in order, will form a thought.

> TIME ONE ROGUE CARBON THING LIVER TWELFTH WE TIDE GORGEOUS NEVER FOR RUN GROWTH OUT MAN OF QUICK SOUL IS ORGANIZE POOL SURPRISE FOOTPRINT

Eliminate...

1. the four words that begin with the same three letters (in any order).

2. the two words that, when put together, form the name of an English city.

3. the four words that complete the following to form a truism: ____ and ____ wait ____ no ____

4. the word that can precede "sand," "silver," and "witted."

5. the word that ends with four consonants.

6. the word that, when a vowel is added to it, becomes the name of an Asian capital.

7. the two words that, when put together, form a phrase meaning "a negative impact that someone or something has on the environment."

LANGUAGE # GOING IN CIRCLES

In each circle, insert one letter into each empty space to form an 8-letter word. Words may read either clockwise or counter-clockwise and may begin with any letter in the circle.

1.

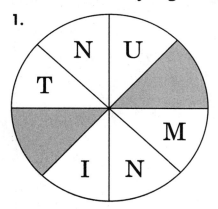

2.

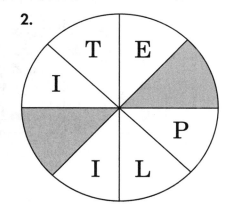

WORD VISIBILITY

LANGUAGE

There are six 5-letter words below. The first letter of the answer is found in the first pair of letters, and it is either the top or the bottom letter. Continue across each pair.

For example, the word GIRL would be found thus:
<u>G</u> A <u>R</u> <u>L</u>
L <u>I</u> T X

1. T O A P K
   S H O R C

2. O I B E M
   W F T O N

3. R E H S W
   B A N E D

4. V U Y O R
   F E R F T

5. G A E P C
   L R A N H

6. C H U J L
   N O I L M

CARD SENSE

LOGIC

Five playing cards were shuffled and put in a pile, one on top of another. Using the clues, can you identify each card's position in the pile?

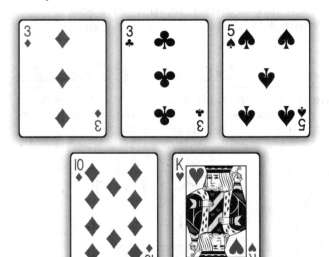

1. The black cards are not adjacent.

2. The red cards are adjacent.

3. The five is not on top.

4. The diamonds are not adjacent.

5. The threes are not adjacent.

HEXAGON HUNT

In this diagram of six-sided figures, there are 10 "special" hexagons. These 10 are special because the six numbers around each one are all different from each other and the center. We've circled one of the 10. Can you find the other 9?

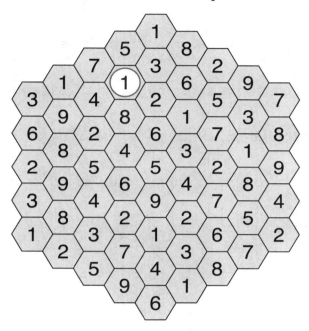

LANGUAGE

COMPOUND IT

Starting at #1, pick a word that will form a compound word with a word chosen in #2. Then with the word you've selected in #2, pick one from #3 to form another compound word. Continue in this manner to #10, so that you've formed nine compound words. In some instances more than one compound word can be formed, but there is only one path to get you to #10.

1. ground, bound, fellow, bird

2. hog, ship, less, bath

3. shape, tie, tub, board

4. breaker, less, walk, room

5. out, over, mate, week

6. standing, back, line, wit

7. pack, ache, woods, man

8. handle, kind, horse, hunt

9. dish, bar, hearted, joy

10. washer, stick, maid, frail

GRAND TOUR

WEEK 20

LANGUAGE ◆ VISUAL

Form a continuous chain of 4-letter words moving through the maze from START to FINISH. The second part of one word becomes the first part of the next word. This puzzle starts with PO-ST-AR (post, star).

START

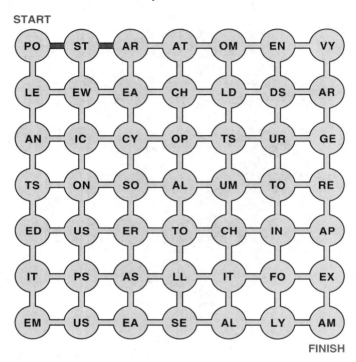

FINISH

V COUNT

VISUAL

Here's an eye exam that's also a V exam! First, read the sentence below. Next, go back and read the sentence again, but this time count all of the V's. How many are there?

VILE VETERINARIAN VIOLET VANCE

VIED FOR EVERY VOLLEYBALL

VICTORY AVAILABLE VERSUS VERY

VIRTUOUS VETERAN VERA VAUGHN

WITH VERVE, VIVACITY, AND VORACITY.

140

LOOSE TILE

WEEK
20

The tray on the right seemed the ideal place to store the set of loose dominoes. Unfortunately, when the tray was full, one domino was left over. Determine the arrangement of the dominoes in the tray and which is the Loose Tile.

CIRCLE SEARCH

Move from circle to adjoining circle, horizontally and vertically only, to form 13 common, everyday words of at least three letters. Don't change the order of the letters in the circles that contain more than one letter. Proper names are not allowed.

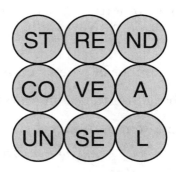

141

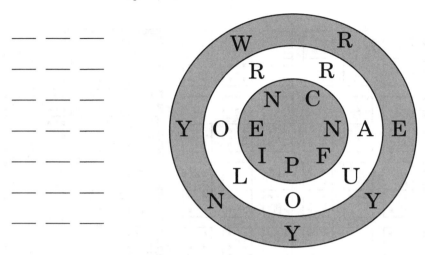

WEEK 20 — SEVEN WORD ZINGER   LANGUAGE

Using each letter once, form seven everyday 3-letter words with the first letter coming from the center, the second from the middle, and the third from the outer circle. Your words may differ from ours.

— — —

— — —

— — —

— — —

— — —

— — —

— — —

FUN WITH FACTS AND FIGURES   MATH

This puzzle tests you on a lot of little facts and figures. Solve the quiz in the order given since each answer is used in the next statement. There are no fractions used here.

1. Take the number of people in four duos and multiply it by the number used to indicate November in dates. _____

2. Next, add the number of letters in the name of the country that contains New Delhi and Mumbai. _____

3. Now, divide by the number of wheels on a tricycle. _____

4. Subtract the number of tentacles on an octopus. _____

5. Add the value of the Roman numeral III. _____

Our answer is the number of letters in the alphabet. *Is yours?*

142

LICENSE PLATES

Each box contains six letters of the first and last names of 19th-century English novelists. The top three are a part of the first name and the bottom three are a part of the last name, in order.

1.
```
J A N
S T E
```

2.
```
H A R
I C K
```

3.
```
A R Y
S H E
```

4.
```
I L Y
B R O
```

5.
```
R A M
T O K
```

6.
```
O R G
E L I
```

LANGUAGE

ANTONYMS QUIZ

An antonym is a word that is opposite in meaning to another word; for example, "cold" is the antonym of "hot." One of the words following each capitalized word is the antonym of that word.

1. DELETERIOUS   a. prosaic   b. helpful   c. brisk

2. DIFFIDENT   a. bold   b. lenient   c. frugal

3. LAVISH   a. cavalier   b. scarce   c. noisome

4. FACILE   a. itinerant   b. philanthropic   c. strenuous

5. TREPIDATION   a. abundance   b. omission   c. serenity

6. ACERBITY   a. indolence   b. sweetness   c. resilience

7. VILE   a. virtuous   b. eccentric   c. haggard

8. COMMEND   a. transcend   b. denounce   c. cavort

"They are ill discoverers that think there is no land, when they can see nothing but sea."
— *Francis Bacon*

ALPHABET SOUP

LANGUAGE ◆ VISUAL

Cross off each letter from the alphabet list that appears in the larger group of letters. Then rearrange the letters not crossed out to form the name of a world capital.

G	U	V	U	K	U	V	G	H	U	G	V	K	D	U	H
K	A	Y	J	L	Y	Q	J	A	H	G	Y	H	V	K	Y
X	I	C	K	G	V	A	T	I	J	Y	K	B	X	G	C
J	H	X	I	P	W	Z	G	H	N	S	I	J	Y	W	F

A B C D E F G H I J K L M N O P Q R S T U V W X Y Z

Capital: _____

CHANGELINGS

LANGUAGE

Can you change the first word into the second word by changing only one letter at a time? Do not rearrange the order of the letters with each change. Each change must result in an everyday word, and words beginning with a capital letter, slang, or obsolete words aren't allowed.

1. HANG

_____

_____

_____

MAPS
(4 changes)

2. TOWN

_____

_____

_____

VOTE
(4 changes)

3. POTS

_____

_____

_____

YAMS
(4 changes)

144

CROSS EXAMINATION

In each set, cross out the three groups of letters so that the remaining groups, in order, spell out a word.

1. COM   BACH   LOUS   PAT   E   LOR

2. PRO   E   VEN   LEC   TRO   TUTE   CUTE

3. TA   PAL   CHOM   STI   E   TER   ION

4. QUI   LEP   STAN   RE   BLE   CHAUN

5. RE   VAL   CEP   POR   TA   CLE   IST

6. DRAW   AC   BIN   CEL   ER   PLAST   ATE

7. DE   FAN   TAS   PLOR   GRY   A   BLE

8. MON   PES   TEL   TI   SURE   CIDE

SLIDE RULE

Slide each column of letters up or down in the box and form as many everyday 3-letter words as you can in the windows where LED is now. We formed 40 words, including LED.

Your list of words:

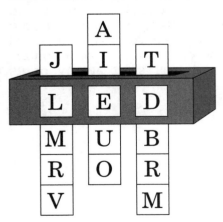

145

FILLING STATION

WEEK 21

LANGUAGE

Place the given consonants on the dashes to form an actor's name, his birthplace, and three of his movies. The vowels have already been placed.

1. B G H H M P R R T Y (actor)

   __ U __ __ __ __ E __   __ O __ A __ __

2. K K N N R R W W Y Y (birthplace)

   __ E __   __ O __ __ ,   __ E __   __ O __ __

3. D F F H P R R S T T T (1936 movie)

   "__ __ E   __ E __ __ I __ I E __

   __ O __ E __ __"

4. G H H R R S (1941 movie)

   "__ I __ __   __ I E __ __ A"

5. B C C L N S (1942 movie)

   "__ A __ A __ __ A __ __ A"

SQUARE LINKS

LANGUAGE

Write one letter in each empty box so that an everyday 8-letter word is spelled out around each black box. Each word may read either clockwise or counter-clockwise, and may start at any of its letters.

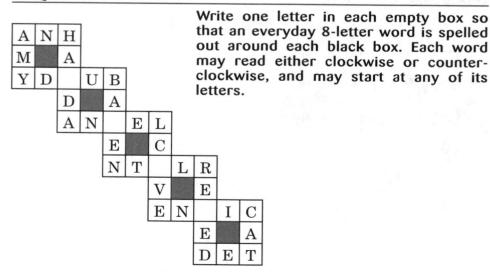

146

MISSING DOMINOES

In this game you use all 28 dominoes that are in a standard set. Each one has a different combination from 0-0, 0-1, 0-2, to 6-6. Domino halves with the same number of dots lie next to each other. To avoid confusion we have used an open circle to indicate a zero. Can you fill in the missing white dominoes to complete the board?

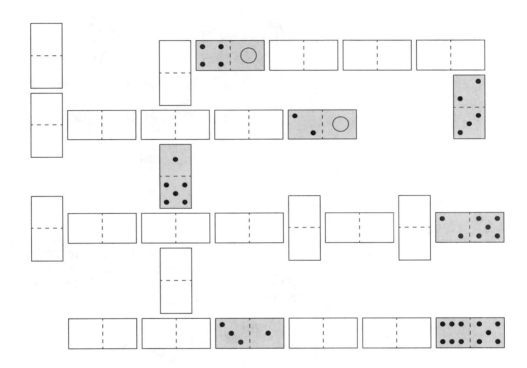

DOMINOES

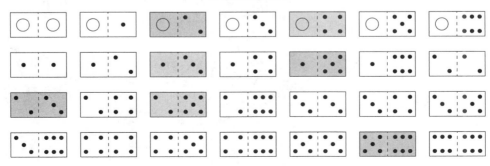

BULL'S-EYE LETTER
LANGUAGE

Add the SAME single letter to each group of three letters, then rearrange them to form six everyday 4-letter words.

— — — —

— — — —

— — — —

— — — —

— — — —

— — — —

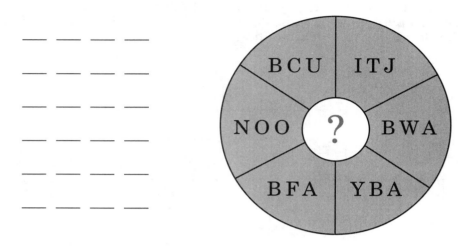

BCU   ITJ

NOO   ?   BWA

BFA   YBA

LETTER, PLEASE
DECODING

The numbers below stand for certain letters on the telephone dial. You will see that one number may stand for more than one letter — for example, 3 may be D, E, or F. By finding the correct letter for each number, you will have spelled out a thought.

2 6 9   7 3 2 4 7 3

3 6 7   7 8 2 2 3 7 7

2 3 4 4 6 7   9 4 8 4

2 6 2 4 8 4 6 6 .

SUDOKU

Directions for solving are on page 131.

2	1			5				8
	4	9			1	5		
8			2		3	4		9
	3				5	8		
		2	3		7	1		
		5	6				7	
5		3	1		6			4
		8	5			2	9	
6				2			5	1

VISUAL

KEEP ON MOVING

The goal is to move from the shaded square to the asterisk. Since the shaded square has the number 3 in it, you must move three squares up, down, left, or right, but not diagonally. In the new square will be another number; move that number of squares up, down, left, or right, continuing in this way until you reach the asterisk. It's okay to cross or retrace your own path.

2	2	2	5	5	2
5	3	4	1	3	5
3	1	3	1	2	3
1	1	3	*	4	5
5	5	1	2	4	4
3	4	5	5	3	4

WORD HUNT

LANGUAGE ◆ SPATIAL

Find words by moving from one letter to any adjoining letter. You may start a word with any letter in the diagram. In forming a word you may return to a letter as often as you wish, but do not stand on a letter using it twice in direct succession. In this Word Hunt, you are searching for 4- and 5-letter words that begin with BU. We found ten 4-letter words, including BURN and nine 5-letter words. Plurals and present-tense verbs ending in "s" are not allowed.

Your list of words:

H	T	S	R	O
S	P	R	Y	T
U	B	U	N	N
N	G	L	K	V
C	H	E	L	Y

OVERLAY

VISUAL ◆ SPATIAL

When you overlay the three diagrams in the top row, which of the three lettered diagrams, A, B, or C, will be formed?

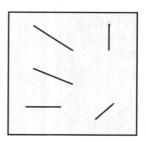

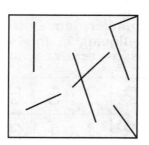

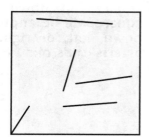

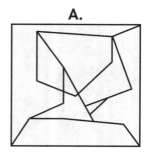

A.

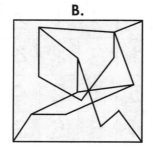

B.

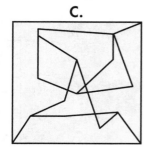

C.

150

SYMBOL-ISM

WEEK
21

This is simply a Cryptogram that uses symbols instead of letters to spell out a truism. Each symbol stands for the same letter throughout. For this puzzle, we've already indicated that ✪ = B and ✳ = H.

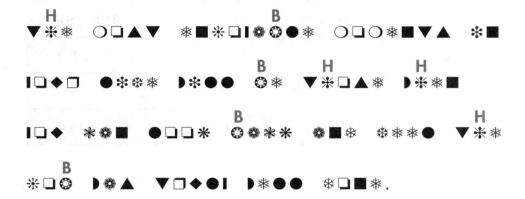

LANGUAGE

ASSOCIATIONS

You'll find eight groups of three words that can be associated in some way with each other (example: mantel, fireplace, logs). Cross out each group as you find it. The initial letters of the remaining words will spell out the answer to the riddle:

WHEN DO CANDLEMAKERS WORK?

CHICKEN HARD ORDINARY EGYPT FLEA BLOND

NERVOUS BUN LIBYA GOOSE GOLD WOBBLY

DIFFICULT BRONZE IRRITATE DAWDLE REDHEAD

CAPABLE MOSQUITO LINGER KETCHUP

BRUNETTE MUFFIN EPISODE SUDAN TARRY

NATIVE CHALLENGING DUCK DESTINY ROLL

SILVER SMOG GNAT

WAYWORDS

LANGUAGE

A 9-word thought can be found beginning with the word LIVE. Then, move to any adjacent box up, down, or diagonally for each following word.

LISTEN	DON'T	REJOICE	PRAISE
BUT	HESITATE	PUSH	FULLY
OTHERS	BELIEFS	THEM	LIVE
CHANGE	ON	YOUR	TODAY

COUNT THE RECTANGLES

VISUAL ◆ SPATIAL

To solve this puzzle, write down the four letters that describe each rectangle that includes the circle in this figure. We found 16 rectangles that include the circle; how many can you locate?

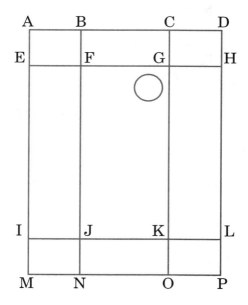

COUNT ON IT!

Use the given letters to form a familiar saying, one letter per dash. All the letters following 1 are the first letters of each word, the letters following 2 are the second letters of each word, etc. It is up to you to determine where each letter goes.

1. B D D G N T T T   2. A A E H H O O R

3. A E I R R T T   4. A E E H N N T   5. E G I T

6. N R S   7. G

$\overline{1}\ \overline{2}\ \overline{3}\ \overline{4}\ \overline{5}\ \overline{6}$ $\overline{1}\ \overline{2}$ $\overline{1}\ \overline{2}\ \overline{3}\ \overline{4}$

$\overline{1}\ \overline{2}\ \overline{3}\ \overline{4}\ \overline{5}$ $\overline{1}\ \overline{2}\ \overline{3}\ \overline{4}\ \overline{5}\ \overline{6}$ $\overline{1}\ \overline{2}\ \overline{3}\ \overline{4}$

$\overline{1}\ \overline{2}\ \overline{3}\ \overline{4}$ $\overline{1}\ \overline{2}\ \overline{3}\ \overline{4}\ \overline{5}\ \overline{6}\ \overline{7}$.

RINGERS

Each Ringer is composed of five rings. Use your imagination to rotate the rings so that you spell out four 5-letter words reading from the outside to the inside when all five rings are aligned correctly.

1.

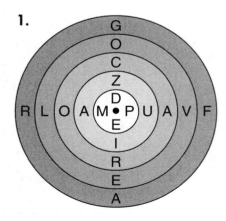

2.

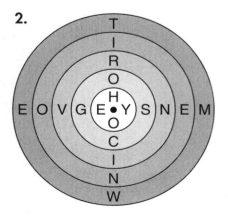

TIPS OF THE ICEBERG   MATH

The chart shows the gratuities each waiter or waitress earned on a recent breakfast shift at the Iceberg Diner. All you have to do is some addition and then answer the following questions:

1. Who made the most in total tips?
2. Who made the least?
3. Which two waitpersons made exactly the same amount?

EMPLOYEE	TIP 1	TIP 2	TIP 3	TIP 4	TIP 5
Hank	$1.15	$1.25	$1.00	$1.30	$1.10
Inez	$2.00	$2.30	$1.00	$1.20	$0.60
Jack	$0.45	$1.20	$2.10	$2.00	$0.40
Ken	$1.50	$1.50	$1.35	$1.25	$1.00
Laura	$1.95	$1.80	$1.20	$1.00	$1.00
Marty	$2.20	$1.50	$1.50	$1.40	$0.90
Noel	$1.10	$2.10	$0.90	$2.00	$1.00

COUNTDOWN

Following the connecting lines, find the only route in this grid that passes through the numbers backward from 9 to 1 consecutively.

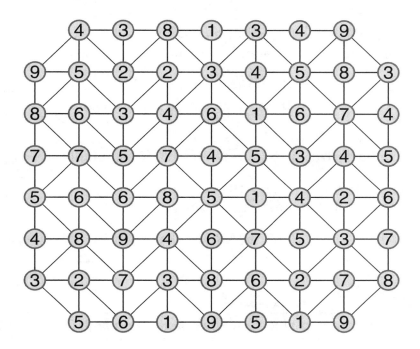

LANGUAGE ◆ SPATIAL

TRI, TRI AGAIN

Fit the nine triangles into the big one so six everyday words are spelled out reading across the arrows. Do not rotate the triangles.

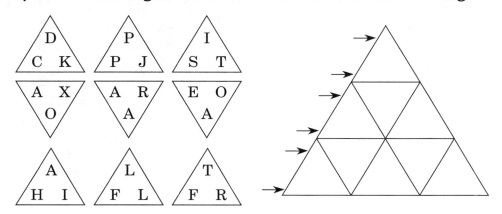

RELATIONSHIPS QUIZ

LANGUAGE

KENNEL is to DOG as STY is to PIG because a DOG lives in a KENNEL and a PIG lives in a STY. Each of the statements below is a relationship of some kind. Can you select the right word from the four following each?

1. INDIANA is to HOOSIER as OHIO is to _____.
   (a) Prairie   (b) Cleveland   (c) Buckeye   (d) Sooner

2. PACIFIC is to CALIFORNIA as ATLANTIC is to _____.
   (a) Portugal   (b) Bolivia   (c) India   (d) Alaska

3. EAT is to GOURMAND as SPEND is to _____.
   (a) dollar   (b) save   (c) restaurant   (d) squanderer

4. RED is to ORANGE as BLUE is to _____.
   (a) green   (b) yellow   (c) brown   (d) water

5. DOUBT is to TRUST as ARDENT is to _____.
   (a) sensitive   (b) stoic   (c) unusual   (d) impolite

MARCHING ORDERS

MATH ◆ LOGIC

Using a different two-step sequence of addition and/or subtraction, can you make your way from Start to Finish in each puzzle? We've started the first one for you using the sequence +2 and −1; continue this sequence to reach Finish. You will not cross your own path or pass through any square twice.

1.   FINISH ↑

4	3	5	4	6	8
1	2	7	5	4	9
4	6	3	7	5	7
3	1	4	6	8	9
2	5	2	9	5	6
0	3	8	6	7	4

↑ START

2.   FINISH ↑

13	14	12	16	14	18
9	11	14	10	20	15
8	6	4	13	12	16
3	2	9	8	8	17
5	4	7	6	10	13
0	3	2	4	8	9

↑ START

MISSING LINKS

WEEK 22

Fill the empty squares in the diagram with the given letters so that everyday words are formed reading across and down.

	R	I	V	E				U	M		E		J		C
O				E			O		E		A		M		I
C			A		C	O		N	T		N			N	
U		C			O		D		R		T		A		D
	O		E	O		E	R			A			A		E
E		E			E			I			E		L		Y
N		A			R		I		T	R	U		T		
	O		A	L			I		T			N		I	
		I				B		N	Y		A			I	S
		B		E	C		R			S		E	T		
C		N		U			R		I			E			O
O			P	I		A			O		S				N
M			T			A		O							O
	E		C		L		R		L		S		O		E
L		Y		F		E	L		C		O		I		A
	L		E			A		D		V		D			B
I		O			U	B				E			I		
	I		E	T	Y		E		E	L		O			E

Letters:

AAAA BB CCC DDDD EE HHHH III
J KK LLLLLL M NNNNN OOO P
RRRR SSS TTTTT U V WW YY

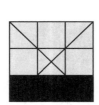
WORD WHEEL

LANGUAGE

Starting with the "L" at the arrow, see how many everyday words of three or more letters you can find going clockwise. Don't skip over any letters. For example, if you saw the letters C, A, R, E, D, you would form five words: CAR, CARE, CARED, ARE, RED. We found 30 words.

STACKED UP

VISUAL ◆ SPATIAL

The box on the left can be formed by three of the numbered boxes superimposed on top of each other; do not turn them in any way. Can you figure out which three work?

1.
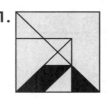

2.
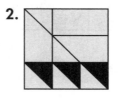

3.
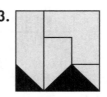

4.
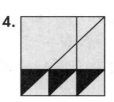

5.
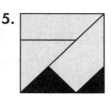

6.

GETTING IN SHAPE

Which two boxes contain the same nine shapes?

1.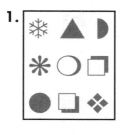

2.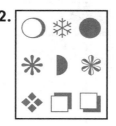

3.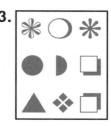

4.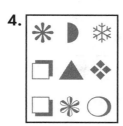

5.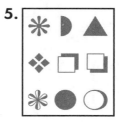

6.

LOGIC

DEDUCTION PROBLEM

Patricia runs an interior painting business. On a recent day, she painted five different rooms of a house (including the living room), with no room getting the same color. The rooms were painted at different times. From this information and the clues below, can you determine each room's color, as well as the order in which they were painted?

1. Patricia applied beige paint immediately before using tan paint, which she used immediately before white paint (which wasn't used on the fifth room she painted).

2. The bathroom and porch (which wasn't painted brown) were painted first and fifth, in some order.

3. Patricia used gray paint immediately before painting the kitchen, which was painted immediately before the den.

ARROW MAZE

VISUAL

Directions for solving are on page 130.

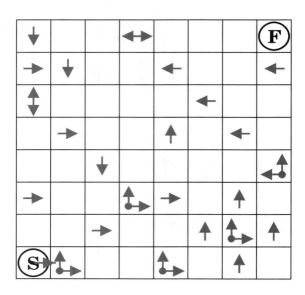

MAGIC NUMBER SQUARE

MATH

Fill in the empty boxes so these groups add up to the number below the diagram: 1. each row; 2. each column; 3. each long diagonal; 4. the four center squares; 5. the four corner squares; and 6. each quarter of the diagram. A number will be used only once.

10	21	17	
23			11
			25

70

"Ours is the age which is proud of machines that think and suspicious of men who try to." — *Howard Mumford Jones*

ANAGRAM MAZE

WEEK 23

Directions for solving are on page 135. Once again, there are 21 words to anagram and the first word you'll be anagramming is DRAB.

1 DRAB	2 CORK	3 FANG	4 WAND	5 VATS	6 BEAT
7 KIWI	8 NAIL	9 FORK	10 LAST	11 HERE	12 LIFT
13 BOWL	14 FUEL	15 FURY	16 SHUT	17 GLEE	18 BARN
19 DELI	20 TELL	21 CHAR	22 GOAT	23 BAND	24 SLAP
25 FILE	26 AGES	27 SHOE	28 BODY	29 ROOF	30 SEAM
31 BALD	32 FILM	33 LOLL	34 LESS	35 LAVA	36 ROOM

VISUAL ◆ SPATIAL

BLOCK PARTY

Study the different views of the block, and draw what should appear on the face that has a question mark.

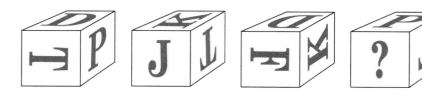

CIRCLE MATH

MATH

Each overlapping circle is identified by a letter having a different number value from 1 to 9. Where some circles overlap, there is a number: It is the SUM of the values of the letters in those overlapping circles. Can you figure out the correct values for the letters? As a starting help, E = 6.

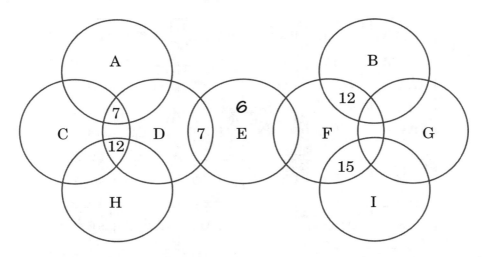

STATE LIMITS

LANGUAGE

The list below consists of the names of seven U.S. States, but we've removed all of the letters between the first and last ones. Can you complete the names?

1. C _____ O

2. N _____ Y

3. H _____ I

4. M _____ N

5. K _____ Y

6. T _____ E

7. M _____ D

RING LOGIC

Complete the diagram by drawing in the links between the rings using the statements. Assume that all the rings in the picture are locked rigidly into position and cannot be moved in any direction. Consider yourself a true ringmaster if you can find the solution in six minutes or less!

1. The pattern looks the same even when it's rotated like a wheel.

2. Ring B is in front of ring Q.

3. Ring H is linked to three rings; its top left is in front of ring Q.

4. Ring M is linked to two rings; its left side is to the front.

5. Ring O is linked to two rings; its right side is to the front.

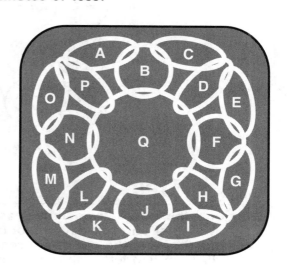

WHAT'S YOUR NUMBER?

Can you figure out the relationship of the numbers in the first two groups of figures and, based on that, what missing number goes into the space with the question mark in the third group of figures?

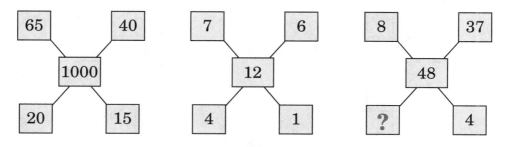

163

CIRCLE SEARCH

LANGUAGE

Directions for solving are on page 141. Here you're looking to form 14 words of at least four letters.

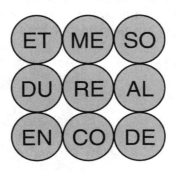

CROSS-UPS

LANGUAGE

Using only the letters given above each diagram, fill in the boxes in such a way that an everyday compound word is formed, one part reading across and the other part reading down. The letter already in the diagram is a letter shared by both parts of the word. Note: Each part of the compound word is an entire word on its own.

1. B D I N S T W

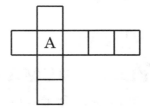

2. A A E F L M O W

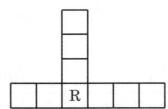

3. A C C H I K M S

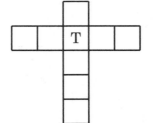

4. C C D I L L O O S

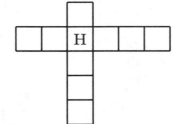

WORD CHARADE

WEEK 23

Find each letter in the diagram according to the instructions, and write each letter on its dash to spell out a 6-letter word.

My first letter appears only in the first, third, and fifth rows.

My second letter appears once in each row and column.

My third letter appears more often than any other letter.

My fourth letter appears only in the third column.

My fifth letter appears only once in the diagram.

My sixth letter is the first letter of an 8-letter name of a flower reading clockwise.

I	Q	U	M	N	J	F	H
T	G	V	F	S	D	P	N
S	F	O	D	I	U	N	C
E	N	F	B	L	R	I	F
B	U	F	A	D	N	K	M
F	J	N	W	X	Q	W	F
N	K	O	J	C	G	F	X
V	A	R	N	P	E	T	H

— — — — — —

CALL TO ORDER

In what order should the groups be placed so that they are arranged from the least complete to the most complete?

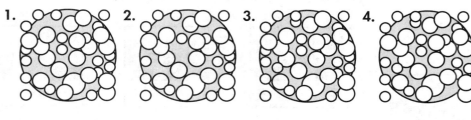

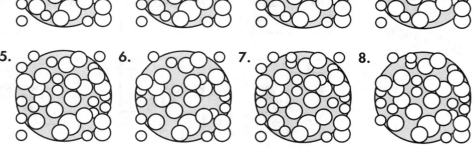

GETTING IN SHAPE

VISUAL

Which two boxes contain the same 12 shapes?

1.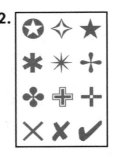

2.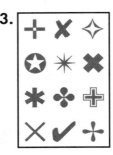

3.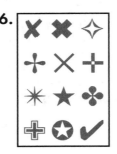

4.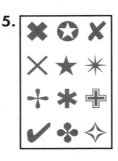

5.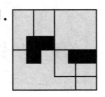

6.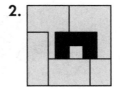

STACKED UP

VISUAL ◆ SPATIAL

Directions for solving are on page 158.

1.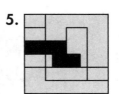

2.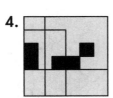

3.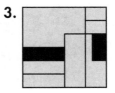

4.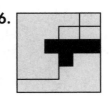

5.

6.

ROUND TRIP

WEEK
24

When this puzzle has been completed correctly, you will have made a round trip through its set of dots. You must visit every dot exactly once, make no diagonal moves, and return to your starting point. Parts of the right path are shown; can you find the rest?

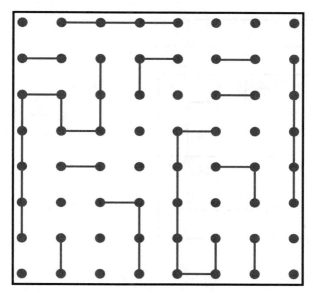

WORD HUNT

Directions for solving are on page 150. This time, you'll be searching for 5-letter words that contain the letter X (such as BOXER). We found 21 words, including BOXER.

J	O	T	S	M	E
I	X	L	I	A	D
C	N	E	X	U	Y
D	B	A	C	T	H
E	T	O	L	E	R
X	P	E	X	D	A

Your list of words:

167

IN THE ABSTRACT

VISUAL ◆ SPATIAL

Directions for solving are on page 136.

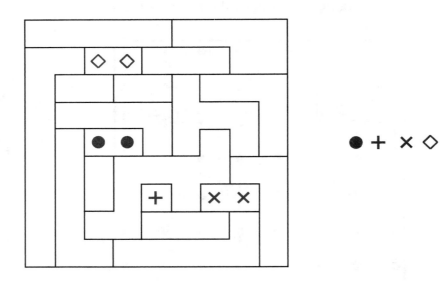

NEXT TO NOTHING

VISUAL

In the first row, the T is next to the number zero and the J is next to the letter O. Circle all of the letters next to zeroes then scramble the circled letters to spell out the name of an animal.

T0	JO	UO	YO
IO	XO	MO	SO
DO	WO	A0	QO
FO	BO	P0	H0
KO	E0	GO	ZO
R0	CO	VO	N0

ALPHABET CIRCLE MAZE

Start at A at the bottom, continue through the alphabet only once, and finish at the Z in the center. You will pass through other letters when going from one letter to the next, but move in only one direction, either around a circle or along a spoke. Don't enter or cross through the Z until you are finished.

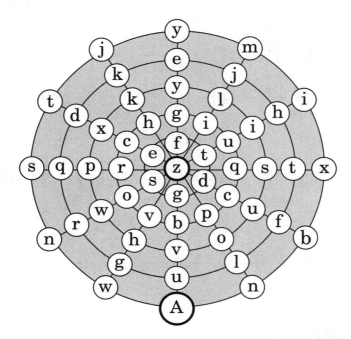

DOVETAILED WORDS

Two related words, with their letters in the correct order, are combined in each row of letters. Can you find both words? In a line like POBOOXDELER, or POboOxDeLEr, you can see the two words POODLE and BOXER.

1. P A A D H E S S I T V E E _____ _____

2. B A T T W O I R N L _____ _____

3. D N O U C R T O S R E _____ _____

4. A C E T L T L A I R C _____ _____

5. J L O I N L Q A U C I L _____ _____

COUNTDOWN

VISUAL

Directions for solving are on page 155.

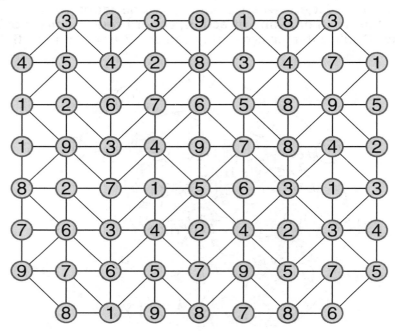

CODE WORD

DECODING

Directions for solving are on page 134.

$$\overline{1} \ \overline{2} \ \overline{3} \ \overline{4} \ \overline{5} \ \overline{6} \ \overline{7} \ \overline{8} \ \overline{9} \ \overline{10} \ \overline{11}$$

M 4 S 9   3 6 10 S   8 5 10   U 9 9 10 5 10 11   W 6 9 2   8 7

10 8 5 7 10 S 9   3 4 4 K   8 7 11   8   S 6 7 1 10 5 10   9 4 7 10

4 F   V 4 6 1 10 ,   W 2 6 3 10   9 5 U 9 2 S   8 5 10   4 F 9 10 7

9 4 3 11   W 6 9 2   8   1 8 S U 8 3   S 2 5 U G   8 7 11   8

11 6 S M 6 S S 6 V 10   3 8 U G 2 .

GOING IN CIRCLES

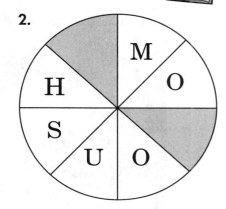

Directions for solving are on page 137.

1.

2.

ANIMAL CHARADES

Directions for solving are on page 134.

My FIRST is in COBRA and in BANK;   _____

My SECOND is in HYENA and in FRANK;   _____

My THIRD is in GOAT but not in FLAG;   _____

My FOURTH is in GAZELLE but not in DRAG;   _____

My FIFTH is in OCELOT and in TOIL;   _____

My SIXTH is in FALCON and in FOIL;   _____

My SEVENTH is in SPARROW but not in THROW;   _____

My EIGHTH is in WEASEL but not in SLOW.   _____

My WHOLE is a ruminant and it wouldn't be strange
    To see this horned critter at home on the range.

_____

MAGNIFIND

VISUAL ◆ SPATIAL

Figure out which areas of the drawing have been enlarged.

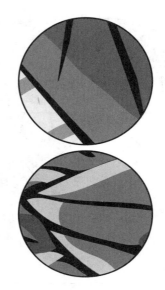

WORD WHEEL

LANGUAGE

Directions for solving are on page 158. Beginning with the "H" at the top of the wheel, we formed 33 words of three or more letters. Do not include proper nouns.

COUNT ON IT!

Directions for solving are on page 153.

1. A D H I K T W Y Y   2. A F H N O O O R R

3. E N O P U U U Y   4. L P T W   5. Y Y

$$\overline{1}\ \overline{2}\ \overline{3} \quad \overline{1}\ \overline{2}\ \overline{3} \quad \overline{1}\ \overline{2}\ \overline{3}\ \overline{4}\ \overline{5}$$

$$\overline{1}\ \overline{2}\ \overline{3}\ \overline{4}\ \overline{5} \quad \overline{1}\ \overline{2} \quad \overline{1}\ \overline{2}\ \overline{3}$$

$$\overline{1}\ \overline{2}\ \overline{3}\ \overline{4}, \quad \overline{1}\ \overline{2}\ \overline{3}\ \overline{4} \quad \overline{1}\ \overline{2}\ \overline{3}.$$

LANGUAGE

WHIRLIGIG

In each numbered section are five letters. Rearrange each group of letters so that when you add "OUT" from the middle of the diagram to the front of each group, you will form 12 common 8-letter words.

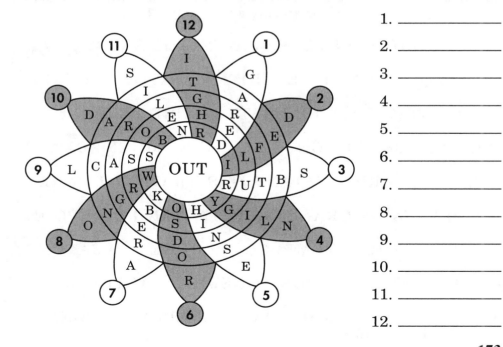

1. _____
2. _____
3. _____
4. _____
5. _____
6. _____
7. _____
8. _____
9. _____
10. _____
11. _____
12. _____

SLIDE RULE

LANGUAGE

Directions for solving are on page 145. Here, you're to form 4-letter words. We found 29 words, including FROM.

Your list of words:

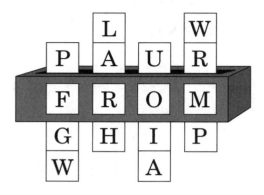

ASSOCIATIONS

LANGUAGE

Directions for solving are on page 151.

WHAT DID THE SEA SAY TO THE SAND?

GRAPEFRUIT NOTICE HOT MANITOBA OPERA

LEMON TEMPT LANCE HASTY TORRID PETROLEUM

ILLUSTRATE LUNCH NEGATIVE MULE GRASP

SPEAR ONTARIO INSTANT GAS TRAITOR DONKEY

DINNER JADE ORANGE UPSTANDING HARPOON

SAVORY   OIL   TEMPLE   PLUNGE   WEATHER

BREAKFAST ADVANCE QUEBEC VANITY DIVE

SWELTERING ERROR DROP BURRO DEPEND

QUOTATION MARKS

Enter the capital letters in the diagram as indicated by the number-letter combinations to form a bit of literary information. For example, one of the B's should be placed in the box where column 6 and row b intersect.

	1	2	3	4	5	6	7	8	9	10	11	12	13	14	15
a															
b															
c															
d															
e															
f															
g															—
h															
i															
j															

A: 8a, 10b, 13b, 5c, 11e, 14e, 5f, 6h, 14h

B: 6b, 8g, 13g, 4j

C: 7a, 2d, 4f, 3h, 15i

D: 7d, 11d, 6g, 1h, 8h, 15h

E: 4a, 11a, 15a, 3b, 1c, 12c, 8d, 10d, 15d, 10e, 1f, 11f, 5g, 12h, 2i, 7i, 3j, 5j

F: 2e, 14f, 11i, 10j

G: 8e

H: 3a, 12b, 4c, 8c, 14d, 11h, 13i

I: 15b, 14c, 6d, 3e, 3f, 2h, 11j

K: 4h, 1j

L: 10a, 14a, 2c, 12f, 1g, 2g, 2j

M: 15e, 11g

N: 9b, 14b, 11c, 4d, 6f, 8f, 7h, 3i, 12j, 13j

O: 9c, 3d, 9f, 15f, 3g, 12g, 10i

R: 9a, 4b, 10c, 9d, 4e, 9e, 2f, 6i, 6j, 7j

S: 6a, 15c, 5d, 5e, 8i

T: 2a, 12a, 1b, 2b, 11b, 7c, 13d, 6e, 12e, 10h, 4i

U: 5i, 14i

V: 10f, 1i

W: 6c, 4g

Y: 7b, 9g, 14g, 8j

HEXAGON HUNT

VISUAL

Directions for solving are on page 139.

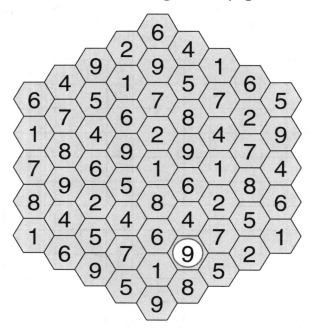

VISION QUEST

VISUAL

Find the row or column that contains five DIFFERENT baking pans.

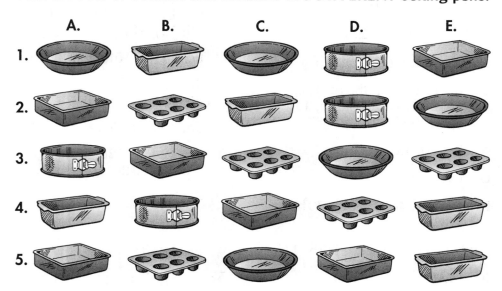

176

SQUARE LINKS

Directions for solving are on page 146.

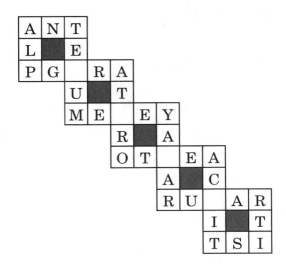

OVERLAY

Directions for solving are on page 150.

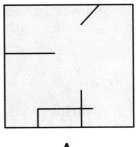

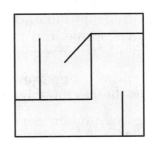

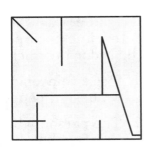

A.

B.

C.

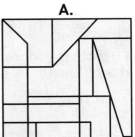

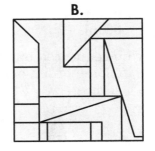

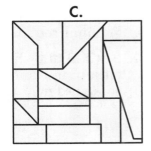

QUICK FILL

LANGUAGE

Directions for solving are on page 130.

A C D E I L T T U V

1. Letter 4 is a consonant.

2. Letter 5 (which is a vowel) is from the first half of the alphabet.

3. Letters 8, 9, and 7, in order, spell out a hot, brewed beverage.

4. In the alphabet, letter 1 appears immediately before letter 10.

5. Letter 3 appears in the word SYMBOL.

6. Letter 2 is a vowel.

7. Letter 6 does not appear in the word DIALECT.

$$\overline{1}\ \overline{2}\ \overline{3}\ \overline{4}\ \overline{5}\ \overline{6}\ \overline{7}\ \overline{8}\ \overline{9}\ \overline{10}$$

DEDUCTION PROBLEM

LOGIC

Raquel and three friends stopped by a pizzeria for lunch. Each person requested a different vegetable topping on his or her slice, along with one of two meat toppings. No two placed their order at the same time. From this information and the clues below, can you determine each person's vegetable and meat topping, along with the order in which they made their requests?

1. The two people who ordered pepperoni are the one who requested peppers and the person who ordered fourth.

2. The person who requested mushrooms (who isn't Nathan) did so immediately before Marsha.

3. The friend who asked for spinach also got sausage and William requested pepperoni.

4. Nathan and the one who requested onions placed their orders either first and third, in some order, or second and fourth, in some order.

CARD SENSE

Directions for solving are on page 138.

1. The five is somewhere above the diamond.

2. The six is somewhere above the spade.

3. The eight is somewhere above the four but isn't on top.

4. The ten is somewhere between the heart and the six.

5. The clubs are not adjacent.

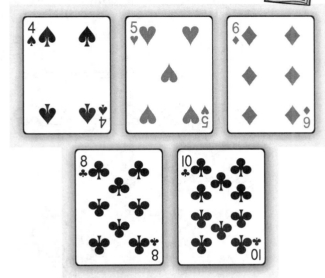

MATH

FUN WITH FACTS AND FIGURES

Directions for solving are on page 142.

1. Take the number of the year of the most recent Winter Olympics and subtract the number of pounds in a ton. _____

2. Next, multiply by the number of points awarded for a touchdown in football. _____

3. Now, subtract the number of degrees Fahrenheit at which water freezes. _____

4. Divide by the number of doughnuts in a baker's dozen. _____

5. Add the number of April Fool's Day in that month. _____

Our answer is the number of reporter's "W" questions. *Is yours?*

GRAND TOUR

LANGUAGE ◆ VISUAL

Directions for solving are on page 140. This time, you'll be looking for a chain of 5-letter words, starting with MO-DEL-TA (model, delta).

START

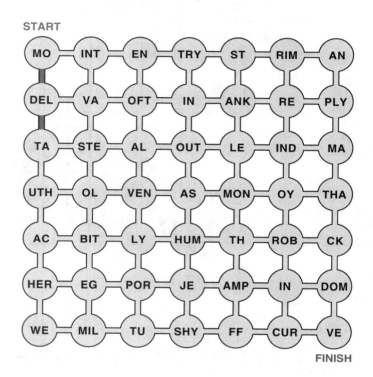

FINISH

COMPOUND IT

LANGUAGE

Directions for solving are on page 139.

1. saw, corner, child, horn

2. stone, horse, birth, pipe

3. cutter, radish, line, wall

4. paper, long, flower, book

5. pot, bow, keeping, haul

6. luck, bellied, shot, string

7. less, table, grass, gun

8. powder, boat, spoon, hopper

9. yard, earth, bill, fruit

10. quake, fold, cake, work

180

ANAGRAM MAZE

WEEK
26

Directions for solving are on page 135. Once again, there are 21 words to anagram and the first word you'll be anagramming is PAGE.

1 VOTE	2 NOEL	3 SUED	4 RATS	5 PAGE	6 DUMB
7 NEAT	8 FERN	9 HIGH	10 CURL	11 YOKE	12 SOCK
13 TABS	14 ZINC	15 GRIN	16 LAID	17 LURE	18 AVID
19 ROBS	20 GOES	21 WEAK	22 JINX	23 MYTH	24 TEEM
25 ROAR	26 PULL	27 FARM	28 BURY	29 AMID	30 MANE
31 VOLT	32 LEAF	33 RISK	34 PEAS	35 BOLD	36 PERT

LANGUAGE

WAYWORDS

Directions for solving are on page 152. Again, you'll be looking for a 9-word thought beginning with WHERE.

ARE	OPTIONS	WHERE	PERFECT
DARKEST	SHADOWS	TOMORROW	THE
THE	MEASURE	ARE	LIGHT
SUSTAIN	BRIGHTEST	GLOWS	BLOSSOMS

"No problem can withstand the assault of sustained thinking."
— *Voltaire*

CROSS EXAMINATION
LANGUAGE

In each set, cross out the three groups of letters so that the remaining groups, in order, spell out a word.

1. PER   IN   VAS   COR   POR   SIZE   ATE

2. CON   PEN   TRO   VER   GER   SIAL   SOME

3. TRA   AC   COM   SIN   MO   PATE   DATE

4. IN   AS   FIN   TRO   I   CLE   TIVE

5. PE   VAN   LAS   TRO   LE   PEP   UM

6. EX   DEL   PE   TUR   PART   DI   TION

7. PER   PET   SYN   U   O   AL   CORE

8. PSY   RHO   COL   DO   DEN   ASTY   DRON

BULL'S-EYE LETTER
LANGUAGE

Directions for solving are on page 148.

— — — — —

— — — —

— — — —

— — — —

— — — —

VEY   UJK

KIC   ?   RBO

MUB   WAL

WORD LINK

Place the words in parentheses after each capitalized word in the diagram so that they cross or connect with the capitalized word. ELM has been placed in the diagram; ALL, PESTER, and SMILED cross or connect with ELM.

ALE (eel, phase, trend)

ALL (elm, pastes, slight)

CREATE (resist, tamper, tie)

EEL (ale, other, pet)

ELM (all, pester, smiled)

ETHER (pastes, resist, slight, tamper)

HAREM (held, polite, robe, simple)

HELD (harem, label, phase, trend)

LABEL (held, robe, simple)

OTHER (eel, phase, rode, trend)

PASTES (all, ether, pester, sat, smiled)

PESTER (elm, pastes, rode, slight)

PET (eel, phase, trend)

PHASE (ale, held, other, pet)

POLITE (harem, resist, tamper, tie)

RESIST (create, ether, polite, simple)

ROBE (harem, label)

RODE (other, pester, smiled)

SAT (pastes, slight, tamper)

SIMPLE (harem, label, resist, tie)

SLIGHT (all, ether, pester, sat, smiled)

SMILED (elm, pastes, rode, slight)

TAMPER (create, ether, polite, sat)

TIE (create, polite, simple)

TREND (ale, held, other, pet)

E							
L							
M							

ELIMINATION

LANGUAGE

Directions for solving are on page 137. Once again, the remaining words will form a thought.

INLET   MONEY   WHITE   NEVER   MINE   TAXI
WORRY   GULF   DOESN'T   HOUSE   STARING   CHEERS
GROW   ABOUT   OATH   LAGOON   FRIENDS   ACTION
PRESORT   ON   ONLY   VAIN   OVAL   INACTION
LOST   OFFICE   TREES   CREEK

Eliminate...

1. the three 4-letter words that, when scrambled together, form an Asian capital and its country.

2. the word that forms the name of a bird when a consonant is added to it.

3. words that are bodies of water.

4. the words that are also Emmy Award-winning TV shows.

5. the four words that form the name of President Obama's place of residence and where he usually works.

6. the word that has a flower in it reading backwards.

7. the five words that form a phrase meaning "arboreal perennials never yield legal tender."

BLOCK PARTY

VISUAL ◆ SPATIAL

Directions for solving are on page 161.

 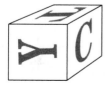  

MISSING DOMINOES

Directions for solving are on page 147.

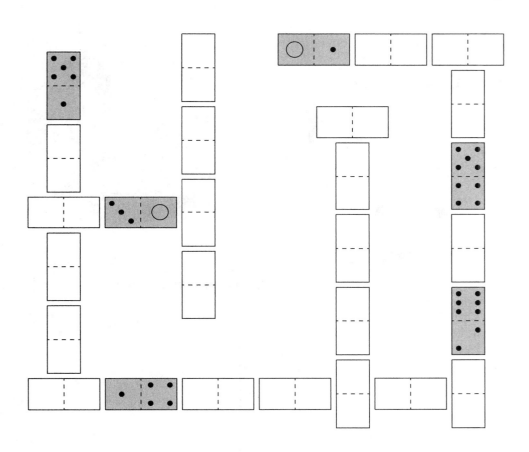

DOMINOES

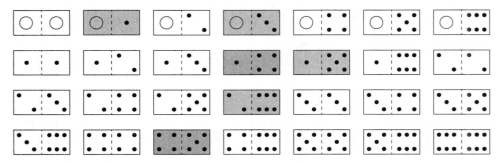

185

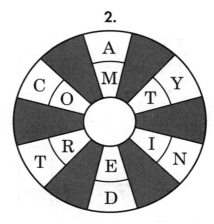

TARGET SHOOT   LANGUAGE

Find the two letters which, when entered into the center circle of each target, will form three 6-letter words reading across.

1.

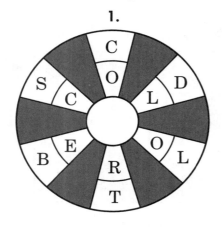

2.

IN THE ABSTRACT   VISUAL ◆ SPATIAL

Directions for solving are on page 136.

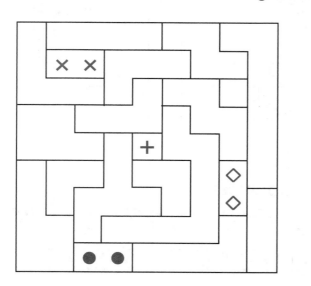

"A fool-proof method for sculpting an elephant: first, get a huge block of marble; then you chip away everything that doesn't look like an elephant." — author unknown

LOOSE TILE

The tray on the right seemed the ideal place to store the set of loose dominoes. Unfortunately, when the tray was full, one domino was left over. Determine the arrangement of the dominoes in the tray and which is the Loose Tile.

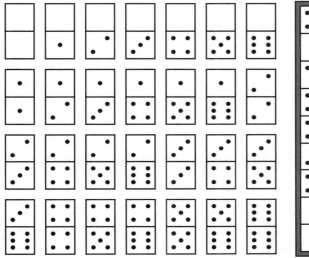

LANGUAGE

SEVEN WORD ZINGER

Directions for solving are on page 142.

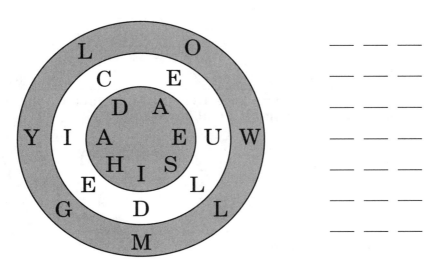

— — —

— — —

— — —

— — — —

— — —

— — —

— — —

FILLING STATION

LANGUAGE

Place the given consonants on the dashes to form a director's name and four of his movies. The vowels have already been placed.

1. B G L N P R S S T V (director)

__ __ E __ E __   __ __ I E __ __ E __ __

2. C C D D F H H K L N N N R R S S T T T (1977 movie)

"__ __ O __ E   E __ __ O U __ __ E __ __

O __   __ __ E   __ __ I __ __   __ I __ __"

3. D D D F H J L M M N N N N P S T T (1984 movie)

"I __ __ I A __ A   __ O __ E __   A __ __

__ __ E   __ E __ __ __ E O __   __ O O __"

4. C H L L P P R R T (1985 movie)

"__ __ E   __ O __ O __   __ U __ __ __ E"

5. C J K P R R S S (1993 movie)

"__ U __ A __ __ I __   __ A __ __"

ALL IN A ROW

MATH

Directions for solving are on page 131. This time, look for the most groups of consecutive numbers adding up to 18.

A. 5 5 5 3 6 9 1 6 4 3 3 3 3 3 9 9 8 1 5 8 1 2 4

B. 6 4 9 5 9 1 3 2 1 5 5 5 1 7 3 2 5 9 4 3 3 3 8 4

C. 8 7 1 3 8 1 5 6 6 9 6 2 1 2 3 4 5 8 9 7 1 5 2 2

188

SUDOKU

WEEK 27

Directions for solving are on page 131.

		5	2				3	
2		6					8	1
	1		6	4				
		3	1		7	9		
5	2						1	7
		1	3		2	5		
				3	9		7	
9	3					8		5
	8				5	1		

EASY PICKINGS

Directions for solving are on page 133.

SI FO   YT HO EU   SB EI LO NI ER VS TE

ET YV ER TR YH TS NH AI NT GE

YR VO UM   RT EI DA DS,   MY ON DU

OH AX DE   BL EA ST TH EI DR

NT KO TX   RH ET LA DY.

189

MAGNIFIND

VISUAL ◆ SPATIAL

Figure out which area of the drawing has been enlarged.

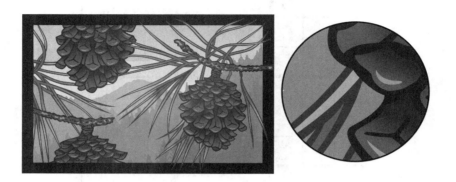

SUDOKU

LOGIC

Place a number into each box so each row across, column down, and small 9-box square within the larger square (there are 9 of these) contains 1 through 9.

	8		2			7	3	
			7	8	4			9
		2				6	8	
9				1			5	8
	6		8	2	3		9	
4	3			7				2
	5	3				2		
6			3	4	2			
	4	1			8		7	

190

VISION QUEST

Find the row or column that contains five DIFFERENT items for mailing.

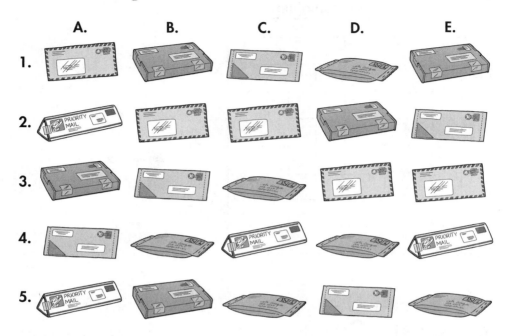

MATH

ALL IN A ROW

Which row below contains the most groups of consecutive numbers adding up to 9? Look carefully, because some groups may overlap.

A. 8 3 3 5 1 6 5 1 4 7 3 2 1 4 2 6 1 8 5 1 2 1 7 6

B. 6 4 3 7 1 2 4 5 8 3 2 2 4 6 2 7 5 3 2 1 3 4 6 8

C. 5 3 7 4 1 3 1 2 3 8 4 2 5 2 6 4 1 2 3 6 8 5 6 1

IN THE ABSTRACT

VISUAL ◆ SPATIAL

Fill in each section with one of the four symbols so no sections containing the same symbol touch. Four sections are already complete.

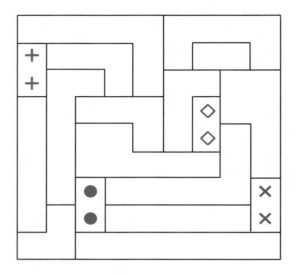

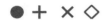

ALPHABET SOUP

LANGUAGE ◆ VISUAL

Cross off each letter from the alphabet list that appears in the larger group of letters. Then rearrange the letters not crossed out to form the name of a snake.

L	N	W	F	Y	G	F	I	N	L	G	N	F	Y	U	N
D	X	H	N	I	L	R	F	X	U	W	H	Y	X	G	H
W	T	Y	Z	M	J	E	C	T	I	Z	D	J	E	L	J
Z	X	G	Y	U	K	M	P	T	V	R	Q	I	S	K	V

A B C D E F G H I J K L M N O P Q R S T U V W X Y Z

Snake: _____

TIPS OF THE ICEBERG

The chart shows the gratuities each waiter or waitress earned on a recent breakfast shift at the Iceberg Diner. All you have to do is some addition and then answer the following questions:

1. Who made the most in total tips?
2. Who made the least?
3. Which two waitpersons made exactly the same amount?

EMPLOYEE	TIP 1	TIP 2	TIP 3	TIP 4	TIP 5
Al	$0.75	$1.20	$1.20	$1.40	$1.25
Brenda	$2.10	$1.50	$1.05	$1.15	$1.00
Charlie	$1.00	$1.00	$1.00	$1.00	$1.80
Dena	$1.10	$1.45	$1.05	$1.00	$1.80
Ed	$1.15	$2.10	$1.10	$1.70	$1.75
Flora	$1.15	$1.40	$2.80	$2.05	$1.40
Greta	$0.90	$0.35	$1.35	$1.60	$1.40

GRAND TOUR

Form a continuous chain of 5-letter words moving through the maze from START to FINISH. The second part of one word becomes the first part of the next word. This puzzle starts with CA-MEL-ON (camel, melon).

START

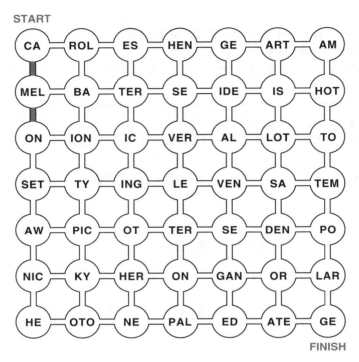

FINISH

EASY PICKINGS

To solve, simply cross out one letter in each pair below. When the puzzle is completed correctly, the remaining letters will spell out a fact.

AT HB RE AZ GH GA MN

LE VI TN CV XO LC UN   MW MA ST

MT IH EL   SN AI TX HT EG KE NG TF LH

DP RG ET AS NI DA EA RN GT.

WEEK 28

VISUAL

ARROW MAZE

Starting at the S and following the arrow up, see if you can find your way to F. When you reach an arrow, you MUST follow its direction and continue in that direction until you come to the next arrow. When you reach a two-headed arrow, you can choose either direction. It's okay to cross your own path.

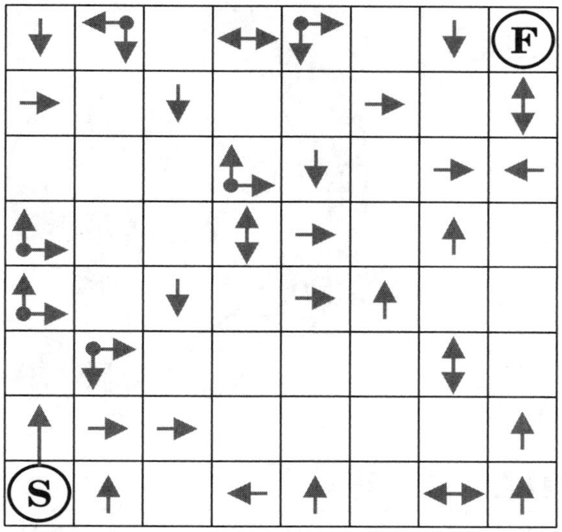

LANGUAGE ◆ SPATIAL

WORD HUNT

Find words by moving from one letter to any adjoining letter. You may start a word with any letter in the diagram. In forming a word you may return to a letter as often as you wish, but do not stand on a letter using it twice in direct succession. In this Word Hunt, you are searching for 4-letter words that begin with J. We found 17 words, including JAZZ.

E	D	N	K	Y
K	O	U	R	E
L	I	J	E	T
T	N	A	D	S
X	B	M	Z	Z

Your list of words:

SEVEN WORD ZINGER

LANGUAGE

Using each letter once, form seven everyday 3-letter words with the first letter coming from the center, the second from the middle, and the third from the outer circle. Your words may differ from ours.

— — —

— — —

— — —

— — —

— — —

— — —

— — —

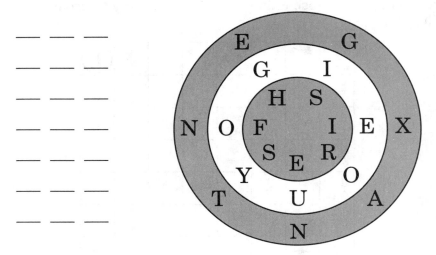

QUICK FILL

LANGUAGE

Determine the 10-letter word from the clues. All the letters in the word are listed.

C D E E K O O P R W

1. Letter 8 is from the first half of the alphabet and letter 10 is from the second half.

2. Letter 9 appears elsewhere in the word.

3. In the alphabet, letter 7 is immediately before letter 4 and letter 7 does not appear in the word POWERED.

4. In the alphabet, letter 3 is immediately before letter 5.

5. Letter 6 is a vowel.

6. Letter 2 appears in the word CONDUCT.

7. Letter 1 is the first letter of the state where the Green Bay Packers are based.

$$\overline{1} \ \overline{2} \ \overline{3} \ \overline{4} \ \overline{5} \ \overline{6} \ \overline{7} \ \overline{8} \ \overline{9} \ \overline{10}$$

CARD SENSE

Five playing cards were shuffled and put in a pile, one on top of another. Using the clues, can you identify each card's position in the pile?

1. The diamonds are adjacent.

2. The tens are not adjacent.

3. The eight is somewhere above both tens.

4. The heart is not on top.

5. The spade is not on the bottom.

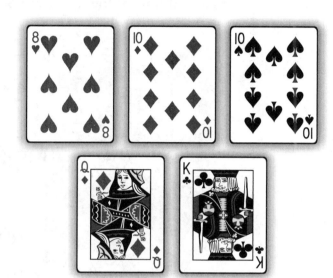

COUNT ON IT!

Use the given letters to fill in the familiar saying, one letter per dash. All the letters following 1 are the first letters of each word, the letters following 2 are the second letters of each word, etc. It is up to you to determine which letter goes where.

1. I T B C H   2. O S E U H   3. S E O N

4. K G T   5. E   6. R

$$\overline{1}\ \overline{2}\ \overline{3}\ \overline{4}\ \overline{5}\ \overline{6}\quad \overline{1}\ \overline{2}\quad \overline{1}\ \overline{2}\ \overline{3}$$

$$\overline{1}\ \overline{2}\ \overline{3}\ \overline{4}\quad \overline{1}\ \overline{2}\ \overline{3}\ \overline{4}\ .$$

197

HEXAGON HUNT

VISUAL

In this diagram of six-sided figures, there are 10 "special" hexagons. These 10 are special because the six numbers around each one are all different from each other and the center. We've circled one of the 10. Can you find the other 9?

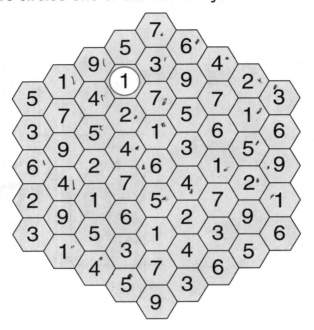

SYMBOL-ISM

DECODING

This is simply a Cryptogram that uses symbols instead of letters to spell out a truism. Each symbol stands for the same letter throughout. For this puzzle, we've already indicated that ♣ = C and ↥ = N.

```
 C  N C   NC           C
♣✳↥♣♣✳❖↥♣❖   ✳↥   ⛄🂠♣✓   🚌✿⊙❖    🎿

    NC                                      N
○❖↥♣✿🚌;   ✿✳   ⛄🂠↥✳   ⬆❖   ↥✓🎿╳○❖↥❖👋

   N
✿↥   ✳╳✿❖╳   ✳✳   ⬆❖   🂠↥❖↥🂠🚌.
```

198

COUNT TO TEN

WEEK
28

Examine the leaves and snowflakes and then answer these questions: 1. Which row contains the most leaves? 2. Which row contains the most snowflakes? 3. Which row contains an equal number of leaves and snowflakes?

1.
2.
3.
4.
5.
6.
7.
8.
9.
10.

DECODING

CODE WORD

Decipher a thought and the Code Word's eleven letters, represented by the numbers 1 through 11. So, if the Code Word were "THUNDERCLAP," 1 in the sentence would be T, 2 would be H, etc.

$$\overline{1}\ \overline{2}\ \overline{3}\ \overline{4}\ \overline{5}\ \overline{6}\ \overline{7}\ \overline{8}\ \overline{9}\ \overline{10}\ \overline{11}$$

2 3 4 6 9 1 N 8 10 K E L 9 N 11 M 9 1 K , 2 E

5 9 N 2 9 4 5 6 10 9 3 N 7 8 2 – 5 8 L 8 10 E 11

F 3 1 6 1 2 3 M M 3 N G 9 M 8 N G

7 10 3 L L 3 9 N 4 5 8 10 9 L 10 E E F 1.

LOOSE TILE

WEEK 29

VISUAL ◆ SPATIAL

The tray on the left seemed the ideal place to store the set of loose dominoes. Unfortunately, when the tray was full, one domino was left over. Determine the arrangement of the dominoes in the tray and which is the Loose Tile.

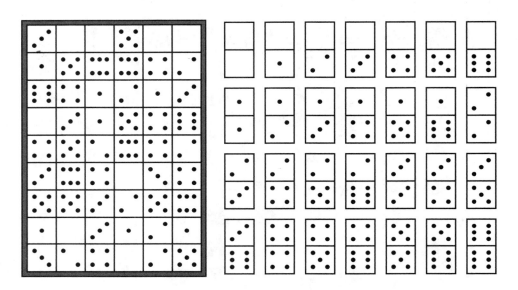

COMPOUND IT

LANGUAGE

Starting at #1, pick a word that will form a compound word with a word chosen in #2. Then with the word you've selected in #2, pick one from #3 to form another compound word. Continue in this manner to #10, so that you've formed nine compound words. In some instances more than one compound word can be formed, but there is only one path to get you to #10.

1. hog, pony, fruit, cloth

2. bound, cake, wash, tail

3. tub, less, pipe, spin

4. line, out, off, drench

5. beat, stage, smart, law

6. suit, coach, breaker, hand

7. bag, gun, case, man

8. load, slinger, fire, work

9. book, storm, place, force

10. melt, trust, stall, brace

200

ONLINE NETWORK

In each two-column group, take the letters in the left-hand column along the paths (indicated by the lines) and place them in their proper boxes in the right-hand column. When done, for each puzzle you'll find three related words reading down the right-hand column.

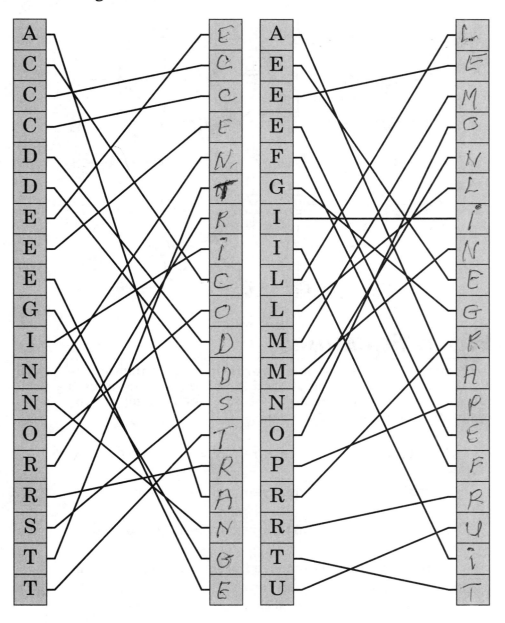

Puzzle 1 — Left column: A, C, C, C, D, D, E, E, E, G, I, N, N, O, R, R, S, T, T

Puzzle 1 — Right column: E, C, C, E, N, T, R, I, C, O, D, D, S, T, R, A, N, G, E

Puzzle 2 — Left column: A, E, E, E, F, G, I, I, L, L, M, M, N, O, P, R, R, T, U

Puzzle 2 — Right column: L, E, M, O, N, L, I, N, E, G, R, A, P, E, F, R, U, I, T

COUNTDOWN

VISUAL

Following the connecting lines, find the only route in this grid that passes through the numbers backward from 9 to 1 consecutively.

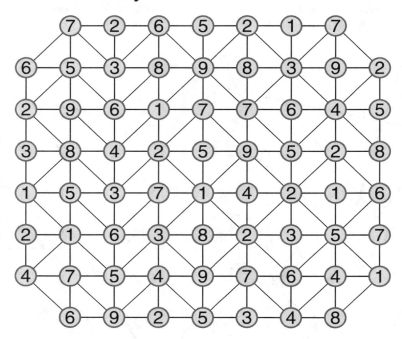

WORD EQUATIONS

LANGUAGE

Determine the three defined words in each equation. The third word is formed when the second is written directly after the first; for example, for "for each + shape = act in a play," you would respond "per + form = perform."

1. debate stance + manicure tool = face outline

2. casino wager + light beam = double-cross

3. dirty disorder + birthday count = voice-mail item

4. religious group + charged atom = orange segment

5. discourage from an action + coal locale = figure out

CIRCLE SEARCH

Move from circle to adjoining circle, horizontally and vertically only, to form 11 common, everyday words of at least three letters. Don't change the order of the letters in the circles that contain more than one letter. Proper names are not allowed.

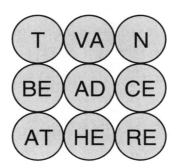

ELIMINATION

Cross off the capitalized words below according to the instructions given. The remaining words, in order, will form a thought.

BUILDING SWEET FACTS CUT CURRICULUM DO WHOLE CAN NOT HARM TRAY RUN FIREPLACE CEASE PEANUT SIGHTED TO APPENDIX GENTLE EXIST OVEN OF WHEN CIRCUIT DRAWN IGNORED WORMS DUE

Eliminate…

1. the three words that can follow "short."

2. the three words that lose their last letter when "ly" is added to the end.

3. the three items that can be made of brick.

4. the three words that form a phrase meaning "vessel bearing annelids and nematodes."

5. the two words where each has two ways of spelling its plural.

6. the three words that appear together in the list and, when scrambled, form the first and last name of the thirty-third President of the United States.

7. the three words that can come before "butter."

WORD CHARADE

LANGUAGE ◆ VISUAL

Find each letter in the diagram according to the instructions, and write each letter on its dash to spell out a 6-letter word.

My first letter is the only letter from the first half of the alphabet in one of the columns.

My second letter is the sixth letter in a word reading diagonally.

M	T	P	E	J	F	X	A
J	E	U	Y	I	C	R	G
L	X	R	W	D	O	U	P
S	C	V	C	M	E	J	C
O	B	I	Q	H	Z	W	X
G	R	N	L	R	A	Y	H
Y	F	W	A	Z	H	N	S
B	Q	J	E	G	D	V	T

My third letter appears three times in one of the rows.

My fourth letter does not appear in the diagram.

My fifth letter appears to the immediate left or immediate right of wherever my first letter appears.

My sixth letter only appears in the top row and in the bottom row.

___ ___ ___ ___ ___ ___

COUNT THE TRAPEZOIDS

VISUAL ◆ SPATIAL

To solve this puzzle, write down the four letters that describe each trapezoid (a four-sided figure with only TWO parallel sides) in this figure. We found 24 trapezoids; how many can you locate?

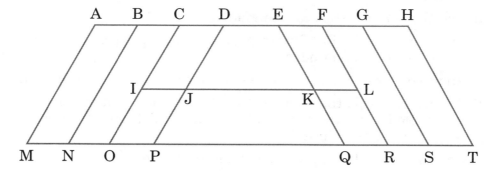

ANAGRAM MAZE

WEEK
29

The diagram contains 36 words, 23 of which are anagrams of other everyday words. Start at the top arrow and anagram DENT. While solving, move up, down, right, or left to the only adjacent word that can be anagrammed. Continue until you arrive at the bottom arrow. There is only one path through the maze.

1 DENT	2 UNDO	3 REAM	4 BANE	5 LOAF	6 BEAK
7 IDLE	8 WISH	9 RUBY	10 BANG	11 MICE	12 REAL
13 PANS	14 CLAP	15 STEP	16 BATH	17 BEAT	18 RIDE
19 TUGS	20 TERM	21 MOAT	22 TINY	23 NONE	24 CLIP
25 TRIO	26 FOUL	27 REFS	28 LOOK	29 SACK	30 TEAK
31 RAGE	32 BARE	33 ROCK	34 ZINC	35 DANK	36 CARS

MATH ◆ LOGIC

WHAT'S YOUR NUMBER?

Can you figure out the relationship of the numbers in the first five boxes and, based on that, what missing number goes into the space with the question mark?

19	20	14
9712	8471	3452

24	7	?
5577	1204	6904

205

LICENSE PLATES

LANGUAGE

Each box contains six letters of the first and last name of a Super Bowl MVP. The top three are a part of the first name and the bottom three are a part of the last name, in order.

1.
```
R R Y
R A D
```

2.
```
E M M
I T H
```

3.
```
R O Y
I K M
```

4.
```
O H N
L W A
```

5.
```
E R R
R I C
```

6.
```
P E Y
A N N
```

RELATIONSHIPS QUIZ

LOGIC

KENNEL is to DOG as STY is to PIG because a DOG lives in a KENNEL and a PIG lives in a STY. Each of the statements below is a relationship of some kind. Can you select the right word from the four following each?

1. SWEET is to SOUR as SHORT is to _____.
   (a) tall   (b) measure   (c) brief   (d) stunted

2. FOOT is to MILE as OUNCE is to _____.
   (a) weight   (b) liquid   (c) cure   (d) pound

3. TEA is to CHINA as COFFEE is to _____.
   (a) aluminum   (b) Colombia   (c) milk   (d) Sweden

4. SHOVEL is to DIG as VISE is to _____.
   (a) hold   (b) sin   (c) chop   (d) scour

5. GLOVE is to HAND as SOCK is to _____.
   (a) finger   (b) leather   (c) foot   (d) shake

MISSING LINKS

WEEK
30

Fill the empty squares in the diagram with the given letters so that everyday words are formed reading across and down.

	R	E	E				P	R		P		R	E			P
O				A				N		N						L
M		F		E	S	T		R		A						U
B		R		M		L		U			I		D	O		
	N		S		D		S		R		H		I			B
S		I		N		R		C		D			I	K		
T			I		L					R		E				R
I		F			L		W	A		T		N				
O			N	C	L			T					O	L		
N		L			M			A		H		E				E
			B		T	R	A		A			H			C
	U		E	D		N			E		E	C		M	
A		O			T		S		D		I			S		N
P		O	M		L		N				E	A		O	
T		A		O		R		R		U			I		
	R			I		Y		P	P	E		R		I	T
R		C		N			I			L			A		
	V		N			T	E		A	N	T		P		O	T

AAAA B CCC DD EEEEEEEEEEEEEE
LL M NN O PPP R SS TTTTT UUUU
W YYY

207

BULL'S-EYE LETTER

LANGUAGE

Add the SAME single letter to each group of three letters and then rearrange the letters to form six everyday 4-letter words.

— — — —

— — — —

— — — —

— — — —

— — — —

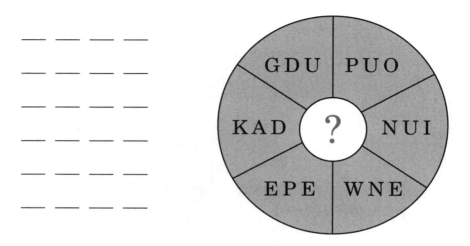

THE LINEUP

LANGUAGE

While scrutinizing the lineup of letters, can you answer the five questions correctly in five minutes or less?

P B A X E D S M A L E W R J U D G M E N T V C Q U A L I F Y Z O N E K

1. Which letter of the alphabet does not appear in the lineup? _____

2. What 8-letter word — with its letters in correct order and appearing together — can you find in the lineup? _____

3. Which letter of the alphabet appears exactly three times in the lineup? _____

4. What 7-letter word — with its letters in correct order and appearing together — can you find in the lineup? _____

5. Other than the answers to Questions 2 and 4, how many everyday words — with their letters in correct order and appearing together — of four or more letters can you find in the lineup? _____

208

WORD WHEEL

Starting with the "P" at the arrow, see how many everyday words of three or more letters you can find going clockwise. Don't skip over any letters. For example, if you saw the letters C, A, R, E, D, you would form five words: CAR, CARE, CARED, ARE, RED. We found 30 words.

LANGUAGE

WAYWORDS

An 8-word thought can be found beginning with the word OFFER. Then, move to any adjacent box up, down, or diagonally for each following word.

OFFER	DREAMS	CANOPY	HOPE
NOTHING	HOPE	LOSING	GENERAL
MORE	ARE	TO	THOSE
THAN	WHAT	WHO	STRAIGHT

STACKED UP

VISUAL ◆ SPATIAL

The box on the left can be formed by three of the numbered boxes superimposed on top of each other; do not turn them in any way. Can you figure out which three work?

1.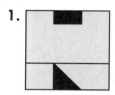

2.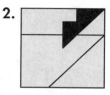

3.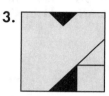

4.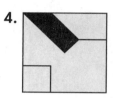

5.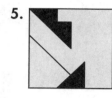

6.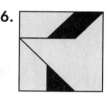

CIRCLE MATH

MATH

Each overlapping circle is identified by a letter having a different number value from 1 to 9. Where some circles overlap, there is a number: It is the SUM of the values of the letters in those overlapping circles. Can you figure out the correct values for the letters? As a starting help, E = 9.

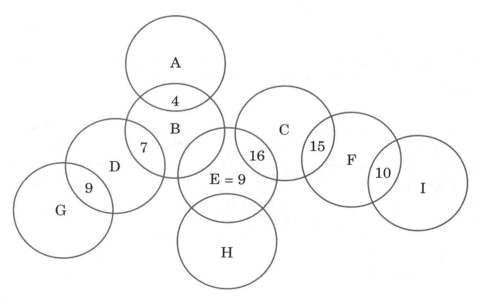

CHANGELINGS

Can you change the first word into the second word (in each set) by changing only one letter at a time? Do not rearrange the order of the letters with each change. Each change must result in an everyday word, and words beginning with a capital letter, slang, or obsolete words aren't allowed. The number in parentheses indicates the number of changes we used for that Changeling.

1. SOOT

2. TOLL

3. LONG

_____

_____

_____

_____

_____

_____

_____

_____

_____

FIRE
(4 changes)

FEES
(4 changes)

LIMB
(4 changes)

SQUARE LINKS

Write one letter in each empty box so that an everyday 8-letter word is spelled out around each solid box. Each word may read either clockwise or counterclockwise, and may start at any of its letters.

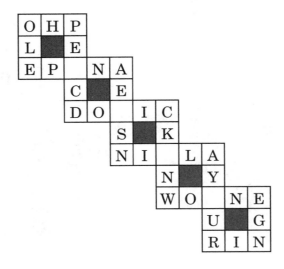

ANIMAL CHARADES

LANGUAGE

Each line contains a clue to a letter of the alphabet. These letters, in the given order, will spell out the name of an animal. The animal's identity is also hinted at in the last sentence of the Charade.

My FIRST is in LEOPARD and in POKE; _____

My SECOND is in COYOTE and in YOKE; _____

My THIRD is in MOLE but not in MERGE; _____

My FOURTH is in TIGER but not in SPLURGE; _____

My FIFTH is in PERCH and in REACH; _____

My SIXTH is in COBRA and in BEACH; _____

My SEVENTH is in IGUANA but not in GRILL. _____

My WHOLE is a bird with a pouch on its bill.

_____

TARGET SHOOT

LANGUAGE

Find the two letters which, when entered into the center circle of each target, will form three 6-letter words reading across.

1.

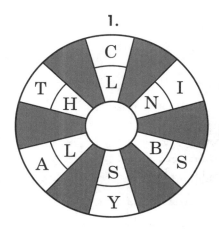

2.

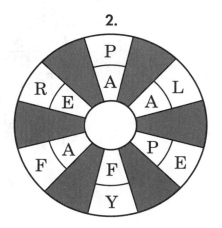

MISSING DOMINOES

In this game you use all 28 dominoes that are in a standard set. Each one has a different combination from 0-0, 0-1, 0-2, to 6-6. Domino halves with the same number of dots lie next to each other. To avoid confusion we have used an open circle to indicate a zero. Can you fill in the missing white dominoes to complete the board?

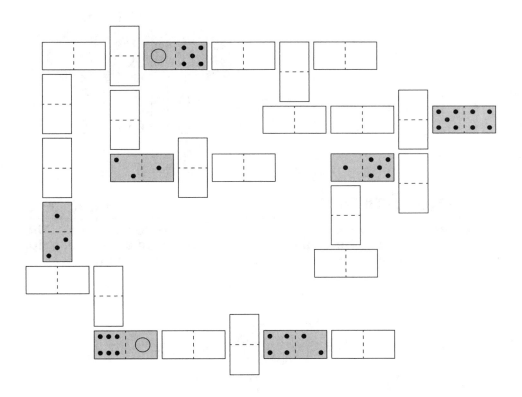

DOMINOES

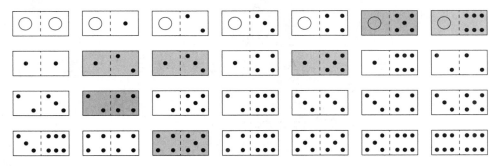

213

SLIDE RULE

Slide each column of letters up or down in the box and form as many everyday 3-letter words as you can in the windows where NAP is now. We formed 24 words, including NAP.

Your list of words:

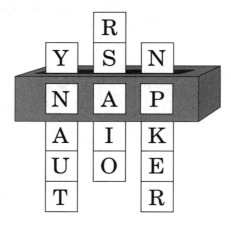

FILLING STATION

Place the given consonants on the dashes to form words. The vowels have already been placed for you, and as an additional help, each entry lists its category beside its given consonants.

1. H L N P P P S (country)

   _ _ I _ I _ _ I _ E _

2. B C H K L L R R S Y (former NBA star)

   _ _ A _ _ E _   _ A _ _ _ E _

3. F G L L N R S (natural wonder)

   _ I A _ A _ A   _ A _ _ _

4. F H H H M N P P R T T T (musical)

   "_ _ E   _ _ A _ _ O _   O _   _ _ E

   O _ E _ A"

5. C L L R R R S T (amusement)

   _ O _ _ E _   _ O A _ _ E _

214

SWITCHEROO

In each group, for the first word and its number equivalent given, determine what the number equivalent is for the second word.

1. DIVE is to 2863 as VIED is to:
   (a) 6823 (b) 6832 (c) 2836 (d) 6328

2. LEAP is to 7614 as PALE is to:
   (a) 7146 (b) 4167 (c) 4761 (d) 4176

3. ABET is to 9425 as BEAT is to:
   (a) 4295 (b) 4925 (c) 5294 (d) 4529

4. ROTE is to 3176 as TORE is to:
   (a) 7361 (b) 7136 (c) 7613 (d) 6371

5. CHAR is to 4281 as ARCH is to:
   (a) 8214 (b) 8421 (c) 8124 (d) 8142

6. MASH is to 5936 as HAMS is to:
   (a) 6539 (b) 6935 (c) 6953 (d) 6359

LANGUAGE ◆ SPATIAL

TRI, TRI AGAIN

Fit the nine triangles into the big one so six everyday words are spelled out reading across the arrows. Do not rotate the triangles.

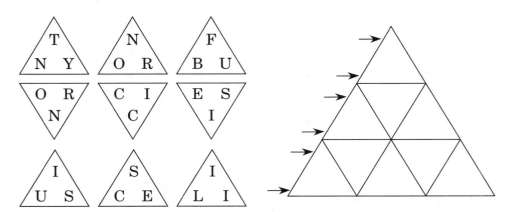

SUDOKU

Directions for solving are on page 190.

			3	5		1	9	
5		9	8	4	6	7		
2				9				8
	8		2			9		6
	9		6	1	5		8	
6		2			4		1	
3				6				5
		4	5	7	8	2		1
	5	1		2	3			

WORD VISIBILITY
LANGUAGE

There are six 5-letter words below. The first letter of the answer is found in the first pair of letters, and it is either the top or the bottom letter. Continue across each pair.

For example, the word GIRL would be found thus: <u>G</u> A <u>R</u> <u>L</u>
                                          L <u>I</u> T X

1. V I N O D
   P A S A R

2. B O U S N
   W L R E H

3. G H O M B
   C L I R M

4. S T W A N
   P O E R T

5. T L B I T
   G E O A S

6. D R E C E
   V O A P H

"Discovery consists of seeing what everybody has seen and thinking what nobody has thought." — Albert Szent-Györgyi

ASSOCIATIONS

You'll find eight groups of three words that can be associated in some way with each other (example: mantel, fireplace, logs). Cross out each group as you find it. The initial letters of the remaining words will spell out the answer to the riddle:

WHAT LIES ON THE BOTTOM OF THE OCEAN AND SHAKES?

RAT BOUND AVERAGE FLANNEL BRAVERY NATIVE

MARIGOLD EARTH SCREWDRIVER DAISY ROBOT

DIAMOND VAGUE COURAGE HAMMER OPTION

JUMP LINEN URGENT PECAN SCARCE EMERALD

CASHEW WAFFLE SQUIRREL VALOR RAPID BURLAP

MOUSE ELEVEN LEAP RUBY CAPTURE ALMOND

LILAC KITCHEN PLIERS

CROSS-UPS

Using only the letters given above each diagram, fill in the boxes in such a way that an everyday compound word is formed, one part reading across and the other part reading down. The letter already in the diagram is a letter shared by both parts of the word. Note: Each part of the compound word is an entire word on its own.

1. C E E K L M P R T

| | A | | | |

2. E H I M O O S

| | | N |

RINGERS

LANGUAGE ◆ SPATIAL

Each Ringer is composed of five rings. Use your imagination to rotate the rings so that you spell out four 5-letter words reading from the outside to the inside when all five rings are aligned correctly.

1.

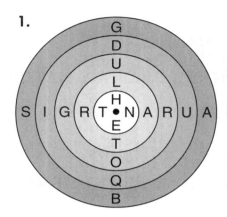

2.

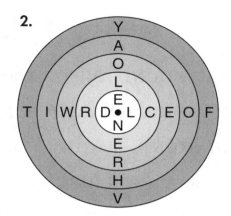

CODED STATES

DECODING

In this list of U.S. states, we've replaced each consonant with an **X** and each vowel (including **Y**) with an **O**. Can you decode each state's name?

1. XOX OOXX

2. XOOXO

3. OXOO

4. XOXXXOXXOXOO

5. XOOXOXX

6. XOXOXO

7. XOXXOXX

8. XOOXX XOXOXO

218

PRESIDENTIAL GOULASH

WEEK **31**

The first half of the 6-letter last name of each U.S. President here starts out correctly, but the half that's supposed to follow is now somewhere else! Can you piece the 18 halves together in order to form the names of the nine Presidents?

1. REAVER

2. PIESON

3. TAYMAN

4. MONGAN

5. HOORCE

6. ARTROE

7. WILLOR

8. TRUTER

9. CARHUR

ALPHABET CIRCLE MAZE

Start at A at the bottom, continue through the alphabet only once, and finish at the Z in the center. You will pass through other letters when going from one letter to the next, but move in only one direction, either around a circle or along a spoke. Don't enter or cross through the Z until you are finished.

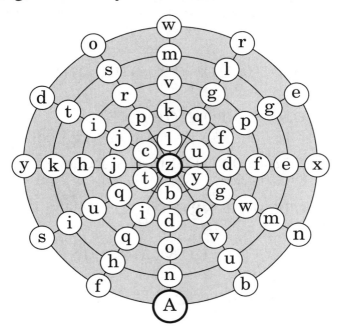

STAR WORDS

VISUAL ◆ LOGIC

Only five of the eight words given will fit together in the diagram. Place them in the directions indicated by the arrows.

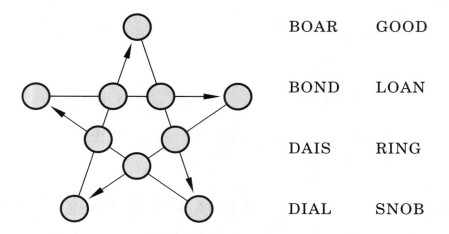

BOAR   GOOD

BOND   LOAN

DAIS   RING

DIAL   SNOB

O COUNT

VISUAL

Here's an eye exam that's also an O exam! First, read the sentence below. Next, go back and read the sentence again, but this time count all of the O's. How many are there?

ON OUR HONOR, OUR ONLY

HONEST-TO-GOODNESS

VACATION OPTIONS FOR

OCTOBER ARE OHIO, THE

POCONOS, KOKOMO, OR,

MORE OBVIOUSLY, TORONTO.

GOING IN CIRCLES

WEEK
32

In each circle, insert one letter into each empty space to form an 8-letter word. Words may read either clockwise or counterclockwise and may begin with any letter in the circle.

1.
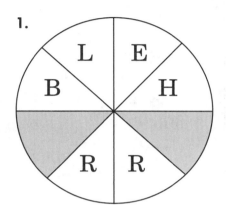

2.
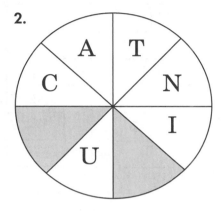

WHO'S WHO?

Lou doesn't smoke and Dan's pants are the same shade as Lou's. Alf, who is speaking aloud to Charles, stands with his back to Bert (whose hair is the same color as Martin's). Can you tell who's who among the six pals?

1   2   3   4   5   6

IN THE ABSTRACT

VISUAL ◆ SPATIAL

Directions for solving are on page 192.

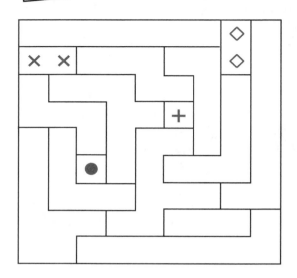

MARCHING ORDERS

MATH ◆ LOGIC

Using a different two-step sequence of addition and/or subtraction, can you make your way from Start to Finish in each puzzle by moving up, down, or diagonally? We've started the first one for you using the sequence +4 and -2; continue this sequence to reach Finish. You will not cross your own path or pass through any square twice.

1.   FINISH ↑

15	16	14	18	16	20
14	13	12	14	10	18
11	6	9	11	10	12
5	8	5	6	9	8
0	3	7	8	12	10
2	6	4	5	7	9

↑ **START**

2.   FINISH ↑

11	8	13	14	18	23
6	10	15	16	21	16
9	10	8	12	18	19
3	4	7	9	17	14
5	2	6	7	15	16
0	3	4	8	11	12

↑ **START**

LETTER, PLEASE

The numbers below stand for certain letters on the telephone dial. You will see that one number may stand for more than one letter — for example, 3 may be D, E, or F. By finding the correct letter for each number, you will have spelled out a thought.

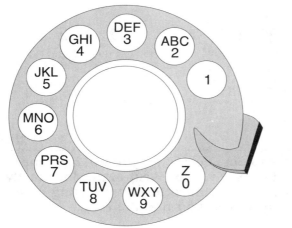

26657 8428

273 7488 273

732559 66

6673 8426

8735377

256257.

VISUAL

HEXAGON HUNT

Directions for solving are on page 198.

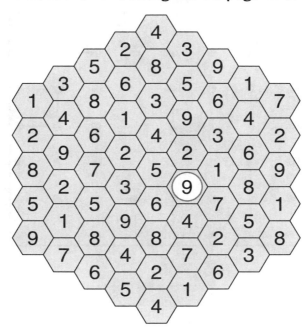

COUNT ON IT!

LANGUAGE

See page 197 for solving directions.

1. M W H L M   2. A I A O A   3. N K R G N

4. E K Y H D   5. T S

$\overline{~1~}\overline{~2~}\overline{~3~}\overline{~4~}$ $\overline{~1~}\overline{~2~}\overline{~3~}\overline{~4~}\overline{~5~}$ $\overline{~1~}\overline{~2~}\overline{~3~}\overline{~4~}$

$\overline{~1~}\overline{~2~}\overline{~3~}\overline{~4~}\overline{~5~}$ $\overline{~1~}\overline{~2~}\overline{~3~}\overline{~4~}$.

ROUND TRIP

VISUAL ◆ LOGIC

When this puzzle has been completed correctly, you will have made a round trip through its set of dots. You must visit every dot exactly once, make no diagonal moves, and return to your starting point. Parts of the right path are shown; can you find the rest?

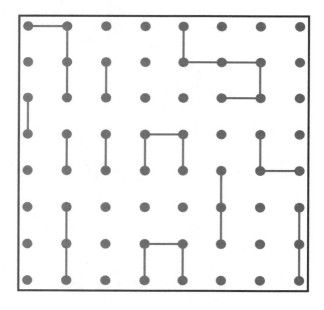

"Time you enjoy wasting, was not wasted."
— *John Lennon*

KEEP ON MOVING

The goal is to move from the shaded square to the asterisk. Since the shaded square has the number 2 in it, you must move two squares up, down, left, or right, but not diagonally. In the new square will be another number; move that number of squares up, down, left, or right, continuing in this way until you reach the asterisk. It's okay to cross your own path.

4	5	1	2	1	3
3	3	5	4	✳	1
1	4	2	2	3	4
2	4	2	3	4	3
4	3	4	3	2	4
2	1	2	5	1	3

CARD SENSE

Directions for solving are on page 197.

1. The four is somewhere between the diamonds.

2. The ten is somewhere between the spades.

3. The five is somewhere between the ace and the club.

4. The card on the bottom of the pile is not red.

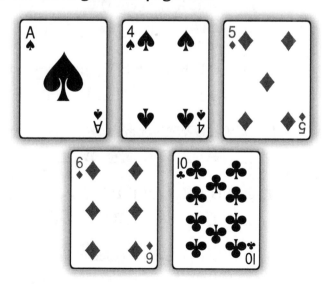

ARROW MAZE

VISUAL

Directions for solving are on page 195.

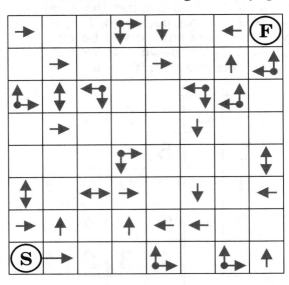

FILLING STATION

LANGUAGE

See page 214 for solving directions.

1. D G M R R S (event)

   __ A __ __ I   __ __ A __

2. M P P R R S S S S V (natural wonder)

   __ I __ __ I __ __ I __ __ I   __ I __ E __

3. D N R S W Y (person)

   __ I A __ E   __ A __ __ E __

4. C G G K L N N P P P S T (book character)

   __ I __ I   __ O __ __ __ O __ I __ __

5. B C D H K R T Y (food)

   __ I __ __ __ A __   __ A __ E

226

ANAGRAM MAZE

Directions for solving are on page 205. This time, there are 21 words to anagram and the first word you'll be anagramming is FACE.

1 LIST	**2** KNEE	**3** RELY	**4** MUCH	**5** BEAU	**6** FACE
7 FEET	**8** LESS	**9** LILY	**10** DROP	**11** DOES	**12** DIET
13 ARID	**14** HEAR	**15** RIPE	**16** CELL	**17** MALT	**18** MINK
19 TINY	**20** MAZE	**21** VANE	**22** FAST	**23** RAPS	**24** SOON
25 HOOT	**26** HAVE	**27** MAKE	**28** AFAR	**29** CAPE	**30** WOOL
31 LIFE	**32** ACME	**33** WHAT	**34** NUTS	**35** NEWT	**36** FOUL

MATH

ALL IN A ROW

Directions for solving are on page 191. This time, look for the most groups of consecutive numbers adding up to 13.

A. 6 4 8 2 9 3 1 2 5 7 4 5 3 1 8 2 6 3 3 4 1 7 5 8

B. 7 3 4 8 1 3 6 2 1 9 5 4 8 2 6 3 4 1 7 2 1 2 9 4

C. 5 2 6 4 7 1 8 3 4 2 4 1 9 5 7 2 4 1 5 2 3 1 2 8

LOOSE TILE

VISUAL ◆ SPATIAL

The tray on the left seemed the ideal place to store the set of loose dominoes. Unfortunately, when the tray was full, one domino was left over. Determine the arrangement of the dominoes in the tray and which is the Loose Tile.

ALPHABET SOUP

LANGUAGE ◆ VISUAL

Cross off each letter from the alphabet list that appears in the larger group of letters. Then rearrange the letters not crossed out to form the name of a fish.

H	R	Y	E	H	R	M	H	R	Y	M	E	R	Y	H	E
M	Y	R	E	H	J	Y	E	R	B	G	J	Y	R	L	M
Y	R	E	J	L	H	D	O	R	K	C	X	G	M	W	Z
G	D	R	O	S	W	F	Q	M	Y	I	V	J	E	Y	P

A B C D E F G H I J K L M N O P Q R S T U V W X Y Z

Fish: _____

228

QUOTATION MARKS

Enter the capital letters in the diagram as indicated by the number-letter combinations to form a quote by President John F. Kennedy. For example, one of the C's should be placed in the box where column 8 and row b intersect.

	1	2	3	4	5	6	7	8	9	10	11	12	13	14	15	16
a																
b																
c																
d																
e																
f																
g																
h																
i																
j																
k																

A: 16b, 10c, 2e, 13e, 7g, 16h, 6i, 6j, 5k

B: 16i

C: 8b, 11e, 5i

D: 1h, 16j

E: 3a, 6a, 15a, 15b, 13c, 9d, 5e, 16e, 3f, 15g, 9h, 14h, 2i, 10i, 14i, 14j, 14k

F: 9a, 3b, 1d, 9e, 7h, 8h, 10k

G: 2f

H: 2a, 6b, 9b, 12e, 6g, 13h, 5j, 13k

I: 14a, 7b, 11b, 3c, 7d, 12d, 15d, 6f, 10g, 12g, 4i, 9j, 11j

K: 1c, 7k

L: 14e, 15e, 13i

M: 6d, 11f, 1i, 15k

N: 5a, 12a, 6c, 1f, 1g, 13g, 16g, 7i, 12j, 15j

O: 11a, 2b, 7c, 16c, 5d, 8e, 2g, 4h, 6h, 11i, 3k, 9k

P: 14b, 3d, 15f, 9i, 12i

R: 10a, 16a, 4d, 10h, 3i

S: 13b, 4c, 12c, 8d, 10d, 16d, 4e, 4f, 9f, 12f, 6k

T: 1a, 13a, 8c, 14c, 13d, 6e, 7f, 3g, 8g, 14g, 3h, 12h, 2j, 7j, 13j, 2k, 12k

U: 10f, 14f, 1j

W: 7a, 5b, 5g, 4j

WAYWORDS

LANGUAGE

Directions for solving are on page 209. This time, you'll be looking for an 11-word thought beginning with SOME.

BRIEF	AND	PARADE	PLEASANT
SOME	THE	WATCH	REQUIRE
OTHERS	JOIN	SOME	AND
IN	BELIEVE	FIND	STAND

CIRCLE MATH

MATH

Directions for solving are on page 210. We've started you off by telling you that A = 6.

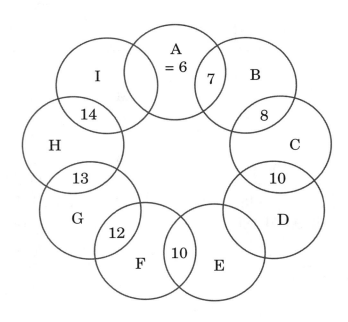

"When patterns are broken, new worlds emerge."
— *Tuli Kupferberg*

230

ANTONYMS QUIZ

WEEK
33

An antonym is a word that is opposite in meaning to another word; for example, "cold" is the antonym of "hot." One of the words following each capitalized word is the antonym of that word.

1. THWART   a. portend   b. iterate   c. abet

2. BOMBASTIC   a. modest   b. formidable   c. turbid

3. MAGNANIMOUS   a. mean   b. besotted   c. weary

4. JUBILANT   a. scholarly   b. remorseful   c. diffuse

5. CUMBROUS   a. clement   b. scanty   c. graceful

6. VEX   a. designate   b. soothe   c. oust

7. PLIANT   a. stubborn   b. striking   c. frank

8. DILIGENCE   a. remorse   b. enmity   c. carelessness

LANGUAGE # QUICK FILL

Directions for solving are on page 196.

D E E L M N O P T Y

1. Letter 10 is a consonant.

2. Letter 8 is from the first half of the alphabet.

3. In the alphabet, letter 5 is immediately before letter 3.

4. Letter 6 appears in the word PLENTY but not in PLANET.

5. Letter 2 is the first letter of the word that completes the following phrase: — said than done.

6. Letter 1 appears in the word MAINLAND.

7. In the alphabet, letter 4 is immediately before letter 7 and neither is a vowel.

8. Letter 9 is the fourth letter of the name of Paris's country.

$$\overline{1}\ \overline{2}\ \overline{3}\ \overline{4}\ \overline{5}\ \overline{6}\ \overline{7}\ \overline{8}\ \overline{9}\ \overline{10}$$

ELIMINATION

LANGUAGE

Directions for solving are on page 203. Once again, the remaining words will form a thought.

BLESSING ROLES IF JOYFUL ELECTRICAL WELL AT IN MAD FIRST QUESTIONAIRE ELATED YOU CHEMICAL SHELL DO SHOCK DAQUIRI IS SUCCEED DISGUISE WED HIDE BELLWEATHER CIVIL YOUR THRILLED ON SURPRISE HELM CANT

Eliminate…

1. the three words that, when put together, form the name of Wisconsin's capital city.

2. the four words that become contractions when an apostrophe is added to each one.

3. the three misspelled words.

4. the three words that mean "happy."

5. the three words that form a phrase that means "felicitation cloaked by camouflage."

6. the three words that can come before "engineering."

7. the three words that, when scrambled, form the name of a character created by the writer Arthur Conan Doyle.

WORD HUNT

LANGUAGE ◆ SPATIAL

Directions for solving are on page 195. This time, you'll be searching for 4-letter words that end with K (such as PACK). We found 38 words, including PACK.

Your list of words:

S	I	P	E	B	D
J	G	L	A	R	U
B	U	C	K	S	I
P	I	N	R	O	P
E	S	M	F	W	C
C	K	A	K	O	O

COUNTDOWN

Directions for solving are on page 202.

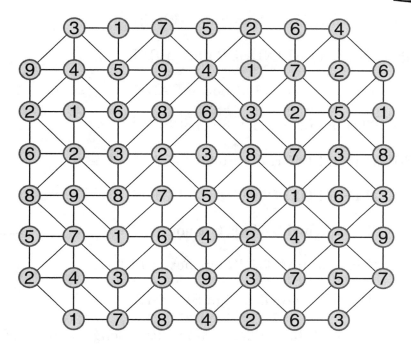

LANGUAGE ◆ SPATIAL

TRI, TRI AGAIN

Directions for solving are on page 215.

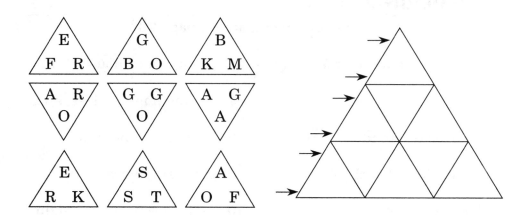

ANIMAL CHARADES
LANGUAGE
Directions for solving are on page 212.

My FIRST is in BELUGA and in LARGE;   ‗‗‗‗‗‗‗

My SECOND is in REINDEER and in BARGE;   ‗‗‗‗‗‗‗

My THIRD is in ADDER but not in DANK;   ‗‗‗‗‗‗‗

My FOURTH is in CANARY but not in PRANK;   ‗‗‗‗‗‗‗

My FIFTH is in FINCH and in CHOICE;   ‗‗‗‗‗‗‗

My SIXTH is in PORPOISE and in VOICE;   ‗‗‗‗‗‗‗

My SEVENTH is in TURTLE but not in SLIGHT;   ‗‗‗‗‗‗‗

My EIGHTH is in PANTHER but not in PLIGHT;   ‗‗‗‗‗‗‗

My NINTH is in LIZARD and in SPREAD.   ‗‗‗‗‗‗‗

My WHOLE is a tall, slender canine with a long, narrow head.

‗‗‗‗‗‗‗‗‗‗‗‗‗‗‗‗‗‗

COMPOUND IT
LANGUAGE
Directions for solving are on page 200.

1. play, corn, handle, free

2. bill, way, field, bar

3. side, board, tender, work

4. walk, week, bench, show

5. boat, stopper, night, end

6. gown, point, house, yard

7. broken, mother, less, stick

8. hood, cat, land, pin

9. slide, fill, mass, mark

10. male, down, rush, weight

GRAND TOUR

Directions for solving are on page 194. This time, you'll be looking for a chain of 5-letter words, starting with OF-FER-AL (offer, feral).

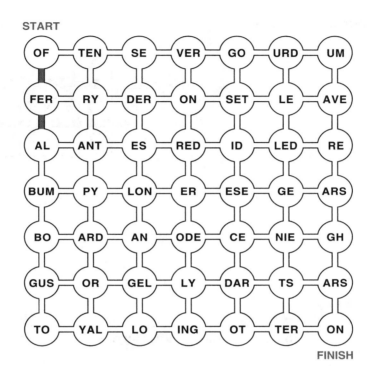

START

FINISH

MATH ◆ LOGIC

WHAT'S YOUR NUMBER?

Can you figure out the relationship of the numbers in the first two figures and, based on that, what missing number goes into the space with the question mark?

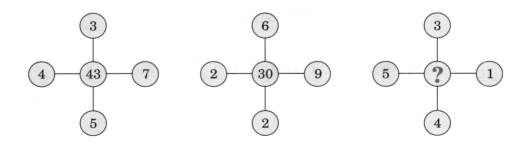

SLIDE RULE

LANGUAGE

Directions for solving are on page 214. Here, you're to form 4-letter words. We found 28 words, including GONE.

Your list of words:

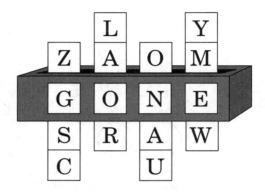

CODE WORD

DECODING

Directions for solving are on page 199. Here, determine a 12-letter Code Word.

$$\overline{1}\ \overline{2}\ \overline{3}\ \overline{4}\ \overline{5}\ \overline{6}\ \overline{7}\ \overline{8}\ \overline{9}\ \overline{10}\ \overline{11}\ \overline{12}$$

K 2 2 8 10 N 5   U 8   W 10 T 9   T 9 2   N 2 10 5 9 B 4 6 12

11 7 N   B 2   3 U 11 9   9 7 6 12 6   4 N   T 9 2 3 — T 9 2 Y

7 L W 7 Y 12   9 7 V 2   T 4   F 10 N 1   W 7 Y 12   T 4

K 2 2 8   7 9 2 7 1 .

THE LINEUP

DAY 34

Directions for solving are on page 208.

TOBOJSKIPFRAGRANTEYZMINDRRECEIVINGQFLEWUX

1. Which letter of the alphabet does not appear in the lineup? _____

2. What 8-letter word — with its letters in correct order and appearing together — can you find in the lineup? _____

3. Which letter of the alphabet appears exactly three times in the lineup? _____

4. What 9-letter word — with its letters in correct order and appearing together — can you find in the lineup? _____

5. Other than the answers to Questions 2 and 4, how many everyday words — with their letters in correct order and appearing together — of four or more letters can you find in the lineup? _____

LANGUAGE

EASY PICKINGS

Directions for solving are on page 194. This time, the remaining letters will spell out a truism.

YT OU   TU HA KS WE   FW IN SR ES GT

PM OL YA CE UE,   RT AB KE SE

CF IA RI ES.

SUDOKU

LOGIC

Directions for solving are on page 190.

7			2		5	8		
1		4	9	3		7		
	5				7			4
9		7						6
	1		7	9	4		8	
3						2		7
5			6				2	
		9		8	2	3		5
		8	3		1			9

BULL'S-EYE LETTER

LANGUAGE

Directions for solving are on page 208.

— — — — —

— — — — —

— — — — —

— — — — —

— — — — —

— — — — —

LBA   NTI

EFL   **?**   EKE

FNA   HOC

238

CIRCLE SEARCH

Directions for solving are on page 203. Here you're looking to form 19 words of at least three letters.

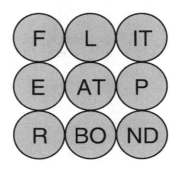

VISUAL ◆ SPATIAL

OVERLAY

When you overlay the three diagrams in the top row, which of the three lettered diagrams, A, B, or C, will be formed?

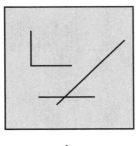
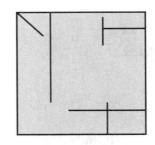
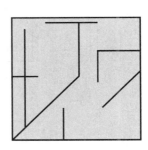

A.

B.

C.

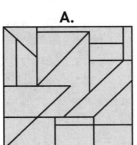
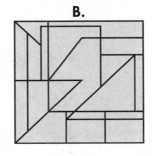
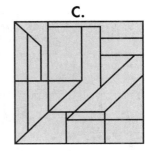

239

Directions for solving are on page 213.

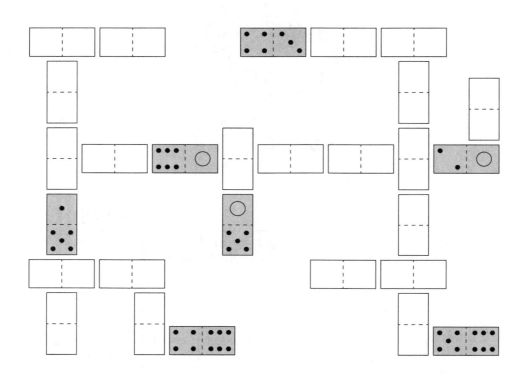

DOMINOES

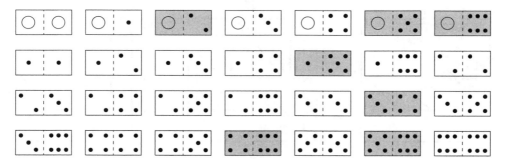

VISUAL ◆ SPATIAL

STACKED UP

WEEK 35

Directions for solving are on page 210.

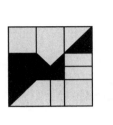

1.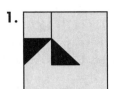
2.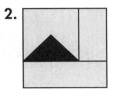
3.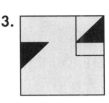

4.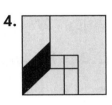
5.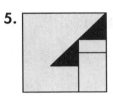
6.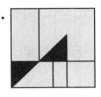

LOGIC

DEDUCTION PROBLEM

Kate and two other women teach at Madison Middle School, as do their husbands (including Mike). Each person teaches a different subject (one teaches social studies) and each wife has her husband's last name. From this information and the clues below, can you determine the full names of each couple and the subject each individual teaches?

1. Stephanie teaches history.

2. Mr. Peters teaches music.

3. Tom's wife is the science teacher.

4. Sam O'Neill has been teaching for ten years.

5. Mrs. Jackson teaches art.

6. Betty's husband is the math teacher.

241

ASSOCIATIONS

Directions for solving are on page 217.

WHY DID THE CHICKEN CROSS THE PLAYGROUND?

DEER TRANCE SCARE OBVIOUS DROP WATERLESS

GRATITUDE MAGENTA EFFORT DIVE OREGANO

TRAP TON GRAPEFRUIT TAPESTRY MOOSE ONION

FRIGHTEN THIRTY ROSEMARY HARVEST PLUNGE

ELEGANT POUND OPERA SCARLET TRAFFIC DRY

HAPPY CRIMSON EPIC TARRAGON ROMANCE

OUNCE SANCTUARY LEMON LISTEN STARTLE

INTEREST ELK DEPUTY ARID LIME ELEMENT

TARGET SHOOT

Directions for solving are on page 212.

1.

2.

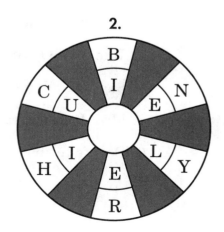

WORD CHARADE

WEEK
35

Directions for solving are on page 204.

My first letter is directly above an N and to the immediate left of an H.

My second letter is the only extra letter in the row that contains the letters in the word JACKPOT.

My third letter appears in the first column but not in the second column.

My fourth letter is the third letter of a string of consecutive letters of the alphabet reading from right to left in one of the rows.

L	G	S	P	B	V	F	N
K	L	C	U	O	E	R	A
Q	P	O	N	M	L	K	J
Z	Q	L	G	D	T	P	H
B	R	F	V	S	H	N	Q
O	Z	C	I	E	L	M	G
P	K	A	O	J	U	T	C
R	O	N	A	D	A	K	I

My fifth letter appears in the bottom four rows but not in the top four rows.

My sixth letter is the first letter of the name of a country that starts reading down in one of the columns then continues reading to the right in one of the rows.

— — — — — —

SKILLS TEST

Can you determine which figure is different from the others?

1   2   3   4   5

WORD LINK

LANGUAGE

Place the words in parentheses after each capitalized word in the diagram so that they cross or connect with the capitalized letter. TAP has been placed in the diagram; TELESCOPE and TRANSACTS cross or connect with TAP.

AJAR (apricot, ate, joy)

APRICOT (ajar, caliph, pot, rye)

ARC (telescope, transacts)

AROMATIC (brace, coyote, extol, ram, transacts)

ATE (ajar, pot, rye)

BRACE (aromatic, brothers, cat, emeralds)

BROTHERS (brace, caliph, coyote, extol, pat, transacts)

CALIPH (apricot, brothers, cap, pinball)

CAP (caliph, coyote, pat)

CAT (brace, coyote, ram)

COOL (pinball, roe, tot)

COYOTE (aromatic, brothers, cap, cat, emeralds)

EMERALDS (brace, coyote, extol, ram, transacts)

EXTOL (aromatic, brothers, emeralds)

JOY (ajar, pot, rye)

PAT (brothers, cap, pinball)

PINBALL (caliph, cool, pat, telescope, transacts)

POT (apricot, ate, joy)

RAM (aromatic, cat, emeralds)

ROE (cool, telescope, transacts)

RYE (apricot, ate, joy)

TAP (telescope, transacts)

TELESCOPE (arc, pinball, roe, tap, tot)

TOT (cool, telescope, transacts)

TRANSACTS (arc, aromatic, brothers, emeralds, pinball, roe, tap, tot)

						T	A	P

ANAGRAM MAZE

WEEK
35

Directions for solving are on page 205. This time, there are 19 words to anagram and the first word you'll be anagramming is SIGN.

1 CULT	2 WAIT	3 SIGN	4 SENT	5 POEM	6 SLOW
_ _ _ _	_ _ _ _	_ _ _ _	_ _ _ _	_ _ _ _	_ _ _ _
7 PURR	8 OOZE	9 WINE	10 CREW	11 PLUS	12 CLAY
_ _ _ _	_ _ _ _	_ _ _ _	_ _ _ _	_ _ _ _	_ _ _ _
13 VEST	14 ANTE	15 HUBS	16 JETS	17 CUFF	18 CATS
_ _ _ _	_ _ _ _	_ _ _ _	_ _ _ _	_ _ _ _	_ _ _ _
19 CALM	20 ALOE	21 FIVE	22 SHUT	23 CURE	24 BOWL
_ _ _ _	_ _ _ _	_ _ _ _	_ _ _ _	_ _ _ _	_ _ _ _
25 PAGE	26 COED	27 FALL	28 WHIM	29 BODY	30 FOIL
_ _ _ _	_ _ _ _	_ _ _ _	_ _ _ _	_ _ _ _	_ _ _ _
31 DECK	32 BRAG	33 FLEE	34 INKS	35 INTO	36 DUMB
_ _ _ _	_ _ _ _	_ _ _ _	_ _ _ _	_ _ _ _	_ _ _ _

GOING IN CIRCLES

Directions for solving are on page 221.

1.

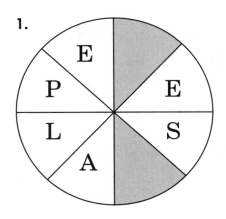

2.

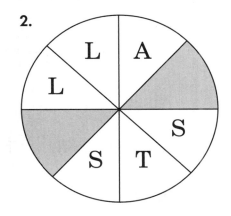

ARROW MAZE

VISUAL

Starting at the S and following the arrow up, see if you can find your way to F. When you reach an arrow, you MUST follow its direction and continue in that direction until you come to the next arrow. When you reach a two-headed arrow, you can choose either direction. It's okay to cross your own path.

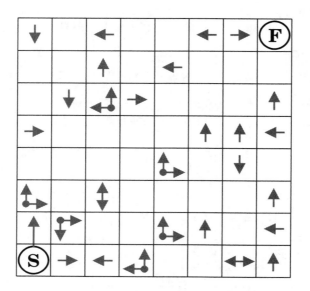

COUNT ON IT!

LANGUAGE

Use the given letters to fill in the familiar saying, one letter per dash. All the letters following 1 are the first letters of each word, the letters following 2 are the second letters of each word, etc. It is up to you to determine which letter goes where.

1. A T L N A T F S   2. R H S O U H U   3. I N E C E

4. E H C R N   5. H E G   6. S

$\overline{1}\ \overline{2}\ \overline{3}\ \overline{4}\ \overline{5}\ \overline{6}$, $\overline{1}\ \overline{2}$ $\overline{1}\ \overline{2}\ \overline{3}\ \overline{4}$

$\overline{1}\ \overline{2}\ \overline{3}\ \overline{4}\ \overline{5}$ $\overline{1}\ \overline{2}$ $\overline{1}$ $\overline{1}\ \overline{2}\ \overline{3}\ \overline{4}$

$\overline{1}\ \overline{2}\ \overline{3}\ \overline{4}\ \overline{5}$.

Y COUNT

Here's an eye exam that's also a Y exam! First, read the sentence below. Next, go back and read the sentence again, but this time count all of the Y's. How many are there?

SLY YANCY YOUNG YELLED "YAY!

YEAH!" AND WRY YVES YORK YODELED

"YIPPEE! YES!," YET WHY DID LOVELY

CYNDY YELTSIN LOUDLY YELP "YIKES!

YOW! YUCK!" ON YVONNE'S YELLOWY

YACHT YESTERDAY?

LOGIC

SUDOKU

Place a number into each box so each row across, column down, and small 9-box square within the larger square (there are 9 of these) contains 1 through 9.

1		6				9		
	5			3		7	6	
	9	3	5		1			2
	6	5	1				2	8
			3		6			
4	3				2	1	7	
3			7		8	6	1	
	8	7		1			4	
		4				8		7

COUNTDOWN

VISUAL

Following the connecting lines, find the only route in this grid that passes through the numbers backward from 9 to 1 consecutively.

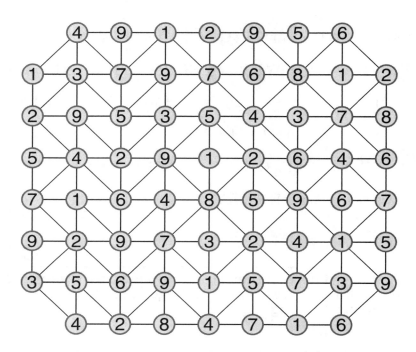

DOVETAILED WORDS

LANGUAGE

Two related words, with their letters in the correct order, are combined in each row of letters. Can you find both words? In a line like POTEORDRLEIER, or POteOrDrLEier, you can see the two words POODLE and TERRIER.

1. G F U O L I L D O E W   _____   _____

2. P W A E L N R G U U I S N   _____   _____

3. T H H O R R R I L L E O R R   _____   _____

4. A B S S P O O N R G B E   _____   _____

5. H P A O S B T I B M E Y   _____   _____

248

VISION QUEST

WEEK 36

Find the row or column that contains five DIFFERENT seats.

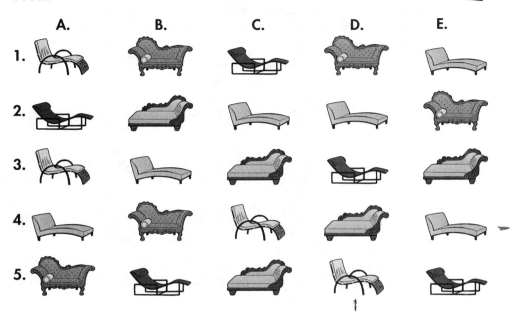

| | A. | B. | C. | D. | E. |

WORD HUNT

LANGUAGE ◆ SPATIAL

Find words by moving from one letter to any adjoining letter. You may start a word with any letter in the diagram. In forming a word you may return to a letter as often as you wish, but do not stand on a letter using it twice in direct succession. In this Word Hunt, you are searching for 5-letter words that end with RT. We found 13 words, including CHART.

C	H	M	U	Q
B	P	A	S	K
C	L	R	T	I
O	U	E	X	R
S	P	A	V	O

Your list of words:

HEXAGON HUNT

VISUAL

In this diagram of six-sided figures, there are 10 "special" hexagons. These 10 are special because the six numbers around each one are all different from each other and the center. We've circled one of the 10. Can you find the other 9?

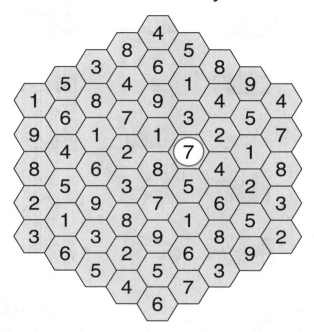

CODE WORD

DECODING

Decipher a quote and the Code Word's eleven letters, represented by the numbers 1 through 11. So, if the Code Word were "THUNDERCLAP," 1 in the quote would be T, 2 would be H, etc.

$$\overline{1}\ \overline{2}\ \overline{3}\ \overline{4}\ \overline{5}\ \overline{6}\ \overline{7}\ \overline{8}\ \overline{9}\ \overline{10}\ \overline{11}$$

1 2 10 9 7 3 11   11 4 O U L 8   10 2 6 11 9   K 6 8 11

O 7   3 4 9 11 9   5 O U 10   5 ' 11 :   5 O 7 8 7 9 11 11 ,

5 10 2 7 K 7 9 11 11 ,   5 2 6 10 7 9 11 11 ,

2 7 8   5 6 10 M 7 9 11 11 .

250

TIPS OF THE ICEBERG

WEEK
36

The chart shows the gratuities each waiter or waitress earned on a recent breakfast shift at the Iceberg Diner. All you have to do is some addition and then answer the following questions:

1. Who made the most in total tips?
2. Who made the least?
3. Which two waitpersons made exactly the same amount?

EMPLOYEE	TIP 1	TIP 2	TIP 3	TIP 4	TIP 5
Hank	$1.10	$2.15	$1.70	$1.95	$1.50
Inez	$1.80	$1.20	$1.40	$1.20	$1.50
Jack	$0.85	$1.10	$1.10	$2.50	$0.95
Ken	$1.60	$0.95	$1.30	$2.20	$1.00
Laura	$1.00	$1.00	$0.80	$1.00	$0.60
Marty	$1.90	$1.40	$1.40	$1.20	$1.20
Noel	$1.00	$1.00	$3.00	$1.15	$1.00

GRAND TOUR

LANGUAGE ◆ VISUAL

Form a continuous chain of 5-letter words moving through the maze from START to FINISH. The second part of one word becomes the first part of the next word. This puzzle starts with VER-SE-DAN (verse, sedan).

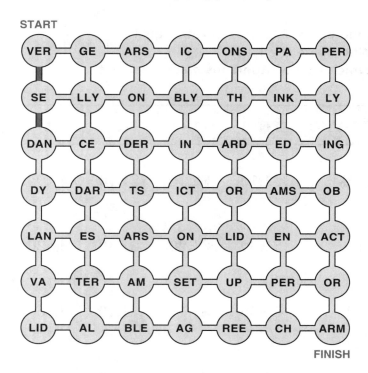

START

VER	GE	ARS	IC	ONS	PA	PER
SE	LLY	ON	BLY	TH	INK	LY
DAN	CE	DER	IN	ARD	ED	ING
DY	DAR	TS	ICT	OR	AMS	OB
LAN	ES	ARS	ON	LID	EN	ACT
VA	TER	AM	SET	UP	PER	OR
LID	AL	BLE	AG	REE	CH	ARM

FINISH

ALL IN A ROW

MATH

Which row below contains the most groups of consecutive numbers adding up to 9? Look carefully, because some groups may overlap. We've underlined an example of a group in each row to start you off.

A. 7 1 3 4 8 2 2 1 4 6 5 3 1 4 <u>7 2</u> 3 1 1 6 8 2 5 1

B. 2 6 4 1 3 7 5 2 8 4 1 1 5 2 2 6 1 5 <u>7 1 1</u> 3 8 2

C. <u>4 1 3 1</u> 8 2 2 3 2 6 4 1 4 7 3 2 8 4 5 1 3 4 7 5

252

ANIMAL CHARADES

Each line contains a clue to a letter of the alphabet. These letters, in the given order, will spell out the name of an animal. The animal's identity is also hinted at in the last sentence of the Charade.

My FIRST is in WOMBAT and in MOIST; _____

My SECOND is in CONDOR and in REJOICED; _____

My THIRD is in EGRET but not in TEEN; _____

My FOURTH is in NUTHATCH but not in CUISINE; _____

My FIFTH is in POLECAT and in POINT; _____

My SIXTH is in IGUANA and in ANOINT; _____

My SEVENTH is in SALMON but not in LAMP; _____

My EIGHTH is in PANTHER but not in STAMP. _____

My WHOLE is a shell-encased reptile,
    One who's not particularly mobile.

_____

STACKED UP

The box on the left can be formed by three of the numbered boxes superimposed on top of each other; do not turn them in any way. Can you figure out which three work?

1.

2.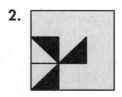

3.

4.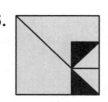

5.

6.

EASY PICKINGS

LANGUAGE

To solve, simply cross out one letter in each pair below. When the puzzle is completed correctly, the remaining letters will spell out a fact.

AT HO ME   HZ AH GN NK SF

SE TV TA CR RO LE ND   IW MN

TS OH EN   MT IO VL SI AE

"TF HO RG RK NE TS TL   DG RU MT PS."

ALPHABET CIRCLE MAZE

VISUAL

Start at A at the bottom, continue through the alphabet only once, and finish at the Z in the center. You will pass through other letters when going from one letter to the next, but move in only one direction, either around a circle or along a spoke. Don't enter or cross through the Z until you are finished.

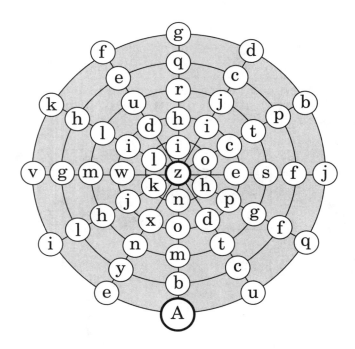

RINGERS

Each Ringer is composed of five rings. Use your imagination to rotate the rings so that you spell out four 5-letter words reading from the outside to the inside when all five rings are aligned correctly.

1.

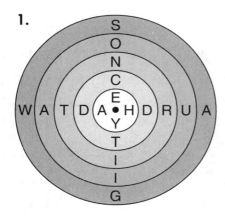

2.

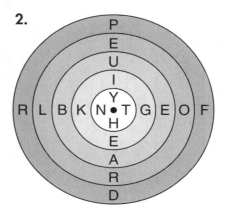

QUICK FILL

Determine the 10-letter word from the clues. All the letters in the word are listed.

B E E N Q S S T U U

1. Letter 2 is from the second half of the alphabet.

2. Letter 5 appears elsewhere in the word.

3. Letter 8 appears more than once in the word PRESENTATION.

4. Letter 1 can be placed in the middle of "hate," "bail," and "duty" to form three new words.

5. In the alphabet, letter 10 is immediately before letter 7.

6. Letter 4 is in the word RESOLUTE but not in DOCUMENT.

7. Letter 6 is a consonant.

8. Letter 3 appears in both SUNBURN and GOBLINS.

9. Letter 9 can be placed as the next-to-last letter of "meat," "shoe," and "grid" to form three new words.

$\overline{1}$ $\overline{2}$ $\overline{3}$ $\overline{4}$ $\overline{5}$ $\overline{6}$ $\overline{7}$ $\overline{8}$ $\overline{9}$ $\overline{10}$

LICENSE PLATES

LANGUAGE

Each box contains six letters of the name of a two-word dessert. The top three are a part of the first word and the bottom three are a part of the last word, in order.

1.
```
N A N
P L I
```

2.
```
M E A
O O K
```

3.
```
C O L
R O W
```

4.
```
A R R
A K E
```

5.
```
P L E
T A R
```

6.
```
I C E
U D D
```

GOING IN CIRCLES

LANGUAGE

In each circle, insert one letter into each empty space to form an 8-letter word. Words may read either clockwise or counterclockwise and may begin with any letter in the circle.

1.

2.

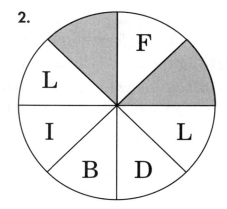

QUOTATION MARKS

Enter the letters in the diagram as indicated to form a thought. For example, the A that goes between W and N has been entered.

	1	2	3	4	5	6	7	8	9	10	11	12	13	14	15	16
a					T			T		E		A		C		E
b		T			H			A		P		A		A		
c	C			O			A			W	A	N		W		T
d			I		S		E		F		R		L		S	
e		G		I		E		O				H				I
f	R		O				F		A		L		K			
g		D		L		V		L				N		U		L
h	I		G		F		I		H				I		N	
i		E				V		N		S		E		C		
j	A		D		E		O		E				M		O	
k		A				O		G		N		S				

In the rows, place the following letters immediately between the indicated letters (reading left to right):

A: W-N, L-K, V-N   H: T-E   N: A-C, I-G, E-C, A-D, O-G
D: I-E   I: C-E, W-T, G-N   O: F-R, L-V
E: P-A, L-S, V-L   K: O-E   P: A-P
F: E-F, N-U   L: G-I, F-I   R: A-A, R-O, U-L
G: I-H, I-N   M: M-O   T: I-S, R-L

In the columns, place the following letters immediately between the indicated letters (reading top to bottom):

D: G-D, S-N   L: I-A   S: A-F, N-E, T-I
E: F-E, H-E, N-O   N: R-I, F-A, E-T   T: R-L
I: E-S   O: E-V   Y: A-H

Place the following letters in the indicated boxes:

A: 16f, 16h   H: 1d   R: 4f, 16j
C: 11i   L: 3k, 5k   S: 3b
E: 7b, 2c, 13e, 14f   M: 15e   T: 5b, 10h, 1k
F: 5c   N: 1b   U: 11g
G: 11k   O: 6a   V: 6j

ANAGRAM MAZE
LANGUAGE ◆ VISUAL

The diagram contains 36 words, 19 of which are anagrams of other everyday words. Start at the top arrow and anagram RING. While solving, move up, down, right, or left to the only adjacent word that can be anagrammed. Continue until you arrive at the bottom arrow. There is only one path through the maze.

1 LOLL	2 BOWL	3 OWNS	4 APES	5 WHAT	6 RING
7 YOKE	8 ARMS	9 FORK	10 BANK	11 FANG	12 ROOF
13 KIWI	14 VETO	15 BEAK	16 MARE	17 AFAR	18 BALL
19 HAIL	20 BODY	21 HALF	22 SKID	23 ICON	24 MAKE
25 FLEE	26 CUPS	27 LION	28 HIGH	29 NONE	30 PENT
31 TONE	32 QUIZ	33 PIER	34 BATS	35 FEAT	36 LILY

WHAT'S YOUR NUMBER?
MATH ◆ LOGIC

Can you figure out the relationship of the numbers in the first two figures and, based on that, what missing number goes into the space with the question mark?

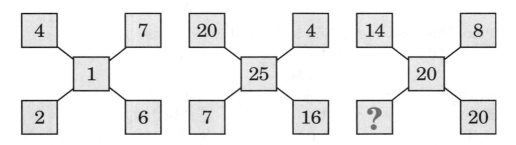

258

CARD SENSE

Five playing cards were shuffled and put in a pile, one on top of another. Using the clues, can you identify each card's position in the pile?

1. The three is directly above the jack.

2. The diamonds are adjacent.

3. The black cards are adjacent.

4. The five is somewhere above the heart.

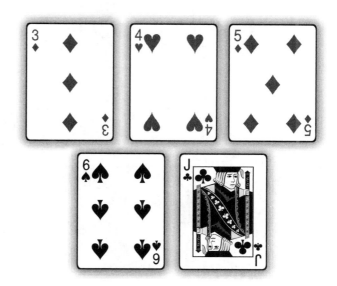

LANGUAGE

COMPOUND IT

Starting at #1, pick a word that will form a compound word with a word chosen in #2. Then with the word you've selected in #2, pick one from #3 to form another compound word. Continue in this manner to #10, so that you've formed nine compound words. In some instances more than one compound word can be formed, but there is only one path to get you to #10.

1. morning, price, horse, clean

2. feathers, power, mule, star

3. nut, train, burst, house

4. hold, quartet, rope, track

5. clan, shop, out, right

6. line, point, beach, moon

7. blank, watch, comb, up

8. weak, lift, sad, coast

9. judge, owl, off, pearl

10. pave, west, steer, shoot

COUNT THE TRIANGLES VISUAL ♦ SPATIAL

To solve this puzzle, write down the three letters that describe each triangle in this figure. We found 30 triangles; how many can you locate?

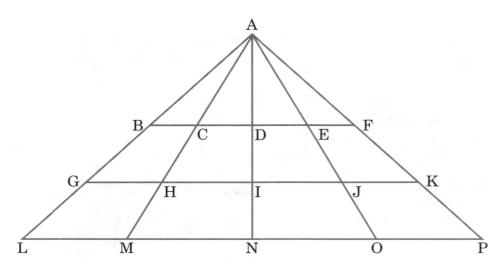

THE LINEUP   LANGUAGE

While scrutinizing this lineup of letters, can you answer the questions correctly in five minutes or less?

JUSTFXZOOMCMARGARINEVRTROUBLEKYQUIPHOW

1. Which letter of the alphabet does not appear in the lineup? _____

2. What 9-letter word — with its letters in correct order and appearing together — can you find in the lineup? _____

3. Which letter of the alphabet appears exactly three times in the lineup? _____

4. What 7-letter word — with its letters in correct order and appearing together — can you find in the lineup? _____

5. Other than the answers to Questions 2 and 4, how many everyday words — with their letters in correct order and appearing together — of four or more letters can you find in the lineup? _____

CIRCLE SEARCH

Move from circle to adjoining circle, horizontally and vertically only, to form 11 common, everyday words of at least three letters. Don't change the order of the letters in the circles that contain more than one letter. Proper names, plurals, and present-tense verbs ending in "s" are not allowed.

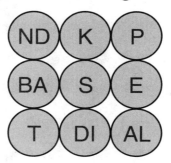

LANGUAGE

ELIMINATION

Cross off the capitalized words below according to the instructions given. The remaining words, in order, will form a thought.

EVERYBODY YOU TRUE GRIT ENERGY ARE CLAN ALLEY TRULY STANDSTILL CRIME RAIN MAN HAPPY PROBLEM IF LABOR CHAT WATTS YOU DOESN'T DEFENSE PINPOINT DON'T CRATE KNOW TREASURY PAY WHY PAPER MOON WEAVER

Eliminate...

1. the four names of U.S. departments of federal government.

2. the three-word saying that means "malfeasant proceedings inhibit remuneration."

3. the three words, each beginning with the same letter, that form three new words when an E is inserted somewhere in each one.

4. the three compound words.

5. the three words that are the last names of actresses.

6. each two-word movie title (with the words of each title together).

7. the word that can be tapped out on a telephone pad as 7762536.

COUNT TO TEN

VISUAL ◆ MATH

Examine the baseball caps and sunglasses and then answer these questions: 1. Which row contains the most baseball caps? 2. Which row contains the most sunglasses? 3. Which row contains an equal number of baseball caps and sunglasses?

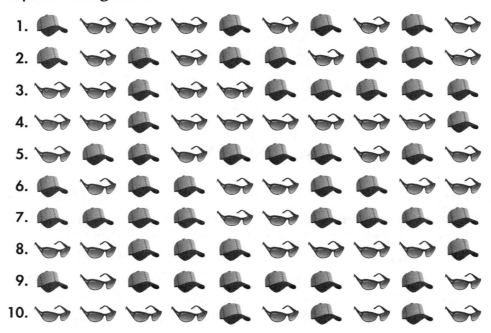

SYMBOL-ISM

DECODING

This is simply a Cryptogram that uses symbols instead of letters to spell out a truism. Each symbol stands for the same letter throughout. For this puzzle, we've already indicated that 🌐 = N and ✏ = C.

                                     N   C

🌑❖☺❖'♦ ♦↝☼❖↗🌑★🌐✳ ↗🌑●↗ ✏↝♦↗↝

               N   N   N

☼↝☺❖ ★🌐 ↗🌑❖ ❖🌐❀ ↗🌑●🌐 ●

                     C   N

✳↝↝❀ ❖❀♥✏🌑●↗★↝🌐 — ↗🌑❖

      N C

●❀♦❖🌐✏❖ ↝✔ ★↗.

262

BULL'S-EYE LETTER

Add the SAME single letter to each group of three letters, then rearrange the letters to form six everyday 4-letter words.

EIW   ALC

HIS   ?   CTA

OHO   TGI

—— —— —— ——

—— —— —— ——

—— —— —— ——

—— —— —— ——

—— —— —— ——

—— —— —— ——

ASSOCIATIONS

You'll find eight groups of three words that can be associated in some way with each other (example: mantel, fireplace, logs). Cross out each group as you find it. The initial letters of the remaining words will spell out the answer to the riddle:

WHO WON WHEN THE TWO WAVES RACED?

SIMPLE   TAFFY   CONCEAL   NORTH   STRICT   HABIT

DALLAS   EASY   EVAPORATE   JAIL   WRITE   EFFORTLESS

YELLOW   SCRIBBLE   SOUTH   TAPESTRY   AUSTIN   TALK

SEVERE   INVASION   PRISON   HIDE   SAY   DEFICIT

HOUSTON   DOODLE   ESCAPADE   BRIG   WEST   HARSH

DISGUISE   UTTER

SUDOKU

LOGIC

Directions for solving are on page 247.

	9		7		3	6		2
	6	2		8			3	
1		7	2				5	4
			5			1		
		5	6		2	9		
		1			9			
6	1				5	2		8
	5			2		3	4	
8		3	4		7		9	

TRI, TRI AGAIN

LANGUAGE ◆ SPATIAL

Fit the nine triangles into the big one so six everyday words are spelled out reading across the arrows. Do not rotate the triangles.

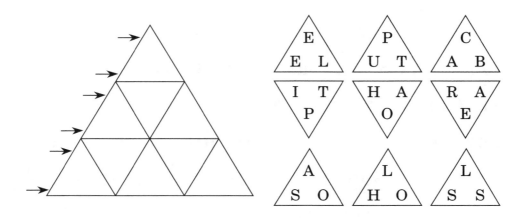

264

WORD CHARADE

WEEK
38

Find each letter in the diagram according to the instructions, and write each letter on its dash to spell out a 6-letter word.

My first letter appears directly below an L and to the immediate left of an F.

My second letter is a consonant in a corner box, but it does not appear in the second row.

My third letter is the only extra letter in a column that contains the letters in the word ROMANCE.

My fourth letter is the second letter of a group of four letters in consecutive alphabetical order in one of the rows.

My fifth letter appears more often than any other letter.

My sixth letter is the middle letter of two 5-letter words that cross each other.

V	K	Z	G	S	C	J	R
H	L	P	B	O	A	V	M
W	T	F	B	R	M	U	O
M	X	R	K	A	I	H	Y
J	A	O	P	Q	R	K	Z
A	U	D	I	T	N	X	P
Y	N	E	G	W	O	U	Q
H	T	O	S	J	E	G	L

— — — — — —

TARGET SHOOT

Find the two letters which, when entered into the center circle of each target, will form three 6-letter words reading across.

1.

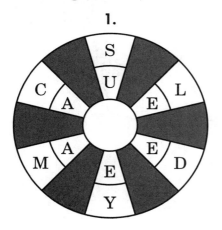

2.

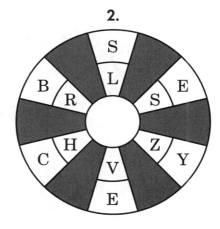

265

SLIDE RULE

LANGUAGE

WEEK 38

Slide each column of letters up or down in the box and form as many everyday 3-letter words as you can in the windows where MAN is now. We formed 40 words, including MAN.

Your list of words:

CIRCLE MATH

MATH

Each overlapping circle is identified by a letter having a different number value from 1 to 9. Where some circles overlap, there is a number: It is the SUM of the values of the letters in those overlapping circles. Can you figure out the correct values for the letters? As a starting help, D = 9.

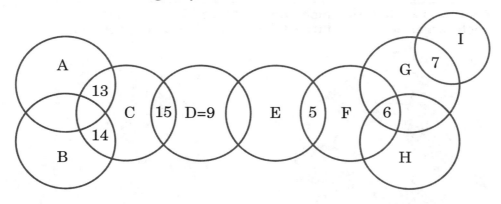

"The most wasted of all days is one without laughter."
— *e.e. cummings*

266

FILLING STATION

Place the given consonants on the dashes to form words. The vowels have already been placed for you, and as an additional help, each entry lists its category beside its given consonants.

1. C H H N T Y (flower)

__ __ A __ I __ __ __

2. N P P P P R Z Z (food)

__ E __ __ E __ O __ I   __ I __ __ A

3. B C D D L N N N Y (movie)

"__ O __ __ I E   A __ __   __ __ __ __ E"

4. G L M N (country)

__ O __ __ O __ I A

5. B D G H L L L M N R R X (inventor)

A __ E __ A __ __ E __   __ __ A __ A __

__ E __ __

LANGUAGE   ORDERLY STATES

The letters in each U.S. state name here are listed in alphabetical order, but without repeats. For example, HAWAII would be shown as AHIW. Can you determine all eight U.S. state names?

1. HIO   _____   5. EGNOR   _____

2. ILNOS   _____   6. ABLM   _____

3. CINOSW   _____   7. ENST   _____

4. ACFILNOR   _____   8. EJNRSWY   _____

IN THE ABSTRACT

VISUAL ◆ SPATIAL

Fill in each section with one of the four symbols so no sections containing the same symbol touch. Four sections are already complete.

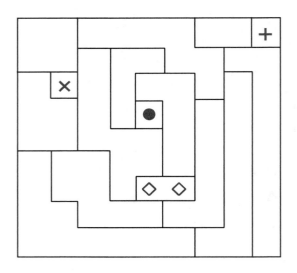

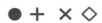

SWITCHEROO

DECODING

In each group, for the first word and its number equivalent given, determine what the number equivalent is for the second word.

1. SHOE is to 7249 as HOSE is to:
   (a) 7924 (b) 2479 (c) 2947 (d) 2794

2. VASE is to 3521 as SAVE is to:
   (a) 2135 (b) 2351 (c) 2531 (d) 2513

3. PROM is to 4965 as ROMP is to:
   (a) 9465 (b) 4596 (c) 9564 (d) 9654

4. FACE is to 6189 as CAFE is to:
   (a) 6918 (b) 8691 (c) 8169 (d) 8196

5. THROW is to 38562 as WORTH is to:
   (a) 26538 (b) 28635 (c) 26385 (d) 23658

6. MARSH is to 18473 as HARMS is to:
   (a) 37148 (b) 38714 (c) 31478 (d) 38417

268

WORD WHEEL

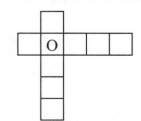

WEEK 39

Starting with the "A" at the arrow, see how many everyday words of three or more letters you can find going clockwise. Don't skip over any letters. For example, if you saw the letters C, A, R, E, D, you would form five words: CAR, CARE, CARED, ARE, RED. We found 27 words.

CROSS-UPS

Using only the letters given above each diagram, fill in the boxes in such a way that an everyday compound word is formed, one part reading across and the other part reading down. The letter already in the diagram is a letter shared by both parts of the word. Note: Each part of the compound word is an entire word on its own.

1. A I I P S T

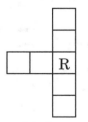

2. E E H P R R S W

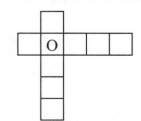

269

MISSING DOMINOES

VISUAL ◆ LOGIC

In this game you use all 28 dominoes that are in a standard set. Each one has a different combination from 0-0, 0-1, 0-2, to 6-6. Domino halves with the same number of dots lie next to each other. To avoid confusion we have used an open circle to indicate a zero. Can you fill in the missing white dominoes to complete the board?

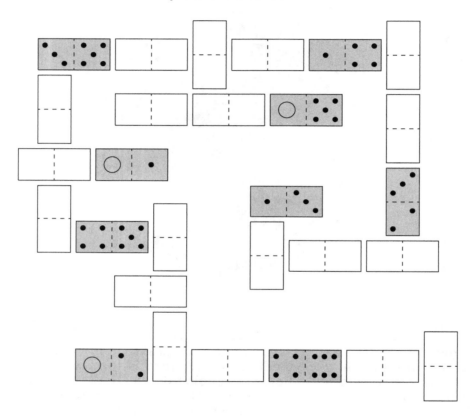

DOMINOES

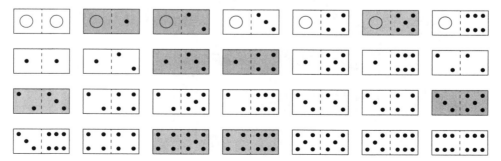

MAGNIFIND

Figure out which areas of the drawing have been enlarged.

LOGIC

RELATIONSHIPS QUIZ

KENNEL is to DOG as STY is to PIG because a DOG lives in a KENNEL and a PIG lives in a STY. Each of the statements below is a relationship of some kind. Can you select the right word from the four following each?

1. DOCTOR is to STETHOSCOPE as NAVIGATOR is to _____.
   (a) hammer   (b) compass   (c) prescription   (d) microscope

2. FLY is to KITE as SAIL is to _____.
   (a) tail   (b) bird   (c) boat   (d) bite

3. ENGLAND is to POUND as JAPAN is to _____.
   (a) sushi   (b) yen   (c) stone   (d) yuan

4. JUROR is to JURY as SOPRANO is to _____.
   (a) aria   (b) verdict   (c) choir   (d) tenor

5. BOOK is to LIBRARY as KEY is to _____.
   (a) island   (b) typewriter   (c) violin   (d) bridge

WHIRLIGIG

WEEK 39

In each numbered section are five letters. Rearrange each group of letters so that when you add "AL" from the middle of the diagram to the front of each group, you will form 12 common 7-letter words.

1. _____
2. _____
3. _____
4. _____
5. _____
6. _____
7. _____
8. _____
9. _____
10. _____
11. _____
12. _____

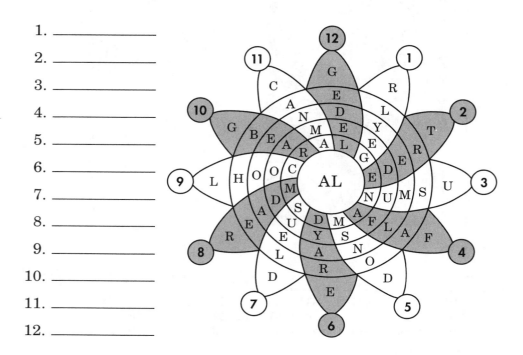

FLOWER IN FLUX

If the flower on the left were changed so that the oval petals were white and the 4-sided petals were black, which of the four flowers on the right would it look like?

1   2   3   4

272

ALPHABET SOUP

WEEK 39

In the first group, cross off each letter from the alphabet list that appears in the larger group of letters. Then rearrange the letters not crossed out to form the name of an animal. In the second group, cross off the letters of the name of this first critter from the alphabet and repeat the process done in the first group to form the name of another animal.

```
C T U I C G R T U D F T U C T B
V M I X V O Q M I K M V Z Q V H
N Y J F N B Z P J W Y G D O Y R
```

A B C D E F G H I J K L M N O P Q R S T U V W X Y Z

Animal: _____

```
J N U F D Z N R D J K N U D N U
G B Y V G Q B Y H Z Y R X Y K B
Q I G V J V F J P H M T X Q I G
```

A B C D E F G H I J K L M N O P Q R S T U V W X Y Z

Animal: _____

LANGUAGE

PRESIDENTIAL FINALES

Each of these "words" is really the last three letters of a U.S. President's first name preceding the last three letters of his last name. For example, John Adams would be shown as OHNAMS. Can you determine the Chief Executive's name suggested by each entry?

1. ACKAMA _____

2. ERTVER _____

3. VERAND _____

4. MASSON _____

5. VINDGE _____

6. LINELT _____

7. MESROE _____

8. ILLTON _____

9. ALDGAN _____

10. SESANT _____

11. ARYLOR _____

12. HAMOLN _____

LETTER, PLEASE

DECODING

The numbers below stand for certain letters on the telephone dial. You will see that one number may stand for more than one letter — for example, 3 may be D, E, or F. By finding the correct letter for each number, you will have spelled out a quotation by Voltaire, French writer and philosopher.

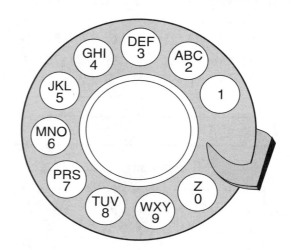

48   47   9484

26657   27   9484

636:   2   8379

76255   686237

7529   2   47328

7278.

CARD SENSE

LOGIC

Directions for solving are on page 259.

1. The spade is adjacent to both threes.

2. The king is adjacent to both clubs.

3. The four is somewhere above the seven.

274

ARROW MAZE

Directions for solving are on page 246.

Directions for solving are on page 246.

LANGUAGE
ANTONYMS QUIZ

An antonym is a word that is opposite in meaning to another word; for example, "cold" is the antonym of "hot." One of the words following each capitalized word is the antonym of that word.

1. ADVANCE   a. triumph   b. retreat   c. masticate

2. METTLE   a. cowardice   b. acrimony   c. elation

3. ILLUSTRIOUS   a. unknown   b. solitary   c. omnipotent

4. LIABILITY   a. specter   b. likeness   c. asset

5. CULTIVATE   a. demur   b. permit   c. neglect

6. ABRIDGED   a. opaque   b. protracted   c. wholesome

7. ABHORRENT   a. delightful   b. addled   c. resentful

8. CONDEMN   a. bestow   b. derive   c. absolve

MARCHING ORDERS

MATH ◆ LOGIC

Using a different two-step sequence of addition and/or subtraction, can you make your way from Start to Finish in each puzzle by moving up, down, or diagonally? We've started the first one for you using the sequence −4 and +5; continue this sequence to reach Finish. You will not cross your own path or pass through any square twice.

1.   FINISH ↑

10	11	14	15	16	12
8	7	9	8	11	15
11	10	12	7	13	10
6	5	9	6	9	14
2	7	4	8	6	8
6	3	8	5	7	9

↑ START

2.   FINISH ↑

20	23	27	30	31	37
18	16	17	29	35	32
13	11	20	16	26	28
8	9	12	16	22	27
4	6	7	10	12	21
2	1	5	6	9	13

↑ START

STAR WORDS

VISUAL ◆ LOGIC

Only five of the eight words given will fit together in the diagram. Place them in the directions indicated by the arrows.

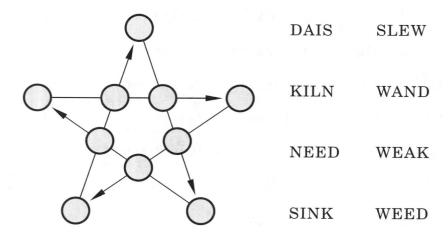

DAIS   SLEW

KILN   WAND

NEED   WEAK

SINK   WEED

276

WAYWORDS

WEEK 40

A 6-word thought can be found beginning with the word **FRIENDS**. Then, move to any adjacent box up, down, or diagonally for each following word.

RECENT	OF	SPELL	JUST
STANDARD	BEST	LIVING	SEEK
PURE	YOUR	CONCLUDE	INSPIRE
FINAL	BREAK	RAISE	FRIENDS

WORD EQUATIONS

Determine the three defined words in each equation. The third word is formed when the second is written directly after the first; for example, for "for each + shape = act in a play," you would respond "per + form = perform."

1. guy's partner + cut a tree limb = horse's gait

2. couch section + word of choice = tank protection

3. debate stance + tennis move = use sparingly

4. textile factory + charged particle = 1,000 x 1,000

5. sharpen + barnyard abode = truthfulness

"Life can only be understood backward, but it must be lived forward."
— *Søren Kierkegaard*

ANAGRAM MAZE

LANGUAGE ◆ VISUAL

Directions for solving are on page 258. This time, there are 17 words to anagram and the first word you'll be anagramming is PART.

1 LOPE	**2** PART	**3** TINY	**4** LOOK	**5** MILL	**6** DANK
7 FEAR	**8** UNDO	**9** BOOK	**10** CHIN	**11** COAL	**12** COAT
13 BANE	**14** SOBS	**15** LOUT	**16** SENT	**17** WHOM	**18** WARY
19 WISH	**20** DUES	**21** SHOE	**22** SACK	**23** JUMP	**24** TIED
25 MICE	**26** CLAP	**27** BANG	**28** FULL	**29** PILE	**30** SLAM
31 TERM	**32** FOUL	**33** PIGS	**34** ZINC	**35** TIME	**36** CLIP

BLOCK PARTY

VISUAL ◆ SPATIAL

Study the different views of the block, and draw what should appear on the face that has a question mark.

278

ONLINE NETWORK

In each two-column group, take the letters in the left-hand column along the paths (indicated by the lines) and place them in their proper boxes in the right-hand column. When done, you'll find three related words reading down each of the two right-hand columns.

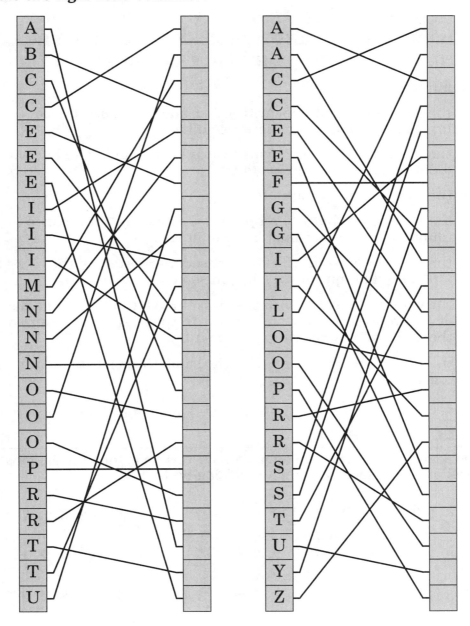

ELIMINATION

LANGUAGE

Directions for solving are on page 261. Once again, the remaining words will form a thought.

PRAY SLANDER STRUNG HONEST DON'T BEET
MUSHROOMS LASSO CRITICISM CRY GRATE
AURAS TAIL IS PEPPERONI FINGER SALARY
OVER WORTH PREY MORE FIGHT GREAT SPILT
THAN SAUSAGE MILK FLATTERY BEAT ASLEEP

Eliminate...

1. the two words that appear together and, when scrambled, form the name of a nine-letter country.

2. the three pairs of homonyms (words that sound alike but with different spellings and meanings).

3. the three names of pizza toppings.

4. the five words that form a phrase that means "forswear to ululate upon precipitated lactic emulsion."

5. the two words, each with four consecutive letters of the alphabet that appear together, in some order.

6. the word that begins with the first three letters of the name of a European country and ends with the first three letters of the name of another European country.

7. the four words that start with the same three letters in any order.

ALL IN A ROW

MATH

Directions for solving are on page 252. This time, look for the most groups of consecutive numbers adding up to 12.

A. ⑥ 5 ⑥ 2 3 ⑧ 1 9 ④ 2 3 1 2 7 1 4 ③ ⑧ ② 2 5 3 7 6

B. 8 2 1 3 5 1 4 6 8 2 2 ⑨ 1 ③ 6 4 1 1 ⑤ ⑦ 4 2 1 5

C. 3 1 5 3 8 2 6 5 2 3 2 8 4 7 2 3 6 5 4 1 8 2 3 7

RING LOGIC

Complete the diagram by drawing in the links between the rings using the statements. Assume that all the rings in the picture are locked rigidly into position and cannot be moved in any direction. Consider yourself a true ringmaster if you can find the solution in under six minutes!

1. Each small ring is linked twice.

2. The right sides of rings F, G, and H are to the front.

3. The bottoms of rings B, D, J, and L are to the front.

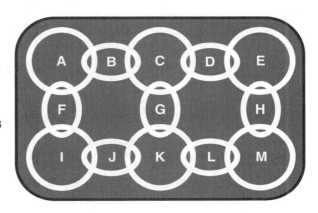

WORD WHEEL

Directions for solving are on page 269. Beginning with the "B" at the arrow, we formed 32 words of three or more letters.

2

FUN WITH FACTS AND FIGURES MATH

This puzzle tests you on a lot of little facts and figures. Solve the quiz in the order given since each answer is used in the next statement. There are no fractions used here.

1. Take the number of consonants in the word RATIONALIZATION and multiply by the number of vowels in the word.   _____

2. Next, add the number of eggs in two dozen.   _____

3. Now, subtract the number of degrees Fahrenheit at which water freezes.   _____

4. Divide by the value of the Roman numeral VIII.   _____

5. Add the number of weeks in half of a year.   _____

Our answer is the number of black squares
on a chessboard. *Is yours?*

SUDOKU

LOGIC

Directions for solving are on page 247.

6			9					5
5	7				2			8
		2	8		1	7		
	6	1		3			5	
8		5		1		6		2
	2			8		1	9	
		6	7		3	9		
4			1				3	6
1					6			7

"Rejoice in the things that are present; all else is beyond thee."
— *Michel de Montaigne*

ALPHABET SOUP

In the first group, cross off each letter from the alphabet list that appears in the larger group of letters. Then rearrange the letters not crossed out to form the name of a beverage. In the second group, cross off the letters of the name of that drink and repeat the process done in the first group to form the name of another beverage.

```
N  P  K  X  K  S  P  L  H  K  X  V  U  K  P  W
Z  G  I  J  V  B  M  N  Z  U  M  N  J  F  M  Z
R  F  O  H  D  R  L  F  R  S  Y  F  Q  R  C  O
```

A B C D E F G H I J K L M N O P Q R S T U V W X Y Z

Beverage: _____

```
O  N  U  F  D  Z  N  C  D  J  D  N  U  D  N  U
S  B  Y  V  O  S  B  Y  H  S  Y  R  X  Y  S  B
Q  W  G  C  J  V  F  J  P  H  O  W  R  Q  W  G
```

A B C D E F G H I J K L M N O P Q R S T U V W X Y Z

Beverage: _____

BOX STARS

Determine which of the four numbered boxes should be placed in the square with the question mark in order to logically complete the sequence.

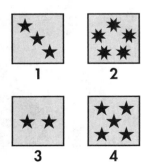

HEXAGON HUNT

VISUAL

Directions for solving are on page 250.

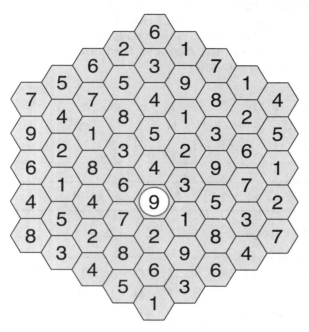

MAGNIFIND

VISUAL ◆ SPATIAL

Figure out which areas of the drawing have been enlarged.

284

ANIMAL CHARADES

Directions for solving are on page 253.

My FIRST is in PERCH and in SCRAWL; _____

My SECOND is in CARIBOU and in BRAWL; _____

My THIRD is in MOUSE but not in SMEAR; _____

My FOURTH is in RACCOON but not in ENDEAR; _____

My FIFTH is in PORPOISE and in ESCORT; _____

My SIXTH is in SARDINE and in DEPORT; _____

My SEVENTH is in PENGUIN but not in
  HEADSTRONG; _____

My EIGHTH is in STARLING but not in SARONG; _____

My NINTH is in LEOPARD and in APPLAUSE. _____

My WHOLE is a critter with massive jaws.

_____

GOING IN CIRCLES

Directions for solving are on page 256.

1.
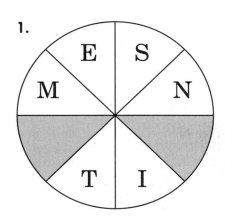

2.
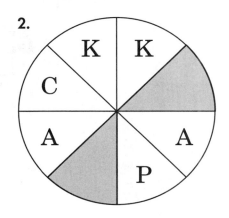

285

KEEP ON MOVING

VISUAL

The goal is to move from the shaded square to the asterisk. Since the shaded square has the number 2 in it, you must move two squares up, down, left, or right, but not diagonally. In the new square will be another number; move that number of squares up, down, left, or right, continuing in this way until you reach the asterisk. It's okay to cross or retrace your own path.

1	5	1	4	4	3
3	1	3	✳	3	1
3	1	3	2	5	3
1	2	2	3	3	2
5	4	2	1	2	5
3	2	1	5	4	1

SQUARE LINKS

LANGUAGE

Write one letter in each empty box so that an everyday 8-letter word is spelled out around each solid box. Each word may read either clockwise or counterclockwise, and may start at any of its letters.

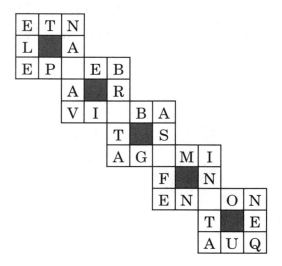

286

Missing Links

WEEK 41

Fill the empty squares in the diagram with the given letters so that everyday words are formed reading across and down.

AAAAAAA BB CC DDDDD EEEEE F
GG HHH I J K LLL M NNNNN OO PP
RRR SSSSSS TTTTT U VV W YYYYY Z

"If a mistake is not a stepping stone, it is a mistake."
— *Eli Siegel*

GRAND TOUR

LANGUAGE ◆ VISUAL

Directions for solving are on page 252. This time, you'll be looking for a chain of 5-letter words, starting with GR-IND-EX (grind, index).

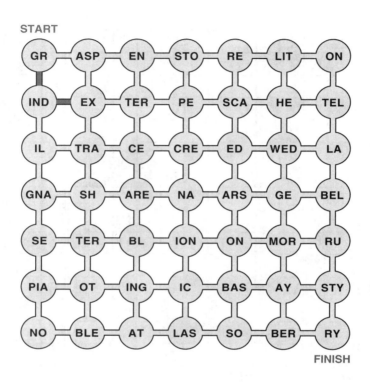

COMPOUND IT

LANGUAGE

Directions for solving are on page 259.

1. bake, great, second, slide

2. fiddle, hand, base, nature

3. walk, ball, cuff, book

4. mark, links, park, store

5. bought, view, down, broad

6. based, cast, turn, town

7. off, coat, ship, bill

8. board, center, red, lead

9. life, room, same, true

10. rifle, size, place, mate

VISION QUEST

Find the row or column that contains five DIFFERENT serving dishes.

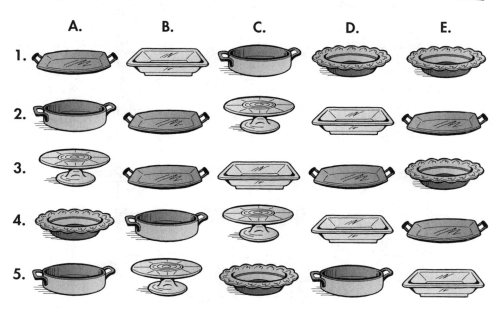

A.   B.   C.   D.   E.

1.

2.

3.

4.

5.

LOGIC

DEDUCTION PROBLEM

Alice, Betty, Cindy, and Dora discussed what they would be when they grew up. Although all of them wanted to be doctors, only one of them actually became one; the others grew up to be a politician, a lawyer, and a professor. As they discussed their hopes, each made a guess about the future, but only the future doctor made a true prediction. From this information and the clues below, can you determine who became what?

1. Alice said Betty would never be a politician.

2. Betty said Cindy would be a doctor and a good one.

3. Cindy said Dora would not be a professor.

COUNTDOWN

VISUAL

Directions for solving are on page 248.

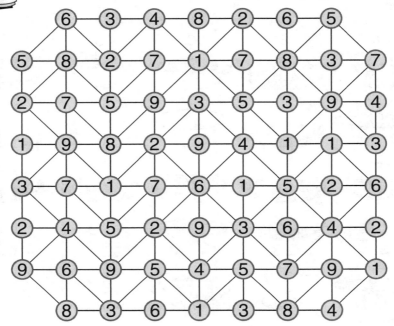

SEVEN WORD ZINGER

LANGUAGE

Using each letter once, form seven everyday 3-letter words with the first letter coming from the center, the second from the middle, and the third from the outer circle. Your words may differ from ours.

— — —

— — —

— — —

— — —

— — —

— — —

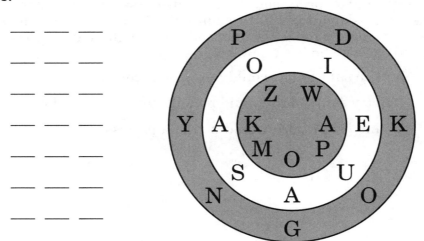

BULL'S-EYE LETTER

WEEK 42

Directions for solving are on page 263.

KCI PIW

ACH **?** POA

JBA PPU

— — — —

— — — —

— — — —

— — — —

— — — —

— — — —

LANGUAGE # THE LINEUP

Directions for solving are on page 260.

VOJDPKISSCLARITYWGZMUTELABYRINTHQEXITTS

1. Which letter of the alphabet does not appear
   in the lineup? _____

2. What 7-letter word — with its letters in correct
   order and appearing together — can you find
   in the lineup? _____

3. Which letter of the alphabet appears exactly
   three times in the lineup? _____

4. What 9-letter word — with its letters in correct
   order and appearing together — can you find
   in the lineup? _____

5. Other than the answers to Questions 2 and 4,
   how many everyday words — with their letters
   in correct order and appearing together — of
   four or more letters can you find in the lineup? _____

STACKED UP

VISUAL ◆ SPATIAL

Directions for solving are on page 253.

1.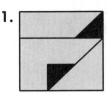
2.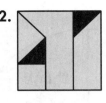
3.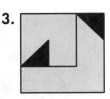
4.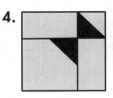
5.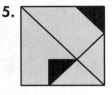
6.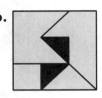

WORD CHARADE

LANGUAGE ◆ VISUAL

Directions for solving are on page 265.

My first letter is the letter in a row that, when it replaces the letter immediately below it, forms a word in that entire lower row.

My second letter appears in the word CAVERNOUS, but not in the column that contains every other letter from that word.

My third letter is the second letter of two 4-letter words that cross each other and might describe a school fundraising event.

S	T	F	E	S	N	H	T
A	G	O	G	B	V	E	I
C	E	R	L	N	R	V	U
E	X	U	C	T	A	N	T
K	Q	S	E	D	U	T	H
F	B	A	K	E	C	I	F
C	O	L	J	P	S	A	U
L	R	E	A	M	O	F	L

My fourth letter is surrounded by an 8-letter word (in a clockwise direction) that is a weatherperson's prediction.

My fifth letter is the seventh letter of an 8-letter word that starts to read up in one column then continues in the column to its right to read down.

My sixth letter appears in every row but one.

___ ___ ___ ___ ___

ASSOCIATIONS

Directions for solving are on page 263.

WHAT IS A COMMUTER'S LEAST FAVORITE BREAD TOPPING?

PROMISE AX TINKER OWN ECUADOR RABBIT

PRICE BANDIT PROHIBIT APPLICATION DIME

TOMAHAWK FINICKY PLEDGE BURGLAR PENNY

WORTH FANTASTIC POSSESS FORBID IRREGULAR

PERU VOW CANVAS HATCHET JUSTICE THIEF

BAN ADEQUATE QUARTER HAVE MIRACLE VALUE

COLOMBIA

LANGUAGE

SLIDE RULE

Directions for solving are on page 266. Here, you're to form 4-letter words. We found 28 words, including READ.

Your list of words:

IN THE ABSTRACT

VISUAL ◆ SPATIAL

Directions for solving are on page 268.

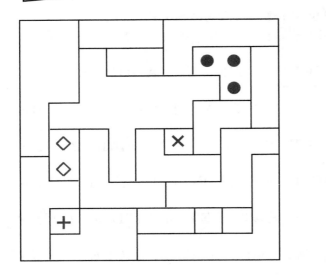

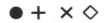

● + × ◇

CIRCLE MATH

MATH

Directions for solving are on page 266. We've started you off by telling you that H = 5.

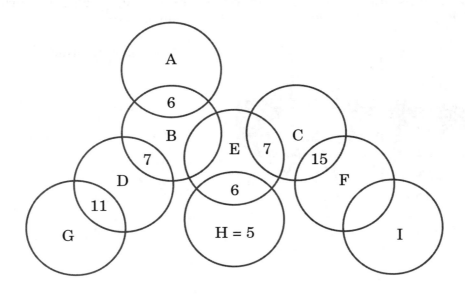

ORDERLY STATES

Directions for solving are on page 267.

1. AEILNPSVY _____

2. ADHKNORT _____

3. AKLS _____

4. AGINRV _____

5. AKNS _____

6. CEINOTU _____

7. ADEHILNORS _____

8. ADIN _____

FILLING STATION

See page 267 for solving directions.

1. C C L M N P R T Y (musician)

__ A U __   __ __ __ A __ __ __ E __

2. C F H L N N R R T V (historical event)

__ __ E __ __ __   __ E __ O __ U __ I O __

3. G G L L R R W (writer)

__ E O __ __ E   O __ __ E __ __

4. C G N P R R R (bird)

__ A __ __ I E __   __ I __ E O __

5. B C H L R S T T W (book)

"__ __ A __ __ O __ __ E' __   __ E __"

295

WHAT'S YOUR NUMBER?

MATH ◆ LOGIC

Can you figure out the relationship of the numbers in the first two groupings and, based on that, what missing number goes into the space with the question mark?

6
7
2
21

5
8
10
4

?
3
12
4

QUICK FILL

LANGUAGE

Directions for solving are on page 255.

A   C   D   E   E   I   I   L   N   T

1. Letter 9 is a consonant.

2. Letter 2 appears in the words "coupon," "jangle," and "turnip."

3. Letter 7 can be placed at the beginning of "rayon" to form a new word.

4. Letter 6 is a vowel that appears in the word NOVELIST but not in COMPLETE.

5. Letter 1 appears in the name of The Buckeye State.

6. Letter 4 appears elsewhere in the word.

7. Letter 5 is from the first half of the alphabet.

8. In the alphabet, letter 3 is immediately before letter 10.

9. Letter 8 is a vowel.

$$\overline{1}\quad \overline{2}\quad \overline{3}\quad \overline{4}\quad \overline{5}\quad \overline{6}\quad \overline{7}\quad \overline{8}\quad \overline{9}\quad \overline{10}$$

WORD HUNT

Directions for solving are on page 249. This time, you'll be searching for 4-letter words that start with M (such as MIND). We found 39 words, including MIND.

T	L	R	T	K
S	E	A	I	N
H	U	M	D	L
C	N	O	E	K
K	A	T	L	D

Your list of words:

OVERLAY

When you overlay the three diagrams in the top row, which of the three lettered diagrams, A, B, or C, will be formed?

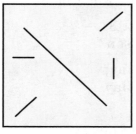 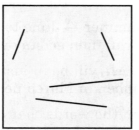 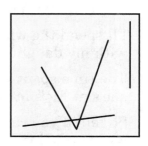

A.   **B.**   **C.**

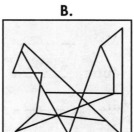 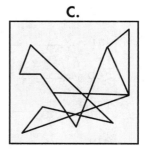

297

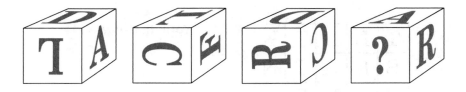

DEDUCTION PROBLEM LOGIC

Remember that old woman who lived in a shoe?
Her children are grown; now she knows what to do.

"Each kid has his own home where I can go stay,
spend one, two, or three months, then go on my way.

I'll move out of my shoe January 1.
Visit Karen and five more before this year's done.

Two months in the loafer owned by my son Joe,
and two months with a daughter, either Karen or Flo.

I'll spend three months with one of sons Roger or Jay,
and the next month with the other (that month won't be May).

I'll spend the whole summer — June to August 31 —
with my daughter Maria, then go stay with a son."

The time spent with each will be in just one stay;
she's at Flo's in November, in March not with Jay.

So tell, if you can, from the words that appear,
where you'll find the old woman each month of next year.

Jan. _____   May _____   Sept. _____

Feb. _____   June _____   Oct. _____

Mar. _____   July _____   Nov. _____

Apr. _____   Aug. _____   Dec. _____

MISSING DOMINOES

WEEK
43

Directions for solving are on page 270.

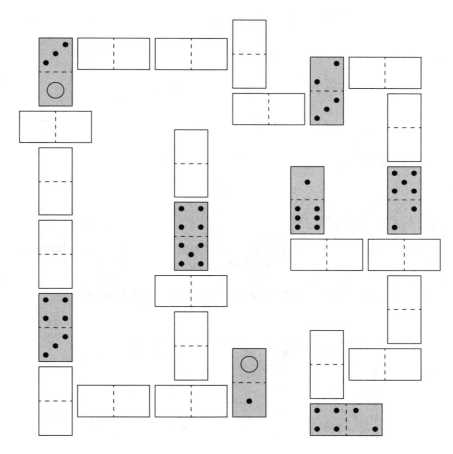

DOMINOES

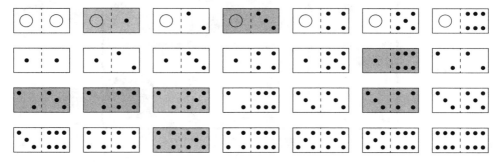

299

EASY PICKINGS

LANGUAGE

Directions for solving are on page 254. This time, the remaining letters will spell out a truism.

YL OU TO HK IS WN GW   GN SO SO DT

PI SL   YL EC SE TS

BI KM SP OF RA IT AS HN VT

IT HC AB IN   LU IO OX KJ IB EN DG

FG DR IL DE NO HD KL YS.

ROUND TRIP

VISUAL ◆ LOGIC

When this puzzle has been completed correctly, you will have made a round trip through its set of dots. You must visit every dot exactly once, make no diagonal moves, and return to your starting point. Parts of the right path are shown; can you find the rest?

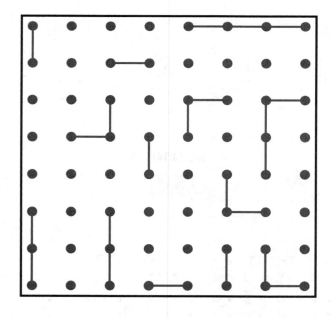

COUNT ON IT! WEEK 43

See page 246 for solving directions.

1. B A T L T I F   2. H N I R H E R   3. E I E S E F

4. N E T E   5. G   6. S

$\overline{1}\ \overline{2}\ \overline{3}$ $\overline{1}\ \overline{2}\ \overline{3}\ \overline{4}$ $\overline{1}\ \overline{2}\ \overline{3}\ \overline{4}\ \overline{5}\ \overline{6}$ $\overline{1}\ \overline{2}$

$\overline{1}\ \overline{2}\ \overline{3}\ \overline{4}$ $\overline{1}\ \overline{2}\ \overline{3}$ $\overline{1}\ \overline{2}\ \overline{3}\ \overline{4}$.

LANGUAGE **WORD VISIBILITY**

There are eight 5-letter words below. The first letter of the answer is found in the first pair of letters, and it is either the top or the bottom letter. Continue across each pair.

For example, the word GIRL would be found thus: G A R L
                                              L I T X

1. J U N E T
   Q O K S R

2. K H A Z P
   G L O M E

3. B H S R T
   C A A O N

4. B R N S L
   T E I I K

5. D N U R E
   E I E M Y

6. M E H E N
   I P T A R

7. T H A S O
   B W I K T

8. P R A P L
   D U I L M

"A wise man will make more opportunities than he finds."
— Francis Bacon

CARD SENSE

LOGIC

Directions for solving are on page 259.

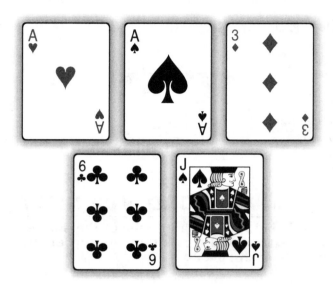

1. The six is somewhere above the heart.

2. The bottom card is not black.

3. The club is not on top.

4. Both aces are somewhere above the jack.

WAYWORDS

LANGUAGE

Directions for solving are on page 277. Here, you'll be looking for a 7-word thought beginning with EXPERIENCE.

IS	LEARNING	BELIEVE	RICH
CREATES	EXPERIENCE	WHAT	PLEASURE
FOR	THAT	NOT	DO
TIMES	EVER	TO	FIRST

WORD LINK

Place the words in parentheses after each capitalized word in the diagram so that they cross or connect with the capitalized word. EAR has been placed in the diagram; AIL, MERCY, and TABLETS cross or connect with EAR.

AIL (apologetic, ear, sly)

APOLOGETIC (ail, cope, doe, mercy, omega, sat, tablets, technical)

CAMEL (omega, tablets, technical)

COPE (apologetic, soda, tee)

DOE (apologetic, soda, tee)

EAR (ail, mercy, tablets)

EAT (octet, tablets, tense)

EDICT (obi, plenty, rod, tad, technical)

HAMSTER (octet, tablets, tad, technical, tense)

LOBE (obi, plenty, rod, technical)

MERCY (apologetic, ear, sly)

OBI (edict, lobe, protection)

OCTET (eat, hamster, protection)

OMEGA (apologetic, camel)

PLENTY (edict, lobe, protection, trend)

PROTECTION (obi, octet, plenty, rod, technical, tense)

ROD (edict, lobe, protection)

SAT (apologetic, soda, tee)

SLY (ail, mercy, tablets)

SODA (cope, doe, sat, technical)

TABLETS (apologetic, camel, ear, eat, hamster, sly)

TAD (edict, hamster, trend)

TECHNICAL (apologetic, camel, edict, hamster, lobe, protection, soda, trend)

TEE (cope, doe, sat)

TENSE (eat, hamster, protection)

TREND (plenty, tad, technical)

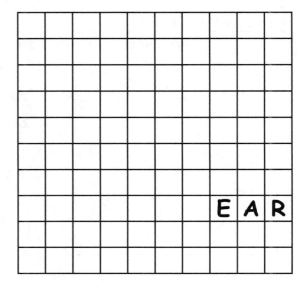

CODE WORD

DECODING

Directions for solving are on page 250. Here, determine a 13-letter Code Word.

$$\overline{1}\ \overline{2}\ \overline{3}\ \overline{4}\ \overline{5}\ \overline{6}\ \overline{7}\ \overline{8}\ \overline{9}\ \overline{10}\ \overline{11}\ \overline{12}\ \overline{13}$$

9 12 12   10 H 9 10   10 H 11   9 M 11 5 7 C 9 8

W 11 1 10   4 8 C 11   W 9 1 ,   9 12 9 1 K 9

1 10 7 12 12   7 1 .   9 3 4 2 8 6 7 8 G   W 7 10 H

8 9 10 2 5 9 12   M 9 5 V 11 12 1   9 8 6

12 9 5 G 11 12 13   2 8 10 4 2 C H 11 6   3 13

H 2 M 9 8   9 M 3 7 10 7 4 8 ,   7 10   1 10 5 7 K 11 1

10 H 11   8 11 W C 4 M 11 5   9 1   9   12 9 8 6

4 F   11 8 6 12 11 1 1   P 5 4 1 P 11 C 10 .

TRI, TRI AGAIN

LANGUAGE ◆ SPATIAL

Directions for solving are on page 264.

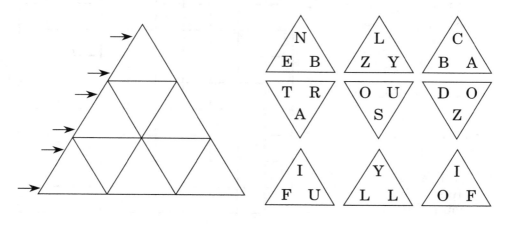

LOOSE TILE

The tray on the right seemed the ideal place to store the set of loose dominoes. Unfortunately, when the tray was full, one domino was left over. Determine the arrangement of the dominoes in the tray and which is the Loose Tile.

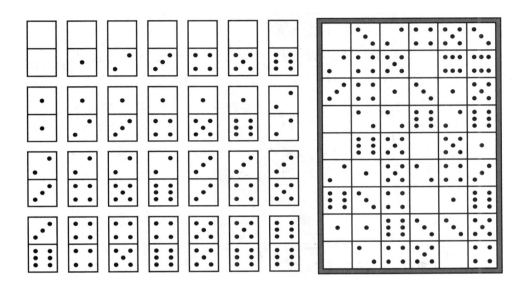

CIRCLE SEARCH

Directions for solving are on page 261. Here you're looking to form 16 words of at least three letters. Remember, proper names, plurals, and present-tense verbs ending in "s" are not allowed.

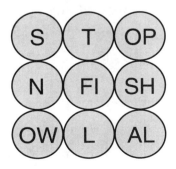

305

ANAGRAM MAZE

LANGUAGE ◆ VISUAL

Directions for solving are on page 258. This time, there are 19 words to anagram and the first word you'll be anagramming is TAKE.

		↓			
1 WAIT	**2** CREW	**3** TAKE	**4** BETS	**5** DROP	**6** FADE
7 WINE	**8** CULT	**9** INTO	**10** PURR	**11** FOIL	**12** FIRE
13 CURE	**14** PAGE	**15** STEP	**16** SALT	**17** PLUS	**18** TEAM
19 ONCE	**20** FALL	**21** DECK	**22** EVER	**23** OILS	**24** CAME
25 LUGE	**26** JETS	**27** FIVE	**28** CUFF	**29** HUNT	**30** BEAU
31 ALOE	**32** LIED	**33** TOGA	**34** CARE	**35** WHIM	**36** OOZE

ALL IN A ROW

MATH

Directions for solving are on page 252. This time, look for the most groups of consecutive numbers adding up to 13.

A. 4 5 4 2 1 6 8 3 7 9 1 3 6 3 7 3 9 2 ⑧⑤ 1 1 4 5

B. 8 1 5 9 7 2 3 4 9 7 1 5 3 3 4 1 6 5 2 7 1 3 8 4

C. 6 3 5 1 4 2 2 1 4 7 3 8 6 2 4 4 3 9 5 2 1 1 6 8

306

SUDOKU

WEEK 44

Directions for solving are on page 247.

			9			3		1
7					4	9		
9	2			6	1		4	
4	5	1		2			3	
		5		3				
	7			4		6	2	5
	3		4	1			9	8
		5	2					3
2		8			9			

TARGET SHOOT

Directions for solving are on page 265.

1.

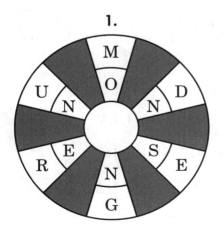

2.

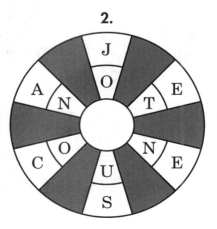

"Turn your face to the sun and the shadows fall behind you."
— Maori proverb

SUDOKU

LOGIC

Place a number into each box so each row across, column down, and small 9-box square within the larger square (there are 9 of these) contains 1 through 9.

5	4		3			1		9
		3			8	4	5	6
		1	6	4				
	6	9		1	2			4
1			7	8		6	9	
			5	9	3			
8	9	4	2			5		
3		2			1		4	7

L COUNT

VISUAL

Here's an eye exam that's also an L exam! First, read the sentence below. Next, go back and read the sentence again, but this time count all of the L's. How many are there?

LIVING IN LOS ANGELES LAST

FALL, SILLY VALLEY GIRL MILLY

MILLER REALLY, REALLY LIKED

TO LICK LITTLE LOLLIPOPS, PLANT

LARGE LILIES, AND LISTEN TO THE

LONELY, LIGHT LILT OF TOLLING

BELLS IN LOCAL CHAPELS.

HEXAGON HUNT

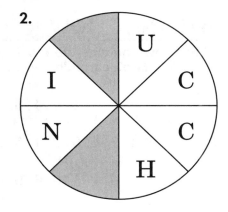

In this diagram of six-sided figures, there are 10 "special" hexagons. These 10 are special because the six numbers around each one are all different from each other and the center. We've circled one of the 10. Can you find the other 9?

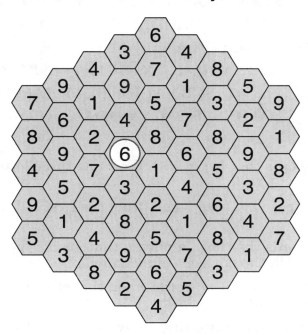

GOING IN CIRCLES

In each circle, insert one letter into each empty space to form an 8-letter word. Words may read either clockwise or counter-clockwise and may begin with any letter in the circle.

1.

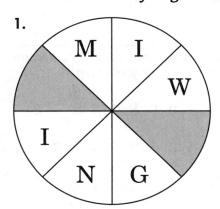

2.

ELIMINATION

LANGUAGE

Cross off the capitalized words according to the instructions given. The remaining words, in order, will form a thought.

EDIFICE SEEN SLANG CHARITY SAUERKRAUT
BROKEN OLIVER GARDEN IS DEBACLE NOEL
TWIST LAGER PLANT LANGUAGE BEGINS
PRETZEL GRADUAL IN GUEST LITTLE ITS
RAGAMUFFIN AT SCHNAPPS PLAY IAMBIC DIED
CALL CLOTHES HOME WOMEN ARGUMENT

Eliminate…

1. the four words that begin with the same three letters in any order.

2. words composed of letters only from the first half of the alphabet.

3. the four words that form a phrase that means "philanthropy commences in the environs of a domicile."

4. words that become new words when the letter V is placed in the middle of each.

5. the words that form two titles of two-word works of literature.

6. words that can follow the word HOUSE.

7. the four German words that have become a part of English.

ALL IN A ROW

MATH

Which row contains the most groups of consecutive numbers adding up to 11? Look carefully, because some groups may overlap.

A. 5 5 1 2 6 9 1 6 4 3 3 3 3 3 2 9 9 8 1 5 8 1 2 4

B. 7 4 9 4 9 4 8 2 1 5 6 4 1 7 3 2 5 9 4 3 3 3 8 4

C. 8 7 2 3 6 1 1 6 6 9 6 2 1 2 3 4 5 8 9 7 1 5 2 2

ONLINE NETWORK

In each two-column group, take the letters in the left-hand column along the paths (indicated by the lines) and place them in their proper boxes in the right-hand column. When done, you'll find three related words reading down each of the two right-hand columns.

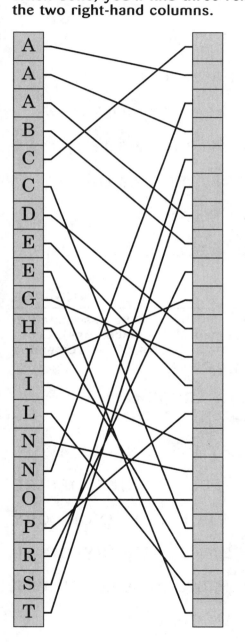

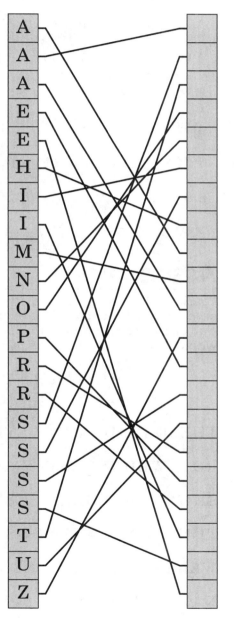

311

CODE WORD

DECODING

Decipher a quote and the Code Word's eleven letters, represented by the numbers 1 through 11. So, if the Code Word were "THUNDERCLAP," 1 in the quote would be T, 2 would be H, etc.

$$\overline{1}\ \overline{2}\ \overline{3}\ \overline{4}\ \overline{5}\ \overline{6}\ \overline{7}\ \overline{8}\ \overline{9}\ \overline{10}\ \overline{11}$$

7 U 2   13 10 3 X 11 6 8 F 3 2 10 3 2 1 9 2,

B 2 6 1 H T 9 2, 3 4 5 M 7 2 9 M 3 8 8 6 V 9

T H 3 4 M 7 8 T 7 T H 9 2 13 10 3 X 6 9 8.

T H 9 M 6 10 K 11 W 3 11 ' 8 8 T 3 2 2 11

5 6 8 K 8 P 3 4 8 7 4 9 H U 4 5 2 9 5

T W 9 4 T 11 T H 7 U 8 3 4 5 10 6 1 H T – 11 9 3 2 8.

ASSOCIATIONS

LANGUAGE

You'll find eight groups of three words that can be associated in some way with each other (example: mantel, fireplace, logs). Cross out each group as you find it. The initial letters of the remaining words will spell out the answer to the riddle:

WHEN ASKED "HOW ARE YOU?,"
HOW DID THE CAT RESPOND?

TUESDAY IDENTITY STEAL STOUT MIRACLE AVOID

ROB WEDNESDAY FAMOUS PLUMP ELF DESIRE

SHUN LASAGNA PERTH WISH FAT INCH CRY

THURSDAY NERVOUS SYDNEY ENERGY BAWL

WANT FUDGE PURSUE IMPLY EVADE PILFER

NAIL CHASE SOB EPIC CANBERRA HUNT

312

COUNT TO TEN

WEEK
45

Examine the items and then answer these questions: 1. Which row contains the most popcorn containers? 2. Which row contains the most soda cups? 3. Which row contains an equal number of both items?

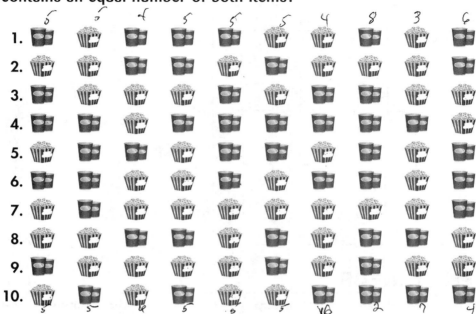

COUNT THE RECTANGLES

To solve this puzzle, write down the four letters that describe each rectangle in this figure. We found 32 rectangles; how many can you locate?

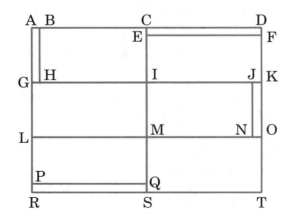

IN THE ABSTRACT

VISUAL ◆ SPATIAL

Fill in each section with one of the four symbols so no sections containing the same symbol touch. Five sections are already complete.

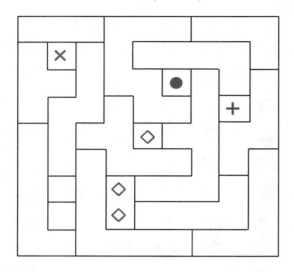

● + ✕ ◇

THE LINEUP

LANGUAGE

While scrutinizing this lineup of letters, can you answer the questions correctly in five minutes or less?

WSDGAZEXBOOKLINIMENTHRCROQUETYJUMPOV

1. Which letter of the alphabet does not appear in the lineup? _____

2. What 8-letter word — with its letters in correct order and appearing together — can you find in the lineup? _____

3. Which letter of the alphabet appears exactly three times in the lineup? _____

4. What 7-letter word — with its letters in correct order and appearing together — can you find in the lineup? _____

5. Other than the answers to Questions 2 and 4, how many everyday words — with their letters in correct order and appearing together — of four or more letters can you find in the lineup? _____

314

ARROW MAZE

Starting at the S and following the arrow to the right, see if you can find your way to F. When you reach an arrow, you MUST follow its direction and continue in that direction until you come to the next arrow. When you reach a two-headed arrow, you can choose either direction. It's okay to cross your own path.

LANGUAGE

ANIMAL CHARADES

Each line contains a clue to a letter of the alphabet. These letters, in the given order, will spell out the name of an animal. The animal's identity is also hinted at in the last sentence of the Charade.

My FIRST is in LION and in GROAN; _____

My SECOND is in JACKAL and in CLONE; _____

My THIRD is in EGRET but not in RUG; _____

My FOURTH is in GOPHER but not in SHRUG; _____

My FIFTH is in PUMA and in GRUMP; _____

My SIXTH is in WALRUS and in STUMP; _____

My SEVENTH is in HAMSTER but not in HEAVEN. _____

My WHOLE has arms that total one more than seven.

_____

ANAGRAM MAZE

LANGUAGE ◆ VISUAL

The diagram contains 36 words, 21 of which are anagrams of other everyday words. Start at the top arrow and anagram MEAL. While solving, move up, down, right, or left to the only adjacent word that can be anagrammed. Continue until you arrive at the bottom arrow. There is only one path through the maze.

1 DUMB	2 SEWN	3 DOSE	4 SNOW	5 SCAR	6 MEAL
7 FERN	8 WENT	9 YOKE	10 ZINC	11 BOLD	12 PERT
13 SOCK	14 KEEN	15 STUN	16 COLA	17 CURL	18 JINX
19 MYTH	20 VOLT	21 PULL	22 TIED	23 FATS	24 NAVE
25 THAW	26 CAME	27 CHUM	28 HIGH	29 ROAR	30 SPAR
31 TIME	32 FARM	33 LYRE	34 RAID	35 PIER	36 PACE

EASY PICKINGS

LANGUAGE

To solve, simply cross out one letter in each pair below. When the puzzle is completed correctly, the remaining letters will spell out a fact.

QT HG ME   HF OH UN NR

SE TE TA SR RO LN SD   IO FD

TM DH EY   YT IE VA SR

AE RF HE   SG RP NR IS NL CG,

AS CU ME UM EI NR,

AG RU MT US MG LN,   JA SN DE

SW IC DN TE BE RY.

MAGNIFIND

Figure out which area of the drawing has been enlarged.

LOGIC

CARD SENSE

Five playing cards were shuffled and put in a pile, one on top of another. Using the clues, can you identify each card's position in the pile?

1. The seven is directly above the heart.

2. The spades are adjacent.

3. The ace is somewhere above the diamond.

4. The red cards are not adjacent.

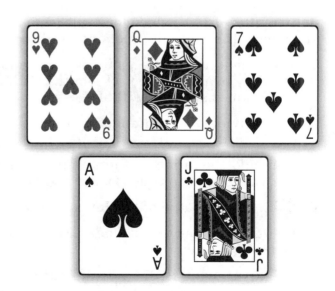

317

SEVEN WORD ZINGER   LANGUAGE

Using each letter once, form seven everyday 3-letter words with the first letter coming from the center, the second from the middle, and the third from the outer circle. Your words may differ from ours.

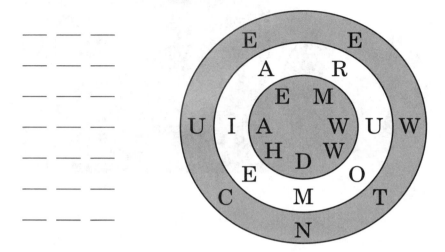

— — —

— — —

— — —

— — —

— — —

— — —

FUN WITH FACTS AND FIGURES   MATH

This puzzle tests you on a lot of little facts and figures. Solve the quiz in the order given since each answer is used in the next statement. There are no fractions used here.

1. Take the number of eggs in five dozen and multiply by the number of months of the year with names starting with J. _____

2. Next, divide by the number opposite the six on a standard clock dial. _____

3. Now, add the number of letters in the name of the state that contains Boston and Cape Cod. _____

4. Subtract the value of the Roman numeral XX. _____

5. Add the number that sounds like the preposition meaning "in favor of." _____

Our answer is the number of strikes in a perfect game of bowling. *Is yours?*

GRAND TOUR

Form a continuous chain of 5-letter words moving through the maze from START to FINISH. The second part of one word becomes the first part of the next word. This puzzle starts with CO-BRA-SH (cobra, brash).

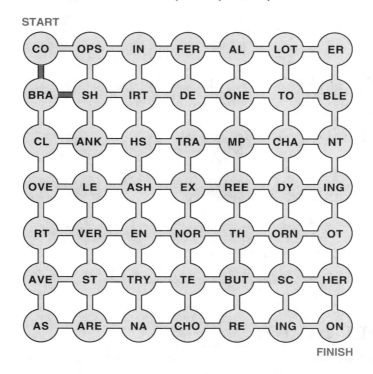

START

CO	OPS	IN	FER	AL	LOT	ER
BRA	SH	IRT	DE	ONE	TO	BLE
CL	ANK	HS	TRA	MP	CHA	NT
OVE	LE	ASH	EX	REE	DY	ING
RT	VER	EN	NOR	TH	ORN	OT
AVE	ST	TRY	TE	BUT	SC	HER
AS	ARE	NA	CHO	RE	ING	ON

FINISH

COMPOUND IT

Starting at #1, pick a word that will form a compound word with a word chosen in #2. Then with the word you've selected in #2, pick one from #3 to form another compound word. Continue in this manner to #10, so that you've formed nine compound words. In some instances more than one compound word can be formed, but there is only one path to get you to #10.

1. blue, wheel, fire, horse

2. berry, place, chair, barrow

3. woman, ground, true, lift

4. off, hood, tail, hog

5. beat, gate, wash, shore

6. bird, line, way, board

7. backer, side, brain, walk

8. ways, child, step, out

9. rank, proof, mother, law

10. shop, land, read, breaker

319

FILLING STATION

LANGUAGE

Place the given consonants on the dashes to form words. The vowels have already been placed for you, and as an additional help, each entry lists its category beside its given consonants.

1. D L L M R (animal)

   A __ __ A __ I __ __ O

2. C D L M M N N R S (television program)

   "__ __ I __ I __ A __   __ I __ __ __"

3. C M N R S T (U.S. city)

   __ A __ __ A __ E __ __ O

4. B D L M R T T (entertainer)

   __ E __ __ E   __ I __ __ E __

5. C C C C H H K L P T (food)

   __ __ O __ O __ A __ E   __ __ I __   __ O O __ I E

TARGET SHOOT

LANGUAGE

Find the two letters which, when entered into the center circle of each target, will form three 6-letter words reading across.

1.

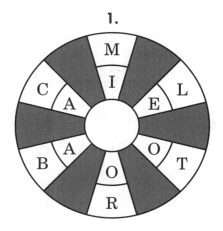

2.

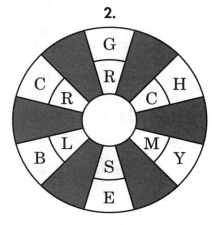

COUNTDOWN

Following the connecting lines, find the only route in this grid that passes through the numbers backward from 9 to 1 consecutively.

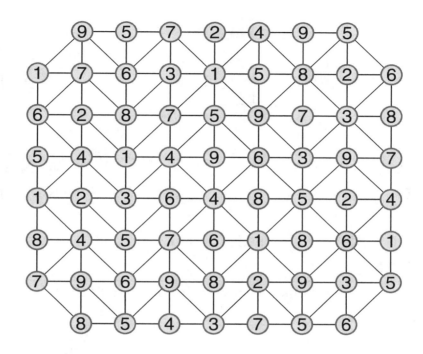

LANGUAGE

COUNT ON IT!

Use the given letters to fill in the familiar saying, one letter per dash. All the letters following 1 are the first letters of each word, the letters following 2 are the second letters of each word, etc. It is up to you to determine which letter goes where.

1. D W I H A T E T   2. H N O A Y H R   3. E U E Y S E

4. N R S   5. E E T

$\overline{1}\ \overline{2}\ \overline{3}\ \overline{4}\ \overline{5}$ $\overline{1}\ \overline{2}\ \overline{3}\ \overline{4}\ \overline{5}$, $\overline{1}$ $\overline{1}\ \overline{2}\ \overline{3}$

$\overline{1}\ \overline{2}\ \overline{3}$ $\overline{1}\ \overline{2}$ $\overline{1}\ \overline{2}\ \overline{3}$ $\overline{1}\ \overline{2}\ \overline{3}\ \overline{4}\ \overline{5}$.

LICENSE PLATES

LANGUAGE

Each box contains six letters of a 2-word sport. The top three are a part of the first word and the bottom three are a part of the last word, in order.

1.
```
A B L
E N N
```

2.
```
E L D
K E Y
```

3.
```
I G U
K A T
```

4.
```
A T E
O L O
```

5.
```
R O N
W I M
```

6.
```
W N H
K I I
```

SUDOKU

LOGIC

Directions for solving are on page 308.

4			3	9			6	
	5	7						3
2			6			8	4	5
9				8		7	3	
	6		1		7		8	
	7	8		3				4
3	4	6			2			9
7						4	2	
	9			5	4			6

322

MISSING DOMINOES

In this game you use all 28 dominoes that are in a standard set. Each one has a different combination from 0-0, 0-1, 0-2, to 6-6. Domino halves with the same number of dots lie next to each other. To avoid confusion we have used an open circle to indicate a zero. Can you fill in the missing white dominoes to complete the board?

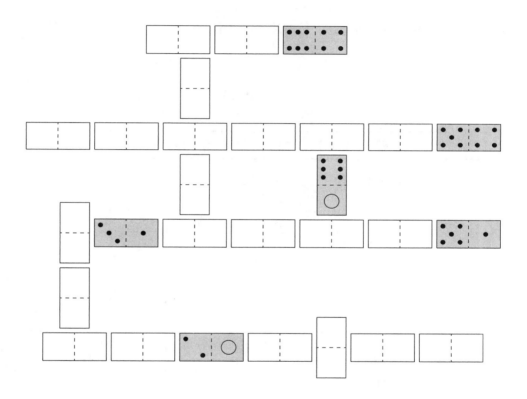

DOMINOES

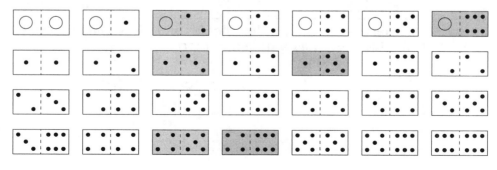

ALPHABET SOUP

LANGUAGE ◆ VISUAL

WEEK 47

In the first group, cross off each letter from the alphabet list that appears in the larger group of letters. Then rearrange the letters not crossed out to form a word. In the second group, cross off the letters of that word and repeat the process done in the first group to form another word. The words put together form a compound word.

E	W	K	H	N	K	H	X	E	K	W	E	N	W	E	K
M	O	N	M	B	O	Q	M	H	T	Q	O	I	M	O	Q
R	G	S	U	P	R	T	J	R	V	G	C	R	Z	U	F

A B C D E F G H I J K L M N O P Q R S T U V W X Y Z

Word: _____

S	Z	E	S	T	E	Z	T	S	E	Z	M	E	A	T	S
F	R	V	X	C	R	V	F	W	R	C	V	R	X	D	M
P	K	O	J	P	I	K	N	L	O	P	Q	K	Y	N	H

A B C D E F G H I J K L M N O P Q R S T U V W X Y Z

Word: _____

BLOCK PARTY

VISUAL ◆ SPATIAL

Study the different views of the block, and draw what should appear on the face that has a question mark.

  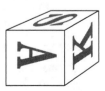 

324

MARCHING ORDERS

WEEK
47

Using a different two-step sequence of addition and/or subtraction, can you make your way from Start to Finish in each puzzle by moving up, down, or diagonally? We've started the first one for you using the sequence −3 and +5; continue this sequence to reach Finish. You will not cross your own path or pass through any square twice.

1. FINISH

12	14	16	19	23	20
8	11	15	17	18	15
7	9	10	13	16	14
6	3	8	9	11	12
2	1	5	10	8	14
4	7	3	7	12	9

START

2. FINISH

20	19	23	26	30	31
16	17	21	22	27	32
14	12	13	26	25	28
6	4	9	14	15	29
1	5	8	10	17	21
2	3	7	11	14	24

START

CHANGELINGS

Can you change the first word into the second word (in each set) by changing only one letter at a time? Do not rearrange the order of the letters with each change. Each change must result in an everyday word, and words beginning with a capital letter, slang, or obsolete words aren't allowed. The number in parentheses indicates the number of changes we used for that Changeling.

1. RIPE

_____

_____

_____

CORN
(4 changes)

2. PINK

_____

_____

_____

CARS
(4 changes)

3. FIND

_____

_____

_____

MATE
(4 changes)

325

VISION QUEST

VISUAL

Find the row or column that contains five DIFFERENT types of neckwear.

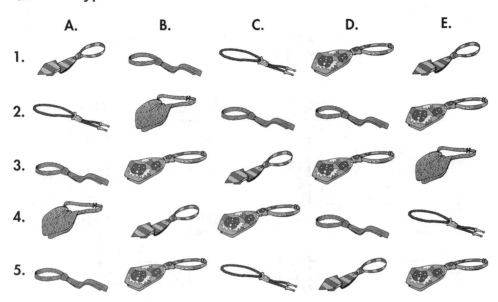

A. B. C. D. E.

1.
2.
3.
4.
5.

SYMBOL-ISM

DECODING

This is simply a Cryptogram that uses symbols instead of letters to spell out a truism. Each symbol stands for the same letter throughout. For this puzzle, we've already indicated that ⊛ = S and ⛏ = R.

RELATIONSHIPS QUIZ

KENNEL is to DOG as STY is to PIG because a DOG lives in a KENNEL and a PIG lives in a STY. Each of the statements below is a relationship of some kind. Can you select the right word from the four following each?

1. BIG is to LITTLE as LOG is to _____.
   (a) wood   (b) sawmill   (c) twig   (d) tree

2. SOIL is to HILL as WATER is to _____.
   (a) glass   (b) ice   (c) pond   (d) drink

3. PERSON is to CHAIR as CUP is to _____.
   (a) saucer   (b) mug   (c) dish   (d) coffee

4. COMMON is to RARE as PRESENT is to _____.
   (a) gift   (b) now   (c) birthday   (d) past

5. DARE is to CHALLENGE as PAIL is to _____.
   (a) bucket   (b) rain   (c) wait   (d) well

SQUARE LINKS

Write one letter in each empty box so that an everyday 8-letter word is spelled out around each black box. Each word may read either clockwise or counterclockwise, and may start at any of its letters.

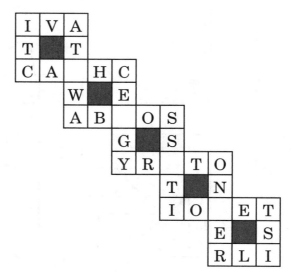

327

WORD VISIBILITY

LANGUAGE

There are six 5-letter words below. The first letter of the answer is found in the first pair of letters, and it is either the top or the bottom letter. Continue across each pair.

For example, the word GIRL would be found thus: <u>G</u> A <u>R</u> L
L <u>I</u> T X

1. W O E A Y
   K N R I D

2. P U D R H
   A L A I O

3. L I U C E
   G R T H N

4. B A S O W
   D Y L A D

5. C E N K R
   M A R O G

6. B H P C E
   F R A D N

OVERLAY

VISUAL ◆ SPATIAL

When you overlay the three diagrams in the top row, which of the three lettered diagrams, A, B, or C, will be formed?

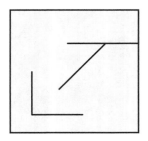
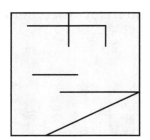
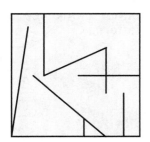

A. **B.** **C.**

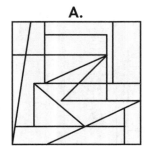
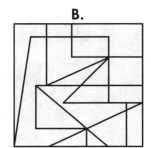
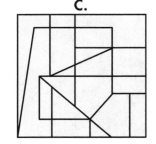

ANTONYMS QUIZ

WEEK 48

An antonym is a word that is opposite in meaning to another word; for example, "cold" is the antonym of "hot." One of the words following each capitalized word is the antonym of that word.

1. EQUITABLE   a. unfair   b. copious   c. random

2. JEER   a. ascend   b. praise   c. disperse

3. DEARTH   a. hatred   b. abundance   c. longing

4. MAUDLIN   a. graceful   b. tepid   c. unemotional

5. LUCID   a. resonant   b. certain   c. obscure

6. SUCCINCT   a. verbose   b. hackneyed   c. comic

7. PROSAIC   a. severe   b. exciting   c. concise

8. INCLEMENT   a. mild   b. active   c. repellent

QUICK FILL

Determine the 10-letter word from the clues. All the letters in the word are listed.

C   E   H   I   M   N   O   O   P   R

1. Letter 10 is a vowel.

2. Letter 1 is in the word PLATFORM but not CREATION.

3. In the alphabet, letter 7 is immediately before letter 2.

4. Letter 6 can be placed in the middle of "rely" and "male" to form two new words.

5. Letter 8 appears more than once in CHOCOLATE.

6. In the alphabet, letter 9 is somewhere before letter 4.

7. Letter 5 appears in the capital of Sweden and the capital of Russia.

8. Letter 3 is not in the word PEPPERONI or HOMEROOM.

$$\overline{1}\ \overline{2}\ \overline{3}\ \overline{4}\ \overline{5}\ \overline{6}\ \overline{7}\ \overline{8}\ \overline{9}\ \overline{10}$$

ORDERLY STATES   LANGUAGE

The letters in each U.S. state name here are listed in alphabetical order, but without repeats. For example, HAWAII would be shown as AHIW. Can you determine all eight U.S. state names?

1. AINORZ   _____

2. AHKLMO   _____

3. AGHINOSTW   _____

4. CEIMNOWX   _____

5. AMNOT   _____

6. AILNOSU   _____

7. AEGIOR   _____

8. ADHKOSTU   _____

CROSS EXAMINATION   LANGUAGE

In each set, cross out the three groups of letters so that the remaining groups, in order, spell out a word.

1. LA   CLAD   NG   UA   ONE   GE   EL

2. BUSH   SIG   ON   HTS   EE   TRI   ING

3. DES   ULT   TI   VERN   TU   ME   TION

4. ME   DENT   IM   TA   BO   AIN   LISM

5. CAT   TEN   AC   IC   IO   PHE   US

6. ST   VE   ELO   GE   TA   IRAN   BLE

7. WHI   SA   PPO   PER   ORW   ICE   ILL

8. PA   HAN   DETA   DKE   STI   RCH   IEF

LOOSE TILE

The tray on the right seemed the ideal place to store the set of loose dominoes. Unfortunately, when the tray was full, one domino was left over. Determine the arrangement of the dominoes in the tray and which is the Loose Tile.

WAYWORDS

A 12-word thought can be found beginning with the word FEW. Then, move to any adjacent box up, down, or diagonally for each following word.

CONSIDER	WITH	THINGS	SUSPEND
UP	FEW	THAN	ARE
PEOPLE	PUT	HARDER	A
REALIZE	TO	EXAMPLE	GOOD

331

KEEP ON MOVING

VISUAL

The goal is to move from the shaded square to the asterisk. Since the shaded square has the number 1 in it, you must move one square up or right, but not diagonally. In the new square will be another number; move that number of squares up, down, left, or right, continuing in this way until you reach the asterisk. You cannot cross your own path.

2	3	1	3	3	3
1	2	1	3	3	5
4	3	4	4	2	✳
3	3	3	1	4	1
3	4	1	3	1	2
1	3	4	5	5	5

DOVETAILED WORDS

LANGUAGE

Two related words, with their letters in the correct order, are combined in each row of letters. Can you find both words? In a line like POTEORDRLEIER, or POteOrDrLEier, you can see the two words POODLE and TERRIER.

1. B A C H B I Y L D   _____   _____

2. D C A A T I R T L Y E   _____   _____

3. P B A A M B N O O D A   _____   _____

4. C O N E U R R A V G E E   _____   _____

5. D S T E I C C A K E L R   _____   _____

TIPS OF THE ICEBERG

The chart shows the gratuities each waiter or waitress earned on a recent breakfast shift at the Iceberg Diner. All you have to do is some addition and then answer the following questions:

1. Who made the most in total tips?
2. Who made the least?
3. Which two waitpersons made exactly the same amount?

EMPLOYEE	TIP 1	TIP 2	TIP 3	TIP 4	TIP 5
Hank	$1.60	$0.65	$0.70	$1.15	$1.10
Inez	$2.80	$2.20	$1.80	$1.30	$1.10
Jack	$1.85	$1.35	$1.80	$4.00	$0.90
Ken	$0.60	$3.00	$4.30	$1.20	$0.80
Laura	$1.20	$1.30	$0.60	$1.40	$0.90
Marty	$2.90	$2.40	$0.40	$2.20	$0.80
Noel	$2.00	$3.00	$4.00	$1.50	$1.00

CIRCLE SEARCH

Move from circle to adjoining circle, horizontally and vertically only, to form 15 common, everyday words of at least three letters. Don't change the order of the letters in the circles that contain more than one letter. Proper names are not allowed.

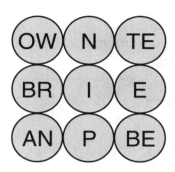

WORD CHARADE

LANGUAGE ◆ VISUAL

Find each letter in the diagram according to the instructions, and write each letter on its dash to spell out a 6-letter word.

My first letter is the seventh letter of the name of a fruit reading backwards in one of the rows.

My second letter is a vowel surrounded by eight consonants.

A	V	H	K	A	M	X	U
J	Z	R	G	T	W	Z	C
T	O	C	I	R	P	A	O
W	P	A	E	I	M	O	H
N	X	K	P	J	A	V	I
J	R	U	Z	N	X	W	N
N	W	S	V	U	G	H	L
P	H	R	N	Z	E	P	O

My third letter appears in the second column but not in the seventh column.

My fourth letter is directly above a U and directly below a J.

My fifth letter appears only in rows three, four, and five.

My sixth letter is a corner letter that is a consonant.

__ __ __ __ __ __

MISSING LINKS

Using only the letters below, fill the diagram with real, everyday words. Be careful — this puzzle isn't as easy as it may look, so a little extra thought will be needed.

	R	A		T	I				F				L	I	M	
O			O			L		F	N	I	S				A
	E	A				O		R			A		A	D	I
T			T			U		S					A	D	I	M
U			H			I	S		N	C					M
N					B			N		E					E
	L	U		I	N		M		F		E	A	C		E
T			I		R			F						E
E			N		S				O	P	E	L		E
		C		U	N		E					E
		R				R					A
P		S		U	N	H	I	N			P
	C	O	R	T		I		U	L
I		A		R		S		U	N	G	W
N		D	C	F	E	E	R	I		G	E
	H	N	N		E		T		E
E	U		G		N	R	B	I	N
	O	A	N	C	E	N	O		Y

AAAA B CC D EE F H IIII
L MM N OOO P Q RRRRRRR
SS TTTTTTTTT U

WORD WHEEL

Starting with the "M" at the arrow, see how many everyday words of three or more letters you can find going clockwise. Don't skip over any letters. For example, if you saw the letters C, A, R, E, D, you would form five words: CAR, CARE, CARED, ARE, RED. We found 30 words.

TRI, TRI AGAIN

Fit the nine triangles into the big one so six everyday words are spelled out reading across the arrows. Do not rotate the triangles.

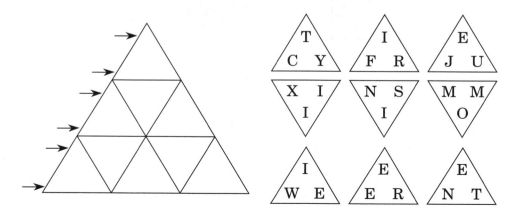

336

LOOSE TILE

The tray on the right seemed the ideal place to store the set of loose dominoes. Unfortunately, when the tray was full, one domino was left over. Determine the arrangement of the dominoes in the tray and which is the Loose Tile.

LANGUAGE

COUNT ON IT!

Directions for solving are on page 321.

1. UABSAP   2. LEAPH   3. ODWN
4. AWN   5. YSY   6. S

$\overline{1}$ $\overline{1}\ \overline{2}\ \overline{3}$ $\overline{1}\ \overline{2}\ \overline{3}\ \overline{4}\ \overline{5}$ $\overline{1}\ \overline{2}\ \overline{3}\ \overline{4}\ \overline{5}\ \overline{6}$

$\overline{1}\ \overline{2}\ \overline{3}\ \overline{4}\ \overline{5}$ $\overline{1}\ \overline{2}$.

CIRCLE MATH

Each overlapping circle is identified by a letter having a different number value from 1 to 9. Where some circles overlap, there is a number: It is the SUM of the values of the letters in those overlapping circles. Can you figure out the correct values for the letters? As a starting help, I = 7.

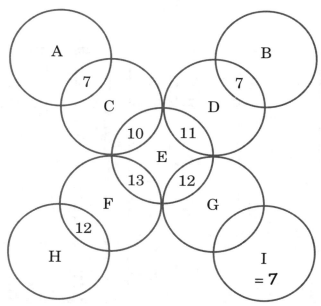

RINGERS

LANGUAGE ◆ SPATIAL

Each Ringer is composed of five rings. Use your imagination to rotate the rings so that you spell out four 5-letter words reading from the outside to the inside when all five rings are aligned correctly.

1.

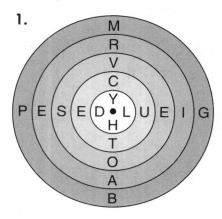

2.

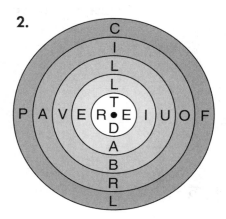

WAYWORDS

Directions for solving are on page 331. Here, you'll be looking for a 14-word thought beginning with THE.

POETRY	FICTION	TO	SENSE
BETWEEN	HAS	AND	MAKE
FORMER	DIFFERENCE	THE	REALITY
THE	DISTANCE	IS	DRESS
TAKEN	THAT	CONTINUES	PARDON

CARD SENSE

Directions for solving are on page 317.

1. The diamond isn't adjacent to the two.

2. The tens aren't adjacent.

3. The bottom card isn't red.

4. The club is adjacent to both hearts.

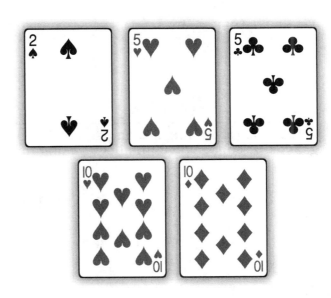

GRAND TOUR

LANGUAGE ◆ VISUAL

Directions for solving are on page 319. This time, you'll be looking for a chain of 5-letter words, starting with GAF-FE-MUR (gaffe, femur).

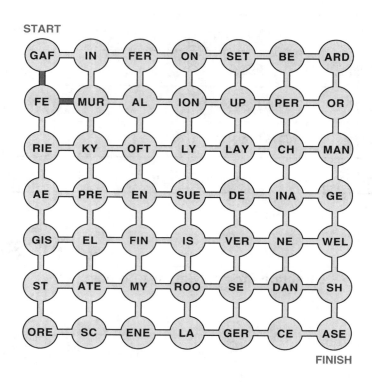

START

FINISH

ALL IN A ROW

MATH

Directions for solving are on page 310. This time, look for the most groups of consecutive numbers adding up to 12.

A. 8 2 1 4 3 7 5 4 1 1 9 2 3 5 2 8 1 1 4 6 5 2 4 1

B. 1 2 3 2 6 1 4 2 4 2 8 3 7 1 1 4 5 9 2 5 3 1 2 4

C. 2 4 1 3 2 8 5 3 9 7 2 1 3 5 6 4 1 3 6 1 1 5 5 2

STAR WORDS

Only five of the eight words given will fit together in the diagram. Place them in the directions indicated by the arrows.

BLOG   LILT

BOOT   LOOT

BOWL   TOOT

GLOB   TWIG

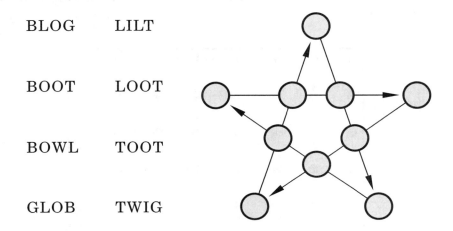

HEXAGON HUNT

Directions for solving are on page 309.

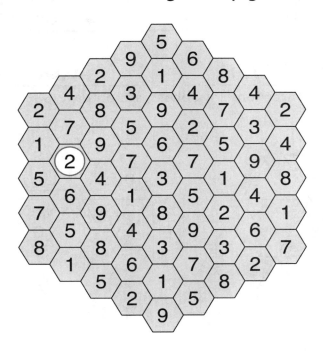

ROUND TRIP

When this puzzle has been completed correctly, you will have made a round trip through its set of dots. You must visit every dot exactly once, make no diagonal moves, and return to your starting point. Parts of the right path are shown; can you find the rest?

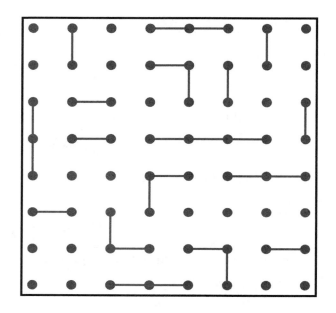

TRI, TRI AGAIN

LANGUAGE ◆ SPATIAL

Directions for solving are on page 336.

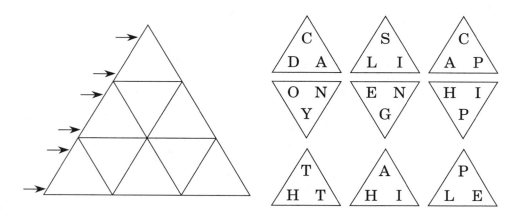

QUOTATION MARKS

Enter the capital letters in the diagram as indicated by the number-letter combinations to form an interesting bit of information. For example, one of the C's should be placed in the box where column 16 and row k intersect.

	1	2	3	4	5	6	7	8	9	10	11	12	13	14	15	16	17	18	19
a																			
b																			
c																			
d																			
e																			
f																			
g																			
h																			
i																			
j										—									
k																			
l																			
m																			

A: 2a, 11a, 19a, 15b, 1c, 6c, 6d, 13d, 7f, 7h, 17h, 3i, 16i, 14k, 8l, 11m

B: 8f, 17i, 6l

C: 2g, 16k

D: 3b, 17b, 3h, 16h, 19k, 3m

E: 14a, 2b, 11c, 5d, 4e, 8e, 10e, 19e, 15f, 1g, 3g, 15g, 2h, 9h, 5i, 11i, 13i, 4j, 6j, 14j, 15j, 7k, 11k, 18k, 4l, 7l, 11l, 19l, 2m

F: 5b, 19b, 15c, 16c, 18c

G: 8a

H: 5a, 9a, 11b, 10c, 4d, 8d, 3e, 14f, 14g, 8i, 12j, 17k, 3l, 18l, 15m

I: 17a, 14d, 14e, 16f, 6g, 10g, 19g, 18j, 2k, 9m

L: 3a, 15e, 16e, 2i, 19j, 1k, 10k, 10l, 7m, 8m

M: 18a, 12c, 2d, 17j

N: 12a, 16b, 2c, 18e, 8g, 11g, 18g, 7j, 4k, 15l, 12m

O: 6a, 6b, 12b, 14c, 1d, 10d, 17d, 3f, 9f, 7g, 14h, 9i, 18i, 3k, 8k, 14l, 16m

P: 16d, 4g, 6k, 9k

R: 8b, 19c, 9d, 15d, 18d, 9e, 1f, 17f, 19f, 6i, 14i, 13j

S: 15a, 14b, 3c, 5c, 12e, 5f, 5h, 10h, 19h, 3j, 12l, 5m, 14m

T: 4a, 16a, 1b, 10b, 9c, 7d, 19d, 2e, 13e, 11f, 13f, 5g, 13g, 1h, 6h, 8h, 12h, 4i, 1j, 8j, 11j, 15k, 2l, 9l, 17l

U: 7a, 7b, 13b, 4f, 10f, 17g, 19i, 6m

V: 2f, 12i, 5j, 10m

W: 7c, 11d, 7e, 13h, 10i, 13k, 17m

Y: 5e, 18h, 9j

343

STACKED UP

VISUAL ◆ SPATIAL

The box on the left can be formed by three of the numbered boxes superimposed on top of each other; do not turn them in any way. Can you figure out which three work?

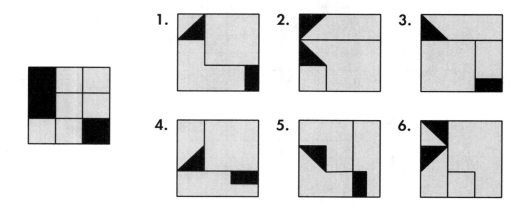

ASSOCIATIONS

LANGUAGE

Directions for solving are on page 312.

WHERE DID THE JUST-MARRIED JOCKEY DECIDE TO STAY?

CLAM TINY PROVIDE HERBAL SPARSE DEER

OYSTER EXCITE SUPPLY EMPHASIZE BANJO

MEAGER HARM RIGID STRESS MUSSEL ICICLE

ELK DALMATIAN HURT CLEAN LESSON SCARCE

EARNEST FURNISH SURGE WASH ACCENT

UNITED CRIMSON INJURE INDELICATE SCARLET

TANK MOOSE LAUNDER EDIFICE RED

SUDOKU

Directions for solving are on page 308.

3	8		7				2	
		9						
1					4	7	9	
		8	5			2		4
	2		4		1		8	
4		7			2	3		
	9	4	1					5
						9		
	3				7		6	2

SLIDE RULE

Slide each column of letters up or down in the box and form as many 3-letter words as you can in the windows where BED is now. We formed 43 words, including BED. Do not include slang words.

Your list of words:

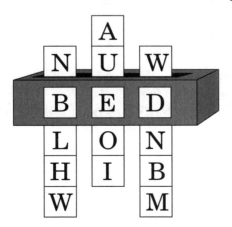

IN THE ABSTRACT
VISUAL ◆ SPATIAL

Directions for solving are on page 314.

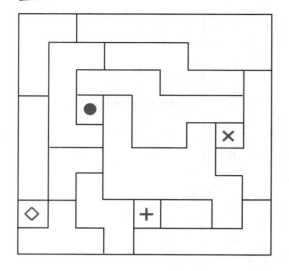

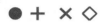

NEXT TO NOTHING
LANGUAGE ◆ VISUAL

In the first row, the G is next to the number zero and the X is next to the letter O. Circle all of the letters next to zeroes then scramble the circled letters to spell out a 7-letter word.

G0	XO	QO	N0
I0	MO	SO	JO
ZO	R0	UO	AO
FO	HO	DO	B0
KO	E0	W0	YO
CO	TO	PO	VO

"The power of imagination makes us infinite."
— *John Muir*

MAGIC NUMBER SQUARES

WEEK 50

Fill in the empty boxes so these groups add up to the number below each diagram: 1. each row; 2. each column; 3. each long diagonal; 4. the four center squares; 5. the four corner squares; and 6. each quarter of the diagram. A number will be used only once per diagram.

1.

37			
	27		21
23		17	
		35	

88

2.

		29	23
	20		
11		44	2

98

DEDUCTION PROBLEM

Al, Bill, Cora, Dan, and Ed were all very confused about what day it was. They made the following statements, only one of which was true:

Al: "The day before yesterday was Sunday."

Bill: "Tomorrow will not be Friday."

Cora: "Tomorrow will be Monday."

Dan: "Today is a weekday — either Monday or Friday or a day in between."

Ed: "No, today isn't a weekday; it's either Saturday or Sunday."

If only one statement is true, what day was it?

TARGET SHOOT

LANGUAGE

Directions for solving are on page 320.

1.

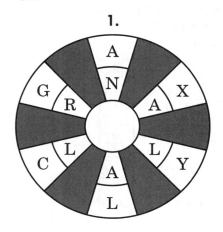

2.

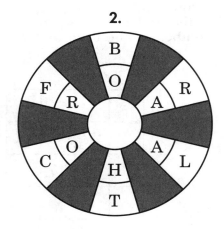

CODE WORD

DECODING

Directions for solving are on page 312. Here, form a 12-letter word.

$$\overline{1} \; \overline{2} \; \overline{3} \; \overline{4} \; \overline{5} \; \overline{6} \; \overline{7} \; \overline{8} \; \overline{9} \; \overline{10} \; \overline{11} \; \overline{12}$$

7 T   7   P L 7 C 5   6 1 5 8 5   T 1 5   Y 5 7 8

10 4   4 P L 10 T   B 5 T 6 5 5 11   6 12 L 5

D 7 Y 4   2 F   L 10 12 1 T   7 11 D   D 7 8 K

7 11 D   6 1 5 8 5   T 1 5   6 2 8 L D ' 4

T 6 5 11 T Y – F 2 3 8   T 10 9 5   Z 2 11 5 4

C 2 11 V 5 8 12 5 ,   T 10 9 5   10 T 4 5 L F   10 4

7 11 2 T 1 5 8   3 11 3 4 3 7 L   P 1 5 11 2 9 5 11 2 11

2 F   T 1 5   4 2 3 T 1   P 2 L 5 .

348

ELIMINATION

Directions for solving are on page 310. Once again, the remaining words will form a thought.

REIN TUNIC FRENCH BISTRO SPEAK
BEAUTY REMINISENCE SUPERIOR RURAL
RAPTOR THE ERIE SWEATER IS QUARENTINE
TRUTH ONTARIO TRANSPORT ONLY THEN
JODHPURS GINGER MOLAR PILGRIMMAGE BAIL
LEAVE CARROT DAILY HURON SKIN AROMA
MURMER PATE IMMEDIATELY PETTICOAT DEEP
ALOOF SPOON MICHIGAN

Eliminate…

1. words that are names of garments.

2. the names of the Great Lakes.

3. words that are composed of letters only from the word FORMULA.

4. the four words that end with the same three letters in any order.

5. the five words that form a phrase that means "pulchritude extends no further than a cutaneous level."

6. the four misspelled words.

7. words that become new words when the letter S is placed in the middle of each.

8. words that can precede the word BREAD.

VISUAL ◆ SPATIAL

BLOCK PARTY

See page 324 for solving directions.

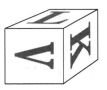   

FUN WITH FACTS AND FIGURES

MATH

Directions for solving are on page 318.

1. Take the total number of consonants in the word GOVERNMENT and subtract the number of vowels in the word. _____

2. Next, multiply by the number of minutes in five hours. _____

3. Now, divide by the current number of members of the U.S. Senate. _____

4. Add the number of golden rings mentioned in the carol "The Twelve Days of Christmas." _____

5. Subtract the number that is the English translation of the Spanish word *uno*. _____

Our answer is the number of pawns on the board at the beginning of a game of chess. *Is yours?*

WORD VISIBILITY

LANGUAGE

See page 328 for solving directions.

1. P R U C G
   W O A N H

2. M A E D O
   S P N G T

3. O X S U A
   I S D R E

4. F L E O R
   B U O P N

5. G H A L A
   D R I M K

6. C O Y U S
   F L C I M

WHAT'S YOUR NUMBER?

Can you figure out the relationship of the numbers in the first two figures and, based on that, what missing number goes into the space with the question mark?

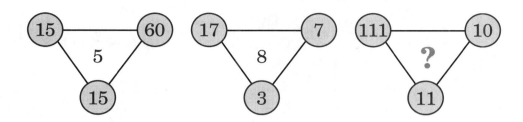

FILLING STATION

Directions for solving are on page 320.

1. B B C K K P P R (thing)

   _ A _ E _ _ A _ _   _ O O _

2. B B C F H N P R R S T T (movie)

   "_ I _ A _ E _   O _   _ _ E
   _ A _ I _ _ E A _"

3. D H L N N R S T (country)

   _ E _ _ E _ _ A _ _ _

4. F L R S V W (decorative item)

   _ _ O _ E _   _ A _ E

5. C N N S S W (U.S. state)

   _ I _ _ O _ _ I _

351

CROSS-UPS

LANGUAGE

Using only the letters given above each diagram, fill in the boxes in such a way that an everyday compound word is formed, one part reading across and the other part reading down. The letter already in the diagram is a letter shared by both parts of the word. Note: Each part of the compound word is an entire word on its own.

1. A E E W

2. A C H O P S W

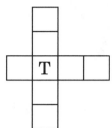

3. D G N N O P R S

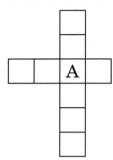

ARROW MAZE

VISUAL

Directions for solving are on page 315.

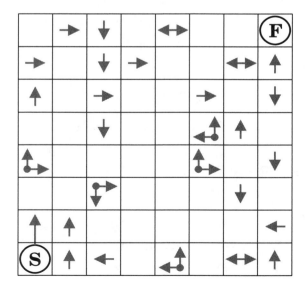

COMPOUND IT

WEEK
51

Directions for solving are on page 319.

1. play, cat, fun, rain

2. coat, bow, book, nap

3. string, fire, tail, mark

4. bone, house, down, pipe

5. dress, line, head, hill

6. strong, backer, light, top

7. weight, box, sail, hold

8. less, over, car, boat

9. lord, pool, look, yard

10. sun, cream, stream, ship

LANGUAGE ◆ SPATIAL **WORD HUNT**

Find words by moving from one letter to any adjoining letter. You may start a word with any letter in the diagram. In forming a word you may return to a letter as often as you wish, but do not stand on a letter using it twice in direct succession. This time, you'll be searching for 5-letter words that start with GR (such as GRACE). We found 16 words, including GRACE.

U	W	L	T	Z
P	O	N	D	C
N	G	R	A	E
E	E	I	P	T
D	F	M	N	D

Your list of words:

"Success does not consist in never making blunders, but in never making the same one a second time."
— *Josh Billings*

ORDERLY STATES

LANGUAGE

Directions are on page 330.

1. ACEHMSTU   _____

2. ACGHIMN   _____

3. ABEKNRS   _____

4. ACHILNORSTU   _____

5. AEGINRSTVW   _____

6. ADELRW   _____

7. ACDLOR   _____

8. AKNRS   _____

COUNTDOWN

VISUAL

Directions for solving are on page 321.

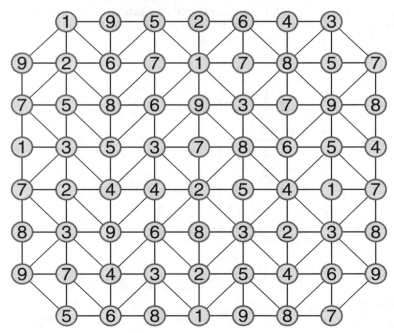

LETTER, PLEASE

The numbers below stand for certain letters on the telephone dial. You will see that one number may stand for more than one letter — for example, 3 may be D, E, or F. By finding the correct letter for each number, you will have spelled out a Bible passage.

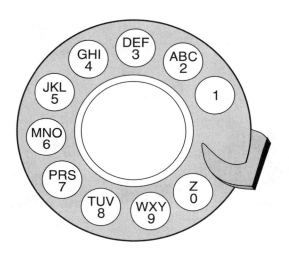

" 3 8 3 7 9 8 4 4 6 4

4 7   7 6 7 7 4 2 5 3

3 6 7   4 4 6   9 4 6

2 3 5 4 3 8 3 7 . "

GOING IN CIRCLES

Directions for solving are on page 309.

1.

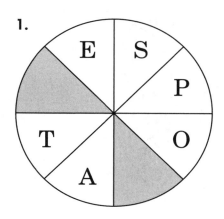

2.

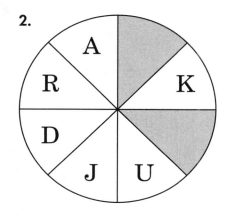

VISION QUEST

VISUAL

Find the row or column that contains five DIFFERENT cats.

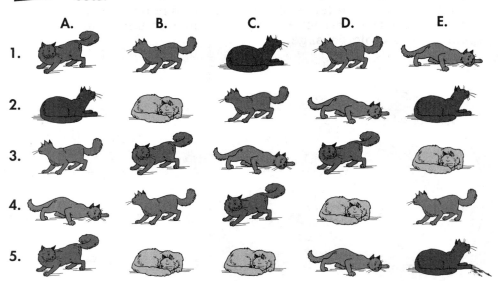

WORD WHEEL

LANGUAGE

Directions for solving are on page 336. Beginning with the "W" at the arrow, we formed 30 words.

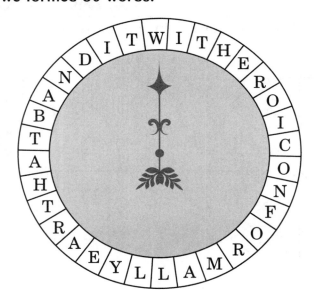

ANAGRAM MAZE

Directions for solving are on page 316. This time, there are 21 words to anagram and the first word you'll be anagramming is SINK.

1 LILY	**2** MINK	**3** ROCK	**4** BARD	**5** SINK	**6** KNOW
7 BRAN	**8** FLUE	**9** LAIN	**10** MALT	**11** HOOT	**12** WOOL
13 BLOW	**14** CELL	**15** AFAR	**16** DAWN	**17** SLAT	**18** ABET
19 LIFE	**20** SAGE	**21** VAST	**22** HOSE	**23** TINY	**24** FLIT
25 HARD	**26** BEAU	**27** MAKE	**28** BANG	**29** MAZE	**30** LIED
31 HAVE	**32** RISE	**33** MOOR	**34** SAME	**35** LAPS	**36** TOGA

LANGUAGE

SKILLS TEST

Each single word below can be combined with two others in the list to form five longer words. All 15 words will be used one time only.

A	HER	ION	SLATE	TO
ALLY	I	LEG	SUB	TRACT
AT	IN	POT	TERN	WE

WORD CHARADE

LANGUAGE ◆ VISUAL

Directions for solving are on page 334.

My first letter appears to the immediate right of a Z and directly above a V.

My second letter is the only letter missing from the word LIFEGUARD in one of the columns.

A	U	L	X	P	K	E	A
Z	J	C	O	B	S	D	O
M	Q	I	Y	J	N	F	W
G	K	G	B	G	V	G	H
F	H	J	W	H	X	L	P
R	D	N	S	Z	M	U	M
I	D	F	B	C	V	I	J
Y	K	A	V	N	C	R	Q

My third letter appears four times in one of the rows.

My fourth letter is the only letter from the second half of the alphabet in one of the columns.

My fifth letter appears only once in the diagram.

My sixth letter does not appear in the diagram.

— — — — — —

ALL IN A ROW

MATH

Directions for solving are on page 310. This time, look for the most groups of consecutive numbers adding up to 14.

A. 1 2 8 5 3 9 2 6 7 2 3 2 1 9 7 4 4 1 2 6 1 5 2 8

B. 6 5 4 5 7 3 8 1 4 2 7 3 1 2 1 6 5 9 8 3 4 2 7 5

C. 3 2 3 6 4 5 1 3 8 4 9 1 6 6 3 4 8 1 2 3 7 6 1 6

MISSING DOMINOES

WEEK
52

Directions for solving are on page 323.

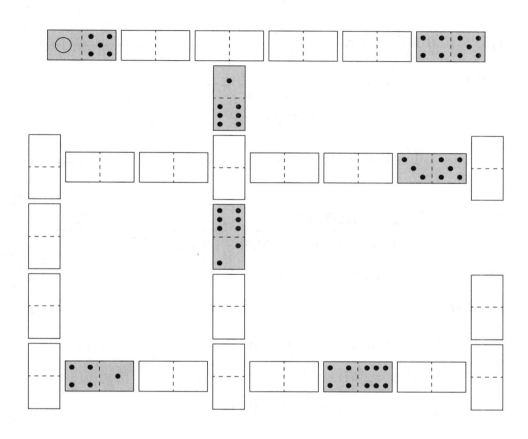

DOMINOES

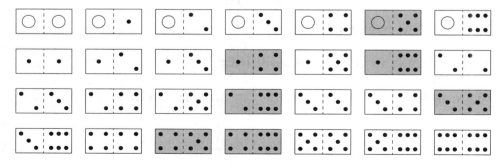

DOVETAILED WORDS

LANGUAGE

Directions for solving are on page 332.

1. Y S A A C I L H T   _____   _____

2. D E E R L A S E E T E   _____   _____

3. F B L L A A Z M E E   _____   _____

4. J G A A R C M K E E N T T   _____   _____

5. K N B L I A D F E E   _____   _____

ANIMAL CHARADES

LANGUAGE

Directions for solving are on page 315.

My FIRST is in SHEEP and in POLE;   _____

My SECOND is in PORPOISE and in SOUL;   _____

My THIRD is in EAGLE but not in GUEST;   _____

My FOURTH is in WHALE but not in WEST;   _____

My FIFTH is in CANARY and in RAIN;   _____

My SIXTH is in ZEBRA and in BRAIN;   _____

My SEVENTH is in MOOSE but not in SOOT;   _____

My EIGHTH is in ELEPHANT but not in PUT;   _____

My NINTH is in GORILLA and in LITTER.   _____

My WHOLE lives in the cold — I'm an arctic critter.

_____

ROUND TRIP

Directions for solving are on page 342.

WEEK
52

SEVEN WORD ZINGER

Directions for solving are on page 318.

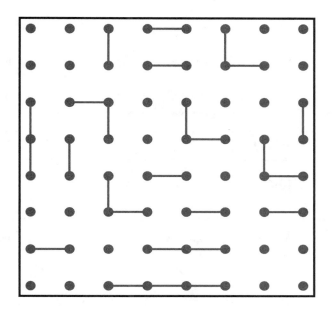

— — —

— — — —

— — — —

— — — —

— — — —

— — — — —

— — — — —

ALPHABET SOUP

LANGUAGE ◆ VISUAL

Directions for solving are on page 324.

F	B	Y	F	B	F	Y	L	B	W	Y	F	B	W	Y	K
Y	T	O	H	E	T	O	H	T	X	H	I	T	E	O	U
O	Q	V	N	M	J	V	Q	S	V	Z	C	N	V	P	C

A B C D E F G H I J K L M N O P Q R S T U V W X Y Z

Word: _____

V	H	L	V	H	Q	L	A	H	L	V	I	V	M	I	H
Q	J	X	L	S	V	M	J	U	L	X	U	C	G	W	U
X	R	O	F	P	K	O	B	P	F	O	Z	F	D	P	Y

A B C D E F G H I J K L M N O P Q R S T U V W X Y Z

Word: _____

CIRCLE MATH

MATH

Directions for solving are on page 338. As a starting help, G = 6.

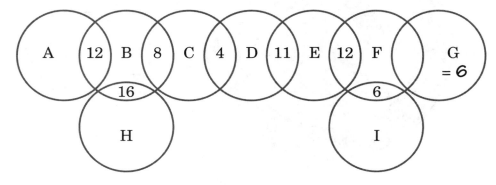

ANSWERS

IN THE ABSTRACT (Week 1)

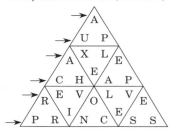

CODE WORD (Week 1)

Code Word: waitperson. Television will never completely replace the newspaper since no one can swat a fly with it.

WHAT'S YOUR NUMBER? (Week 1)

Ten. The bottom number is 14 more than twice the top number.

RELATIONSHIPS QUIZ (Week 1)

1. c; 2. d; 3. b; 4. a; 5. b; 6. c.

MAGNIFIND (Week 1)

EASY PICKINGS (Week 1)

"The Sun Also Rises" was written by Ernest Hemingway.

COUNT THE TRIANGLES (Week 1)

There are 13 triangles: ABC, ABD, ACD, AGM, BDJ, BGJ, DJM, EGH, EGI, EHI, FKL, FKM, FLM.

ANTONYMS QUIZ (Week 1)

1. b; 2. a; 3. a; 4. c; 5. b; 6. a; 7. c; 8. a.

SUDOKU (Week 1)

1	6	5	7	4	9	8	2	3
8	9	2	1	3	6	7	5	4
3	4	7	2	8	5	6	9	1
6	2	4	8	5	7	1	3	9
5	1	8	4	9	3	2	6	7
7	3	9	6	1	2	4	8	5
4	5	1	9	2	8	3	7	6
2	7	3	5	6	1	9	4	8
9	8	6	3	7	4	5	1	2

TRI, TRI AGAIN (Week 1)

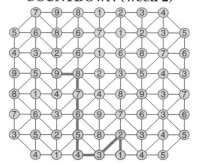

TIPS OF THE ICEBERG (Week 1)

1. Brenda ($6.00); 2. Greta ($3.40); 3. Dena and Flora ($4.95).

COUNTDOWN (Week 2)

SYMBOL-ISM (Week 2)

Those who think after speaking often ponder apologies.

ROUND TRIP (Week 2)

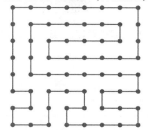

FUN WITH FACTS AND FIGURES (Week 2)

1. 10 x 6 = 60; 2. 60 ÷ 12 = 5; 3. 5 + 24 = 29; 4. 29 − 5 (Texas) = 24; 5. 24 + 1 = 25.

ANAGRAM MAZE (Week 2)

1		3	4	5	
7	8	9		11	
			16	17	
	20	21	22		
	26				
	32	33	34	35	36

The path through the maze, with just one anagram given for each, is: 1. hare; 7. fire; 8. coal; 9. paws; 3. feel; 4. clay; 5. tape; 11. fast; 17. lime; 16. hubs; 22. salt; 21. vine; 20. bake; 26. barn; 32. bale; 33. pier; 34. file; 35. goes; 36. slow.

ALL IN A ROW (Week 2)

Row C. Row A contains five groups: 731, 1334, 222221, 3215, and 155. Row B contains five groups: 11162, 1622, 2252, 191, and 92. Row C contains six groups: 1118, 4421, 713, 56, 6221, and 137.

JACK IN THE BOX (Week 2)
drizzle

THE LINEUP (Week 2)

1. C; 2. squeeze; 3. M; 4. argument; 5. exam, lobe, know.

COUNT TO TEN (Week 2)

1. the sixth row; 2. the first row; 3. the seventh row.

WAYWORDS (Week 2)
The sun loses nothing by shining on all.

GRAND TOUR (Week 2)

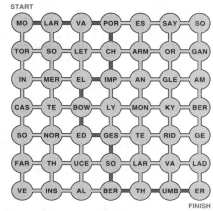

molar, larva, vapor, porch, chimp, impel, elbow, bowed, edges, gesso, sober, berth, thumb, umber.

BLOCK PARTY (Week 2)

LOOSE TILE (Week 2)

The 5-6 tile is the loose tile.

ASSOCIATIONS (Week 2)

agitate, disturb, shake; blue, red, green; cake, cookie, tart; cardinal, bishop, priest; dark, gloomy, somber; energy, force, vigor; field, tract, plot; Finland, Sweden, Norway. "Here comes the fudge."

365

HEXAGON HUNT (Week 3)

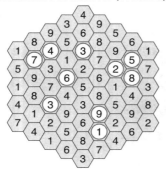

SLIDE RULE (Week 3)

ear, eat, elm, ham, hat, hay, him, hit, hum, hut, pan, par, pat, pay, pin, pit, ply, pun, put, sat, say, shy, sin, sir, sit, sly, sum, sun, wan, war, way, why, win, wit.

CIRCLE SEARCH (Week 3)

eon, fan, farm, garment, gate, neon, one, stone, tee, teen, test, ton, tone.

ELIMINATION (Week 3)

1. broth, consommé, bouillon; 2. love, sight (love at first sight); 3. bull (pit bull), stop (pit stop), fall (pitfall); 4. paradise (pair of dice) 5. paint, the, town, red (paint the town red); 6. shy, pry, nigh, eye; 7. dragon, radical, adroit. "A closed mouth will gather no feet."

WORD WHEEL (Week 3)

mar, mark, market, marketing, ark, tin, ting, gold, golden, old, olden, den, denote, not, note, ten, tend, tendril, end, drill, rill, ill, log, ogle, glean, lean, ant, anti, antic, tic.

KEEP ON MOVING (Week 3)

Move three squares left, two squares down, four squares right, three squares up, and two squares left to the asterisk.

TARGET SHOOT (Week 3)

1. EV: eleven, clever, peeved; 2. CU: locust, occupy, vacuum.

DOVETAILED WORDS (Week 3)

1. adobe, brick; 2. square, circle; 3. luggage, satchel; 4. shout, whisper; 5. hockey, soccer; 6. forty, fifty.

NEXT TO NOTHING (Week 3)

pelican

SQUARE ROUTE (Week 3)

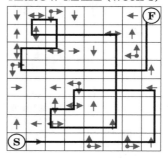

ARROW MAZE (Week 3)

WORD VISIBILITY (Week 3)

1. queen; 2. boxer; 3. tooth; 4. lyric; 5. slick; 6. thyme.

ONLINE NETWORK (Week 3)

peace, tranquility, calm; dolphin, whale, porpoise.

LICENSE PLATES (Week 4)

1. Elvis Presley; 2. Buddy Holly; 3. Carl Perkins; 4. Chuck Berry; 5. Little Richard; 6. Bill Haley.

ASSOCIATIONS (Week 4)

dry, arid, waterless; face, confront, challenge; garnet, opal, topaz; Guatemala, Honduras, Belize; inert, static, dormant; leak, seep, drip; marsh, swamp, moor; pony, horse, steed. "Someday my prints will come."

SUDOKU (Week 4)

9	2	8	4	7	6	3	5	1
3	5	4	9	1	2	7	8	6
1	7	6	5	8	3	2	4	9
8	9	2	6	4	1	5	3	7
4	6	3	7	9	5	8	1	2
5	1	7	3	2	8	9	6	4
6	8	1	2	3	7	4	9	5
7	4	5	8	6	9	1	2	3
2	3	9	1	5	4	6	7	8

SQUARE LINKS (Week 4)

election, straight, ignorant, footpath, overtime.

RINGERS (Week 4)

1. sweep, force, bumpy, adopt; 2. organ, rapid, finer, stump.

STAR WORDS (Week 4)

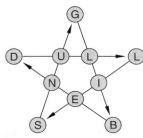

Your sequence of words may begin in any outer circle.

CIRCLE MATH (Week 4)

A = 5, B = 9, C = 4, D = 1, E = 6, F = 7, G = 8, H = 3, and I = 2.

BULL'S-EYE LETTER (Week 4)

The Bull's-Eye Letter is C: disc, talc, chip, achy, tick, card.

ALPHABET SOUP (Week 4)

red

GOING IN CIRCLES (Week 4)

1. motivate; 2. knockout.

CODED STATES (Week 4)

1. Washington; 2. New Mexico; 3. Kentucky; 4. Iowa; 5. Idaho; 6. Arkansas; 7. Texas; 8. North Dakota.

OVERLAY (Week 4)

Diagram A.

COMPOUND IT (Week 4)

1. ginger; 2. bread; 3. basket; 4. ball; 5. park; 6. way; 7. side; 8. arm; 9. band; 10. wagon (gingerbread, breadbasket, basketball, ballpark, parkway, wayside, sidearm, armband, bandwagon).

MISSING DOMINOES (Week 5)

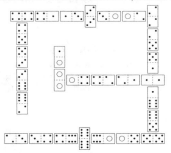

SEVEN WORD ZINGER (Week 5)

aim, bee, coy, ear, lye, sir, who.

STACKED UP (Week 5)

Boxes 3, 5, and 6.

VISION QUEST (Week 5)

Column D.

PRESIDENTIAL RHYMES (Week 5)

1. John Adams; 2. James Polk; 3. Jimmy Carter; 4. George Bush; 5. Martin Van Buren; 6. Harry Truman; 7. John Tyler; 8. Warren Harding; 9. Gerald Ford; 10. Zachary Taylor.

SLIDE RULE (Week 5)

bail, bait, balk, ball, bank, bell, belt, bent, boil, boll, bolt, bonk, book, boon, boot, bulk, bull, bunk, bunt, nail, neon, nook, noon, null, rail, rain, rank, rant, rein, rent, roil, roll, rook, root, ruin, runt, tail, talk, tall, tank, tell, tent, toil, toll, took, tool, toot.

DOUBLE DUTY (Week 5)

Rembrandt van Rijn

WORD CHARADE (Week 5)

I	M	E	G	P	Q	L	O
N	A	U	A	J	I	W	B
P	C	P	Z	C	S	Y	D
G	R	V	F	Q	(N)	J	F
I	N	(U)	(A)	T	R	E	
U	K	X	J	W	L	K	S
X	D	R	M	T	B	Z	M
E	G	(C)	Q	M	I	P	(L)

launch

EASY PICKINGS (Week 5)

Be prepared, be observant, and be helpful.

WORD HUNT (Week 5)

beam, chum, doom, dorm, drum, farm, film, firm, foam, form, from, helm, loam, loom, norm, prim, prom, roam, skim, slim, team, zoom.

ROUND TRIP (Week 5)

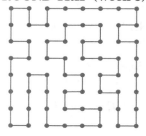

ANAGRAM MAZE (Week 5)

		3	4	5	6
					12
13	14	15	16		18
19			22	23	24
25	26				
	32	33	34		

The path through the maze, with just one anagram given for each, is: 3. does; 4. lean; 5. none; 6. much; 12. tubs; 18. clam; 24. node; 23. live; 22. pets; 16. lied; 15. sack; 14. meat; 13. inch; 19. hate; 25. sour; 26. tern; 32. slip; 33. ride; 34. ecru.

SKILLS TEST (Week 5)

thank, thick, think, track, trick, truck, trunk, tweak.

SUDOKU (Week 6)

4	7	8	6	9	3	1	5	2
6	2	5	4	1	7	9	3	8
3	1	9	5	2	8	4	6	7
5	9	7	3	6	1	2	8	4
8	6	1	9	4	2	5	7	3
2	4	3	8	7	5	6	1	9
1	8	4	2	3	6	7	9	5
7	5	2	1	8	9	3	4	6
9	3	6	7	5	4	8	2	1

LICENSE PLATES (Week 6)

1. Havana, Cuba; 2. Jakarta, Indonesia; 3. Tokyo, Japan; 4. Dublin, Ireland; 5. Manila, Philippines; 6. Kingston, Jamaica.

THE LINEUP (Week 6)

1. U; 2. coffee; 3. F; 4. relieving; 5. skim, dime, foxy.

MAGNIFIND (Week 6)

CODE WORD (Week 6)

Code Word: regulations. One great advantage of many parking lots is that they give us something to blame the bumped fenders on.

368

ALPHABET SOUP (Week 6)
silk

TRI, TRI AGAIN (Week 6)

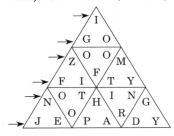

ANIMAL CHARADES (Week 6)
oriole.

GRAND TOUR (Week 6)

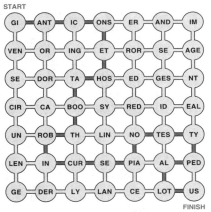

giant, antic, icons, onset, ethos, hosta, taboo, booth, throb, robin, incur, curse, sepia, piano, notes, testy, typed, pedal, allot, lotus.

FUN WITH FACTS AND FIGURES (Week 6)
1. 7 − 6 = 1; 2. 1 x 12 = 12; 3. 12 ÷ 3 (Ohio, Oklahoma, Oregon) = 4; 4. 4 + 40 = 44; 5. 44 − 5 = 39.

MARCHING ORDERS (Week 6)

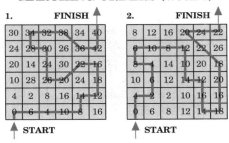

SKILLS TEST (Week 6)
1. "Let us be thankful for the fools. But for them the rest of us could not succeed." 2. "In his private heart no man much respects himself."

COUNTDOWN (Week 7)

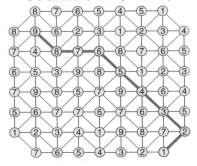

WAYWORDS (Week 7)
A lazy man's only exercise is pushing his luck.

QUOTATION MARKS (Week 7)
"Keep away from small people who try to belittle your ambitions. Small people always do that, but the really great make you feel that you, too, can become great."

369

ANAGRAM MAZE (Week 7)

1	2	3			6
7		9	10		12
13	14		16	17	18
	20	21			
		27			
31	32	33			

The path through the maze, with just one anagram given for each, is: 6. fats; 12. lake; 18. café; 17. stud; 16. page; 10. lain; 9. goat; 3. lion; 2. arch; 1. dubs; 7. coin; 13. bear; 14. went 20. cats; 21. owns; 27. care; 33. lone; 32. star; 31. jest.

ALL IN A ROW (Week 7)

Row A. Row A contains six groups: 3416, 284, 4352, 68, 3461, and 158. Row B contains four groups: 374, 6242, 35123, and 941. Row C contains five groups: 63212, 1256, 833, 3362, and 2417.

LETTER, PLEASE (Week 7)

"In America, any boy may become President, and I suppose it's just one of the risks he takes."

U COUNT (Week 7)

There are 30 U's.

IN THE ABSTRACT (Week 7)

CROSS-UPS (Week 7)

1. watermelon; 2. floorboard; 3. coffeepot.

FILLING STATION (Week 7)

1. Philadelphia; 2. dishwasher; 3. "Pretty Woman"; 4. fried chicken; 5. Meryl Streep; 6. magnifying glass.

SKILLS TEST (Week 7)

Christopher brought in $550 on Monday, $650 on Tuesday, $450 on Wednesday, $700 on Thursday, and $400 on Friday.

LOOSE TILE (Week 7)

The 2-5 is the loose tile.

CIRCLE SEARCH (Week 7)

ale, egad, eve, even, evening, gad, gene, gin, inn, inning, rev, reveal, reveals, revs, salad, sale, seven.

VISION QUEST (Week 8)

Row 2.

SEVEN WORD ZINGER (Week 8)

ado, cap, eve, nun, pit, shy, you.

ARROW MAZE (Week 8)

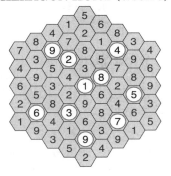

DEDUCTION PROBLEM (Week 8)

The man who took Green's hat took Brown's coat. Black took White's hat, but he didn't take Brown's coat, so Black took Green's coat. White, then, took Green's hat and Brown's coat. By elimination, Brown took Black's hat. Green, then, took Brown's hat. By elimination, Brown took White's coat and Green took Black's coat. In summary:

Mr. Black, White's hat, Green's coat
Mr. Brown, Black's hat, White's coat
Mr. Green, Brown's hat, Black's coat
Mr. White, Green's hat, Brown's coat

CHANGELINGS (Week 8)

1. FINE, wine, wire, wore, WORD. 2. GOES, hoes, hops, hope, HOME. 3. LOSE, dose, dome, dame, GAME.

CODED STATES (Week 8)

1. West Virginia; 2. Illinois; 3. California; 4. Rhode Island; 5. Maryland; 6. Massachusetts; 7. Oregon; 8. Mississippi.

WORD HUNT (Week 8)

4-letter words: bass, boss, hiss, kiss, lass, less, loss, mass, miss, muss, sass, toss; **5-letter words:** amass, amiss, bless, bliss, brass, crass, cross, dress, floss, glass, grass, gross, guess, press, tress, truss.

CIRCLE MATH (Week 8)

A = 5, B = 7, C = 6, D = 3, E = 8, F = 1, G = 2, H = 9, and I = 4.

GOING IN CIRCLES (Week 8)

1. tropical; 2. welcomed.

LETTER, PLEASE (Week 8)

"A little sincerity is a dangerous thing, and a great deal of it is absolutely fatal."

HEXAGON HUNT (Week 8)

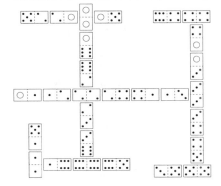

WORD EQUATIONS (Week 8)

1. tot + ally = totally; 2. brow + sing = browsing; 3. tar + get = target; 4. win + Dow = window; 5. pro + gram = program; 6. minis + try = ministry.

MISSING DOMINOES (Week 8)

COMPOUND IT (Week 9)

1. cook; 2. book; 3. store; 4. front; 5. line; 6. up; 7. hold; 8. over; 9. coat; 10. tail (cookbook, bookstore, storefront, frontline, lineup, uphold, holdover, overcoat, coattail).

WORD WHEEL (Week 9)

for, fore, ore, rebel, rebellion, bell, ell, lion, ion, one, ones, oneself, self, elf, elfin, fin, fine, fines, finesse, ess, sea, sear, search, ear, arc, arch, chaste, chasten, has, haste, hasten, ten, tend, end.

BULL'S EYE LETTER (Week 9)

The Bull's-Eye Letter is B: hobo, crab, curb, buck, oboe, tube.

WHIRLIGIG (Week 9)

1. bedroom; 2. because; 3. beneath; 4. between; 5. benefit; 6. beanbag; 7. beastly; 8. believe; 9. behaved; 10. betting; 11. beehive; 12. beatnik.

WHAT'S YOUR NUMBER? (Week 9)

3. The sum of the left and top numbers equals the sum of the middle and right numbers.

ANIMAL CHARADES (Week 9)

barracuda

COUNT ON IT! (Week 9)

Look before you leap.

WORD CHARADE (Week 9)

spigot

QUICK FILL (Week 9)

reciprocal

TARGET SHOOT (Week 9)

1. BB: dabble, bobbin, rabbit; 2. OL: evolve, cooler, frolic.

ALL IN A ROW (Week 9)

Row B. Row A contains four groups: 7261, 46312, 2932, and 781. Row B contains six groups: 367, 79, 1483, 54133, 41335, and 3571. Row C contains five groups: 52315, 277, 358, 691, and 538.

FILLING STATION (Week 9)

1. blackjack; 2. Spencer Tracy; 3. "American Idol"; 4. Venetian blinds; 5. Captain Ahab; 6. Thanksgiving.

STACKED UP (Week 9)

Boxes 2, 4, and 6.

MINUS ONE (Week 9)

1. A; 2. L; 3. I; 4. C; 5. E. The name is Alice.

WORD LINK (Week 10)

P	L	E	A	S	E	S			Z
	O		S	A	L	T	I	N	E
C	O	N	S	I	D	E	R		S
	K		E	L	E	M	E	N	T
J	I	L	T		R				Y
	N		S	A	L	A	R	Y	
E	G	G			Y		E		
D		R		A		F	E	A	T
G	R	E	E	N		O	G	R	E
E		W		T	H	R	O	N	E

HEXAGON HUNT (Week 10)

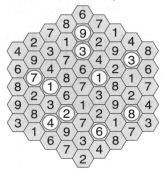

T COUNT (Week 10)
There are 31 T's.

SUDOKU (Week 10)

6	8	4	5	9	3	7	2	1
9	5	7	1	4	2	8	3	6
3	2	1	8	6	7	9	5	4
7	4	9	3	2	5	6	1	8
2	1	5	6	8	4	3	9	7
8	6	3	7	1	9	2	4	5
1	7	2	4	3	6	5	8	9
5	3	8	9	7	1	4	6	2
4	9	6	2	5	8	1	7	3

QUICK FILL (Week 10)
watermelon

ONLINE NETWORK (Week 10)
reveal, disclose, show; Jupiter, Neptune, Mars.

COUNT THE RECTANGLES (Week 10)
There are 14 rectangles: ABFE, ABJI, ACLI, ADMI, ADPN, BCLJ, BDMJ, CDHG, CDML, EFJI, GHML, IKON, IMPN, and KMPO.

ELIMINATION (Week 10)
1. light; 2. minute (minuet); 3. response (pon); 4. adoration (ado, ration); 5. irritates (sea); 6. tranquil, serene, calm, quiet; 7. factory (actor). New solutions may generate new problems.

ASSOCIATIONS (Week 10)
anaconda, python, rattlesnake; femur, tibia, ulna; bonbon, gumdrop, lollipop; depart, leave, go; Frankfurt, Munich, Berlin; pep, vitality, animation; cardinal, robin, sparrow; pants, slacks, trousers. A falsehood.

CODE WORD (Week 10
Code Word: abolishment. During middle age many people comment about how slim they used to be while others go on about how slim they're going to be.

COUNT TO TEN (Week 10)
1. row 4; 2. row 7; 3. row 8.

ALL IN A ROW (Week 10)
Row B. Row A contains five groups: 1152, 414, 12312, 126, and 45. Row B contains eight groups: 36, 171, 14211, 351, 1233, 72, 252, and 5211. Row C contains five groups: 81, 351, 13212, 342, and 423.

IN THE ABSTRACT (Week 11)

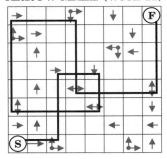

THE LINEUP (Week 11)
1. B; 2. rhododendron; 3. U; 4. kumquat; 5. three (foxy, jump, hill).

ARROW MAZE (Week 11)

ANIMAL CHARADES (Week 11)
herring

MAGNIFIND (Week 11)

CARD SENSE (Week 11)

By clue 2, the top and bottom cards are the three of hearts and the seven of diamonds, in some order. Since the bottom card isn't the seven of diamonds (clue 3), it is the three of hearts. By elimination, the top card is the seven of diamonds. By clue 1, the queen of spades and the queen of clubs are second and fourth from the top, in some order, so the ace of spades is third. The queen of clubs is fourth from the top (clue 3). By elimination, the queen of spades is second from the top. In summary, from top to bottom: seven of diamonds, queen of spades, ace of spades, queen of clubs, three of hearts.

ANAGRAM MAZE (Week 11)

1	2	3	4	5	
				11	
		15	16	17	
19	20	21			
25			28	29	30
31	32	33	34		36

The path through the maze, with just one anagram given for each, is: 1. mart; 2. file; 3. rage; 4. step; 5. rock; 11. arch; 17. lied; 16. icon; 15. vote; 21. trio; 20. sued; 19. drop; 25. rise; 31. cafe; 32. code; 33. bane; 34. fate; 28. chum; 29. ruby; 30. buds; 36. scar.

EASY PICKINGS (Week 11)

The biggest mammal is the whale.

SEVEN WORD ZINGER (Week 11)

any, dim, egg, end, one, vat, who.

FUN WITH FACTS AND FIGURES (Week 11)

1. $4 + 10 = 14$; 2. $14 - 6$ (Poland) $= 8$; 3. $8 \times 4 = 32$; 4. $32 \div 8 = 4$; 5. $4 + 6 = 10$.

GRAND TOUR (Week 11)

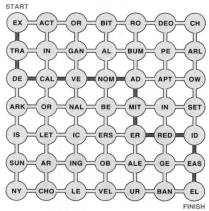

extra, trade, decal, calve, venom, nomad, admit, miter, erred, redid, ideas, easel.

COUNT ON IT! (Week 11)

A grudge is a heavy thing to carry.

FILLING STATION (Week 11)

1. anteater; 2. "Saturday Night Live"; 3. greeting card; 4. South Korea; 5. Clint Eastwood.

TARGET SHOOT (Week 11)

1. FF: guffaw, coffee, baffle; 2. GI: raging, edgier, legion.

COUNTDOWN (Week 12)

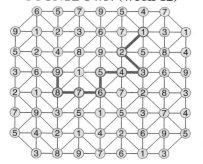

COMPOUND IT (Week 12)

1. needle; 2. work; 3. table; 4. top; 5. sail; 6. boat; 7. yard; 8. stick; 9. ball; 10. room (needlework, worktable, tabletop, topsail, sailboat, boatyard, yardstick, stickball, ballroom).

WHIRLIGIG (Week 12)

1. backboard; 2. backfield; 3. backpedal; 4. backstage; 5. backwards; 6. backwater; 7. backwoods; 8. backtrack; 9. backspace; 10. backslash; 11. backfired; 12. backdated.

BLOCK PARTY (Week 12)

LETTER, PLEASE (Week 12)

Good things come when you least expect them.

GOING IN CIRCLES (Week 12)

1. stumbled; 2. downtown.

MISSING DOMINOES (Week 12)

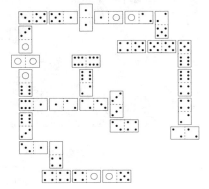

LICENSE PLATES (Week 12)

1. Barcelona, Spain; 2. Tokyo, Japan; 3. Paris, France; 4. Athens, Greece; 5. Sydney, Australia; 6. Beijing, China.

SUDOKU (Week 12)

7	4	2	5	1	9	3	8	6
9	6	8	2	7	3	5	1	4
1	3	5	4	6	8	7	2	9
4	1	7	3	5	6	2	9	8
5	2	6	8	9	4	1	3	7
3	8	9	1	2	7	4	6	5
8	9	3	7	4	1	6	5	2
2	7	1	6	8	5	9	4	3
6	5	4	9	3	2	8	7	1

MARCHING ORDERS (Week 12)

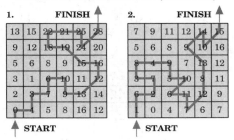

SYMBOL-ISM (Week 12)

We learn with our eyes and ears, and the mouth really has little to do with it.

ALPHABET SOUP (Week 12)

pig

CHANGELINGS (Week 12)

1. BAND, bond, bone, tone, TUNE.
2. BEAR, pear, peas, pews, PAWS.
3. MOSS, boss, bogs, begs, BEDS.
(Using the same number of changes, other answers may be possible.)

VISION QUEST (Week 13)

Row 4.

WHAT'S YOUR NUMBER? (Week 13)

37. The number in the top middle box is equal to the sum of the numbers in the other boxes.

RELATIONSHIPS QUIZ (Week 13)

1. a; 2. d; 3. a; 4. b; 5. c.

SQUARE LINKS (Week 13)

pacifier, blessing, slippers, gorgeous, porridge.

WORD VISIBILITY (Week 13)

1. sunny; 2. dodge; 3. youth; 4. camel; 5. faint; 6. peace.

OVERLAY (Week 13)

Diagram C.

ANTONYMS QUIZ (Week 13)

1. c; 2. a; 3. c; 4. a; 5. b; 6. a; 7. c; 8. a.

GOING IN CIRCLES (Week 13)

1. beginner; 2. airplane.

LOOSE TILE (Week 13)

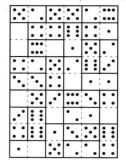

The 1-3 is the Loose Tile.

SKILLS TEST (Week 13)

1. gorilla; 2. giraffe; 3. cheetah; 4. rhinoceros; 5. wildebeest.

STATE LIMITS (Week 13)

1. Utah; 2. New York; 3. Vermont; 4. Connecticut; 5. Montana; 6. West Virginia; 7. California.

WAYWORDS (Week 13)

Good friends often love the same books.

TIPS OF THE ICEBERG (Week 13)

1. Dena ($12.80); 2. Al ($5.85); 3. Brenda and Charlie ($6.20).

KEEP ON MOVING (Week 14)

Move 2 squares left, 4 squares down, 2 squares left, 2 squares up, and 3 squares right to the asterisk.

DOVETAILED WORDS (Week 14)

1. calico, tabby; 2. fudge, sundae; 3. queen, royal; 4. skinny, plump; 5. romance, comedy.

CIRCLE SEARCH (Week 14)

copy, cost, hum, humid, mid, paid, pave, pyramid, ram, vest.

WORD CHARADE (Week 14)

Z	J	E	O	K	C	I	B
L	P	(F)	R	M	O	V	H
(D)	H	B	V	L	R	S	(D)
C	Q	G	J	E	N	P	O
N	J	Y	V	C	(F)	H	Q
L	H	(G)	I	K	I	(Y)	M
P	(F)	N	O	Z	E	C	R
I	V	(A)	M	Y	D	S	G

gadfly

MISSING LINKS (Week 14)

M	A	C	H	I	N	E		B	R	A	C	K	E	T	
A		E				B		O		R		M			
J	E	A	L	O	U	S		S		O		O	F	F	E	R
O			I				O	B	S	T	R	U	C	T		L	E
R	E	F	U	S	A	L			C			I		O		N
C		M				E	I	G	H	T	H			W	E	D
S		M			M			O			E				
T	U	R	B	A	N		O		G				J	A	R
A			A		A		W		A		L	A	Z	Y		R	A	V	E	N
T			R				E				E			E
I		S	K	I	P			E			E		N		E
E	C	H	O			A			B				N		C
G		L		D	E	V	I	O	U	S			I	N	K
G	R	A	I	N		D		M		E		L	
		T		L		M		U		Q	U	E	E	N
P	A	R	A	K	E	E	T		U		U			A
E		R			A		N			E			I
A	W	A	Y		A	X	L	E		L	A	P	E	L

WORD WHEEL (Week 14)

asp, spa, spar, spare, par, pare, parent, are, rent, tin, tinny, inn, nymph, phase, has, self, selfish, elf, elfish, fish, shall, shallot, hall, all, allot, lot, other, the, there, her, here.

QUICK FILL (Day 23)

partiality

SUDOKU (Week 14)

2	5	1	8	9	6	7	3	4
6	4	8	3	7	1	5	2	9
7	3	9	2	4	5	8	6	1
4	9	3	5	6	2	1	7	8
8	2	7	9	1	4	6	5	3
1	6	5	7	8	3	9	4	2
3	8	4	6	5	9	2	1	7
9	1	6	4	2	7	3	8	5
5	7	2	1	3	8	4	9	6

CODED PRESIDENTS (Week 14)

1. George Bush; 2. James Monroe; 3. Woodrow Wilson; 4. Grover Cleveland; 5. Zachary Taylor; 6. Jimmy Carter; 7. William McKinley; 8. Franklin Pierce; 9. Benjamin Harrison; 10. John Tyler.

CIRCLE MATH (Week 14)

A = 6, B = 7, C = 3, D = 4, E = 2, F = 8, G = 5, H = 9, and I = 1.

ASSOCIATIONS (Week 14)

operate, run, work; rotate, turn, revolve; ointment, balm, salve; Mediterranean, Caspian, Baltic; physics, biology, chemistry; population, residents, community; scarlet, crimson, rose; spoon, knife, fork. Feats of clay.

WAYWORDS (Week 14)

It is easy to bear another person's sorrow.

CARD SENSE (Week 14)

The top card is not the nine or king of hearts (clue 1), four of spades (clue 2), or seven of clubs (clue 3); it is the four of diamonds. The nine of hearts is somewhere above the seven of clubs (clue 3), which is somewhere above the four of spades (clue 2). By clue 4, a red card is between the seven of clubs and the four of spades, so the nine of hearts is second from the top, the seven of clubs is third, the king of hearts is fourth, and the four of spades is fifth. In summary from top to bottom: four of diamonds, nine of hearts, seven of clubs, king of hearts, four of spades.

GRAND TOUR (Week 15)

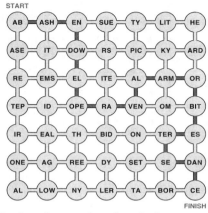

abash, ashen, endow, dowel, elope, opera, raven, venal, alarm, armor, orbit, bites, ester, terse, sedan, dance.

ALL IN A ROW (Week 15)

Row A. Row A contains seven groups: 7112, 43121, 1631, 6311, 119, 3251, and 5141. Row B contains four groups: 38, 812, 56, and 3143. Row C contains five groups: 74, 128, 722, 263, and 4151.

STAR WORDS (Week 15)

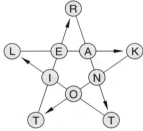

Your sequence of words may begin in any outer circle.

HEXAGON HUNT (Week 15)

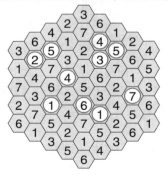

377

ROUND TRIP (Week 15)

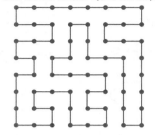

TRI, TRI AGAIN (Week 15)

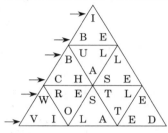

WORD EQUATIONS (Week 15)

1. car + pet = carpet; 2. inn + ate = innate; 3. par + snip = parsnip; 4. sat + ire = satire; 5. con + test = contest.

RING LOGIC (Week 15)

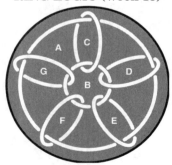

STACKED UP (Week 15)
Boxes 1, 3, and 4.

SWITCHEROO (Week 15)
1. c; 2. a; 3. b; 4. d; 5. d; 6. c.

SUDOKU (Week 15)

3	8	2	5	7	4	6	9	1
6	9	4	3	1	8	7	2	5
7	5	1	6	2	9	3	4	8
2	4	9	1	5	3	8	6	7
5	1	6	4	8	7	2	3	9
8	3	7	9	6	2	5	1	4
4	7	8	2	3	1	9	5	6
1	6	3	7	9	5	4	8	2
9	2	5	8	4	6	1	7	3

SLIDE RULE (Week 15)
bar, bat, bay, boo, boy, but, buy, far, fat, foe, for, fro, fry, fur, oar, oat, ore, our, out, par, pat, pay, pot, pro, pry, put, war, way, who, why, woe, woo, wry.

IN THE ABSTRACT (Week 16)

NEXT TO NOTHING (Week 16)
Charles

MAGIC NUMBER SQUARES (Week 16)

1.

18	6	13	9
17	5	14	10
7	19	8	12
4	16	11	15

2.

10	11	13	16
14	15	9	12
7	6	20	17
19	18	8	5

SKILLS TEST (Week 16)
1. happen, pencil; 2. become, omelet; 3. orchid, hidden; 4. honest, esteem; 5. attend, endure; 6. bother, hermit.

TARGET SHOOT (Week 16)
1. AV: heaven, flavor, travel; 2. PT: depths, tiptoe, captor.

COUNT THE TRIANGLES
(Week 16)
There are 20 triangles: ABC, ADE, AGH, AKL, BDF, BGI, BKM, CEF, CHI, CLM, DGJ, DKN, EHJ, ELN, FIJ, FMN, GKO, HLO, IMO, and JNO.

CIRCLE MATH (Week 16)
A = 9, B = 4, C = 2, D = 6, E = 5, F = 7, G = 1, H = 3, and I = 8.

CROSS-UPS (Week 16)
1. freshwater; 2. cobblestone.

ELIMINATION (Week 16)
1. uncomplimentary; 2. "Carousel"; 3. links (lynx); 4. trudge, planks; 5. mote (mate, mete, mite, mute); 6. minimizing; 7. heart (earth). Live your life and let others live theirs.

ARROW MAZE (Week 16)

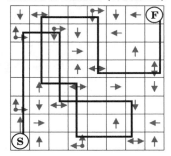

BLOCK PARTY (Week 16)

FUN WITH FACTS AND FIGURES
(Week 16)
1. 6 x 6 = 36; 2. 36 + 30 = 66; 3. 66 ÷ 6 = 11; 4. 11 − 2 = 9; 5. 9 x 10 = 90.

DOVETAILED WORDS (Week 17)
1. juice, orange; 2. nurse, medic; 3. station, depot; 4. wrist, elbow; 5. stove, range.

FILLING STATION (Week 16)
1. New Delhi; 2. Pablo Picasso; 3. "Dirty Harry"; 4. Huckleberry Finn; 5. Aretha Franklin.

WORD HUNT (Week 17)
4-letter words: chop, coop, crop, drop, flop, glop, hoop, loop, prop, shop, slop, stop; **5-letter words:** droop, scoop, sloop, snoop, stoop, swoop, troop; **6-letter words:** bishop, carhop, dollop, gallop, laptop, tiptop, unstop.

WHAT'S YOUR NUMBER?
(Week 16)
40. The number inside the triangle is equal to two times the sum of the top two numbers divided by the bottom number.

VISION QUEST (Week 17)
Column C.

WORD WHEEL (Week 17)

grin, grind, grinds, grindstone, rind, rinds, stone, ton, tone, one, new, newest, ewe, ewes, west, star, start, tar, tart, art, artful, artfully, full, fully, lye, yea, year, yearbook, ear, boo, book, booklet, let.

ANAGRAM MAZE (Week 17)

		3	4	5	6
					12
13	14	15	16		18
19			22	23	24
25	26				
	32	33	34		

The path through the maze, with just one anagram given for each, is: 3. east; 4. abut; 5. came; 6. thaw; 12. tied; 18. does; 24. fete; 23. slit; 22. sewn; 16. went; 15. stun; 14. prod; 13. cola; 19. pier; 25. nave; 26. keen; 32. fats; 33. hear; 34. coat.

SKILLS TEST (Week 17)

N, because an alphabetic sequence spirals counterclockwise into the center of the diagram.

CARD SENSE (Week 17)

The bottom card isn't the king of diamonds (clue 1), four of hearts (clue 2), or seven of clubs (clue 3), so it's one of the two threes. By clue 2, one three is somewhere above the four of hearts and one three is somewhere below it. Since no two adjacent cards are the same suit (clue 4), the three of hearts and four of hearts are not adjacent, in either order, and the three of clubs and seven of clubs are not adjacent, in either order. The seven is somewhere above the king (clue 3). Since the king isn't above a heart (clue 1), it's below the four of hearts. The bottom card, then, is the three of clubs, and the king of diamonds is the fourth card. By elimination, the four of hearts is the third card, the seven of clubs the second, and the three of hearts is the first card. In summary from top to bottom: three of hearts, seven of clubs, four of hearts, king of diamonds, and three of clubs.

BULL'S-EYE LETTER (Week 17)

The Bull's-Eye Letter is A: ahoy, plan, okra, anti, jazz, waxy.

CIRCLE SEARCH (Week 17)

chalet, chat, mat, match, meal, meat, much, mud, rich, rid, rim.

MAGNIFIND (Week 17)

STACKED UP (Week 17)

Boxes 4, 5, and 6.

SLIDE RULE (Week 17)

aced, acne, acre, aped, aunt, bead, bean, beat, been, beet, bend, bent, bunt, burn, read, reed, rend, rent, rued, rune, runt, scan, scat, seat, seed, seen, send, sent, span, spat, sped, sued, suet, sure.

CODE WORD (Week 17)

Code Word: righteously. Although everyone in a small town knows what everyone else is doing, they still have to read the newspaper to find out who's been caught at it.

SQUARE LINKS (Week 17)

flamingo, nonsense, assemble, backbone, wardrobe.

WORD CHARADE (Week 18)

violet

ALL IN A ROW (Week 18)

Row C. Row A contains five groups: 616, 8212, 481, 8131, and 652. Row B contains four groups: 931, 21451, 94, and 742. Row C contains six groups: 9211, 3451, 517, 76, 43213, and 364.

MISSING DOMINOES (Week 18)

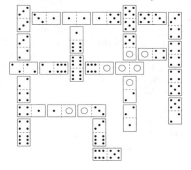

COMPOUND IT (Week 18)

1. dish; 2. pan; 3. handle; 4. bar; 5. tender; 6. foot; 7. note; 8. book; 9. shop; 10. worn (dishpan, panhandle, handlebar, bartender, tenderfoot, footnote, notebook, bookshop, shopworn).

ANIMAL CHARADES (Week 18)

nighthawk

ROUND TRIP (Week 18)

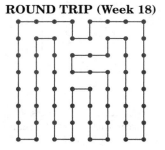

SEVEN WORD ZINGER (Week 18)

art, duo, emu, eve, gut, ply, sea.

IN THE ABSTRACT (Week 18)

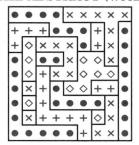

DEDUCTION PROBLEM (Week 18)

None of the buttons dispenses according to its label, so, from Ellen's experience, we know that the creamer button dispenses sugar and the sugar button, creamer. From Mary's experience, it's the tea button that dispenses coffee, while from Mike's experience, it's the cocoa button that dispenses tea. By elimination, the coffee button dispenses cocoa. In summary:

present labeling	correct labeling
cocoa	tea
coffee	cocoa
tea	coffee
creamer	sugar
sugar	creamer

LOOSE TILE (Week 18)

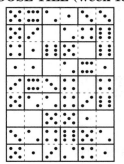

The 0-4 is the Loose Tile.

COUNT ON IT! (Week 18)

Make a friend when you don't need one.

ARROW MAZE (Week 18)

QUICK FILL (Week 18)
roundabout

SUDOKU (Week 19)

5	6	4	3	7	8	1	2	9
2	3	1	9	6	4	8	5	7
7	8	9	5	2	1	4	6	3
4	2	7	8	1	3	5	9	6
8	9	5	6	4	2	3	7	1
3	1	6	7	5	9	2	8	4
1	5	2	4	9	6	7	3	8
6	7	8	1	3	5	9	4	2
9	4	3	2	8	7	6	1	5

ALL IN A ROW (Week 19)
Row A. Row A contains six groups: 18, 315, 522, 414, 432, and 36. Row B contains four groups: 54, 216, 432, and 3213. Row C contains five groups: 1431, 351, 126, 63, and 4122.

ONLINE NETWORK (Week 19)
fight, battle, struggle; cobra, moccasin, python.

COUNT TO TEN (Week 19)
1. row 8; 2. row 5; 3. row 7.

EASY PICKINGS (Week 19)
Make sure to laugh at least once a day.

ANIMAL CHARADES (Week 19)
pigeon

CODE WORD (Week 19)
Code Word: tambourines. Memory is often unfair: The beauty of a rose fades in time, but the sting of the thorn remains.

ANAGRAM MAZE (Week 19)

The path through the maze, with just one anagram given for each, is: 6. snow; 12. went; 11. stun; 10. fats; 4. nave; 3. pier; 2. raid; 1. hare; 7. came; 13. thaw; 14. prod; 15. chum; 21. lyre; 22. pace; 23. spar; 29. tied; 35. cola; 34. keen; 33. sewn; 32. dose; 31. scar.

WHAT'S YOUR NUMBER? (Week 19)
7. The sum of the numbers in the circles divided by the number in the square equals the number in the diamond.

IN THE ABSTRACT (Week 19)

THE LINEUP (Week 19)
1. H; 2. arrogant; 3. N; 4. receiving; 5. three (skip, mind, flew).

ELIMINATION (Week 19)

1. rogue, gorgeous, growth, organize; 2. liver, pool (Liverpool); 3. time, tide, for, man (time and tide wait for no man); 4. quick (quicksand, quicksilver, quick-witted); 5. twelfth; 6. soul (Seoul); 7. carbon, footprint (carbon footprint). One thing we never run out of is surprise.

GOING IN CIRCLES (Week 19)

1. mountain; 2. explicit.

WORD VISIBILITY (Week 20)

1. shark; 2. often; 3. renew; 4. furor; 5. graph; 6.chill.

CARD SENSE (Week 20)

The two black cards are not adjacent (clue 1) but the three red cards are adjacent (clue 2), so the top and bottom cards are the three of clubs and the five of spades in some order. The five of spades isn't the top card (clue 3), so it is the bottom card and the three of clubs is on top. Since the diamonds are not adjacent (clue 4), the king of hearts is the third card and the three of diamonds and ten of diamonds are second and fourth in some order. The three of diamonds isn't second from the top (clue 5); it is fourth and the ten of diamonds is second. In summary, from top to bottom: three of clubs, ten of diamonds, king of hearts, three of diamonds, five of spades.

HEXAGON HUNT (Week 20)

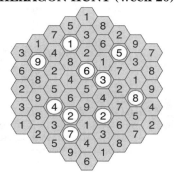

COMPOUND IT (Week 20)

1. fellow; 2. ship; 3. board; 4. walk; 5. out; 6. line; 7. man; 8. handle; 9. bar; 10. maid (fellowship, shipboard, boardwalk, walkout, outline, lineman, manhandle, handlebar, barmaid).

GRAND TOUR (Week 20)

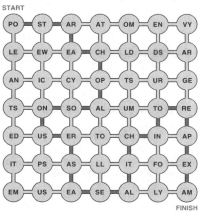

post, star, area, each, chop, opal, also, soon, onus, user, eras, asea, ease, seal, alit, itch, chin, into, tore, reap, apex, exam.

V COUNT (Week 20)

There are 20 V's.

LOOSE TILE (Week 20)

The 1-2 is the Loose Tile.

CIRCLE SEARCH (Week 20)

and, cost, counsel, cove, land, lave, rend, rest, reveal, revere, reverend, severe, veal.

SEVEN WORD ZINGER (Week 20)

coy, ear, fly, ire, now, nun, pry.

FUN WITH FACTS AND FIGURES (Week 20)

1. 8 x 11 = 88; 2. 88 + 5 (India) = 93 ; 3. 93 ÷ 3 = 31; 4. 31 − 8 = 23; 5. 23 + 3 = 26.

LICENSE PLATES (Week 20)

1. Jane Austen; 2. Charles Dickens; 3. Mary Shelley; 4. Emily Brontë; 5. Bram Stoker; 6. George Eliot.

ANTONYMS QUIZ (Week 20)
1. b; 2. a; 3. b; 4. c; 5. c; 6. b; 7. a; 8. b.

ALPHABET SOUP (Week 20)
Rome

CHANGELINGS (Week 20)
1. HANG, pang, pans, mans, MAPS; 2. TOWN, torn, tore, tote, VOTE; 3. POTS, pats, hats, hams, YAMS.
(Using the same number of changes, other answers may be possible.)

CROSS EXAMINATION (Week 21)
1. bachelor; 2. electrocute; 3. tachometer; 4. leprechaun; 5. receptacle; 6. accelerate; 7. deplorable; 8. pesticide.

SLIDE RULE (Week 21)
jab, jam, jar, jet, jib, job, jot, jut, lab, lad, led, let, lid, lit, lob, lot, mad, mar, mat, met, mob, mod, mom, mud, mum, ram, rat, red, rib, rid, rim, rob, rod, rot, rub, rum, rut, vat, vet, vim.

FILLING STATION (Week 21)
1. Humphrey Bogart; 2. New York, New York; 3. "The Petrified Forest"; 4. "High Sierra"; 5. "Casablanca".

SQUARE LINKS (Week 21)
handyman, abundant, tentacle, lavender, dedicate.

MISSING DOMINOES (Week 21)

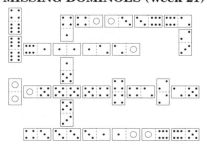

384

BULL'S-EYE LETTER (Week 21)
The Bull's-Eye Letter is L: loon, club, jilt, bawl, ably, flab.

LETTER, PLEASE (Week 21)
Any recipe for success begins with ambition.

SUDOKU (Week 21)

2	1	7	4	5	9	6	3	8
3	4	9	8	6	1	5	2	7
8	5	6	2	7	3	4	1	9
7	3	1	9	4	5	8	6	2
9	6	2	3	8	7	1	4	5
4	8	5	6	1	2	9	7	3
5	2	3	1	9	6	7	8	4
1	7	8	5	3	4	2	9	6
6	9	4	7	2	8	3	5	1

KEEP ON MOVING (Week 21)
Move 3 squares down, 5 squares up, 2 squares left, 2 squares down, 3 squares right, and 1 square down to the asterisk.

WORD HUNT (Week 21)
4-letter words: bulb, bulk, bull, bunk, bunt, burn, burp, bury, bush, bust;
5-letter words: bugle, bulge, bulky, bully, bunch, bunny, burnt, burro, burst.

OVERLAY (Week 21)
Diagram C

SYMBOL-ISM (Week 21)
The most enjoyable moments in your life will be those when you can look back and feel the job was truly well done.

ASSOCIATIONS (Week 21)
chicken, goose, duck; hard, difficult, challenging; Egypt, Libya, Sudan; flea, mosquito, gnat; blond, redhead, brunette; bun, muffin, roll; gold, bronze, silver; dawdle, linger, tarry. On wick-ends.

WAYWORDS (Week 22)
Live your beliefs, but don't push them on others.

COUNT THE RECTANGLES (Week 22)
There are 16 rectangles that contain the circle: ACKI, ACOM, ADLI, ADPM, BCKJ, BCON, BDLJ, BDPN, EGKI, EGOM, EHLI, EHPM, FGKJ, FGON, FHLJ, FHPN.

COUNT ON IT! (Week 22)
Better to dare great things than dare nothing.

RINGERS (Week 22)
1. glaze, forum, avoid, recap; 2. torso, mince, weigh, envoy.

TIPS OF THE ICEBERG (Week 22)
1. Marty ($7.50); 2. Hank ($5.80); 3. Inez and Noel ($7.10).

COUNTDOWN (Week 22)

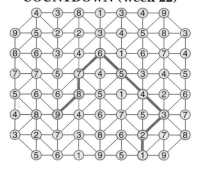

TRI, TRI AGAIN (Week 22)

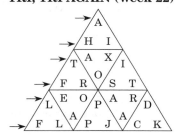

RELATIONSHIPS QUIZ (Week 22)
1. c; 2. a; 3. d; 4. a; 5. b.

MARCHING ORDERS (Week 22)

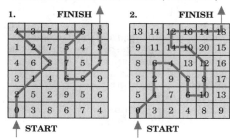

MISSING LINKS (Week 22)

D	R	I	V	E	R		L	U	M	B	E	R	J	A	C	K
O				E			O		E		A		M			I
C			A	C	C	O	U	N	T	A	N	T		I	N	N
U		C		O			D		R		T		A			D
M	O	R	E	O	V	E	R		H	A	D		L	A	B	E	L
E		E		E			I		E			L		Y		
N		A		R		D	I	S	T	R	U	S	T	E	D	
T	O	T	A	L		I		T		N		I			
		I			E	B	O	N	Y		A		S		
		O	B	J	E	C	T		R		S	K	E	T	C	H
C		N		U			I		R							O
O			S	P	I	N	A	C	H							N
M			T		A		O			S						O
P	E	N	C	I	L		R		L		S	H	O	W	E	R
L		Y		F		R	E	L	I	C		O		I		
A	L	L	E	Y		A		D		V		D		A	B	
I		O			T	U	B	A		E		O	I	L		
N	I	N	E	T	Y		E		Y	E	L	L	O	W	E	

WORD WHEEL (Week 22)
locate, locater, cat, cater, caterpillar, ate, pill, pillar, ill, lark, larks, larkspur, ark, arks, spur, urban, urbane, ban, bane, anew, new, newer, ewe, ewer, err, erratic, rat, tic, icon, con.

STACKED UP (Week 22)
Boxes 2, 4, and 5.

GETTING IN SHAPE (Week 23)
Boxes 3 and 5.

DEDUCTION PROBLEM (Week 23)

The fifth paint was not beige, tan, or white (clue 1) or gray (clue 3), so brown was used fifth. By clue 2, the porch was painted first and the bathroom was painted brown. Since the fourth paint was not beige or tan (clue 1) or gray (clue 3), it was white. By clue 1, the beige paint was second and the tan paint was third. By elimination, the porch was painted gray. The kitchen was painted beige and the den was painted tan (clue 3). By elimination, the living room was painted white, fourth. In summary:

bathroom, brown, fifth
den, tan, third
kitchen, beige, second
living room, white, fourth
porch, gray, first

ARROW MAZE (Week 23)

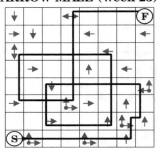

MAGIC NUMBER SQUARE (Week 23)

10	21	17	22
24	15	19	12
23	16	20	11
13	18	14	25

ANAGRAM MAZE (Week 23)

1	2		4	5	6
	8		10		12
13	14		16		18
19		21	22		24
25	26	27			30
					36

The path through the maze, with just one anagram given for each, is: 1. bard; 2. rock; 8. lain; 14. flue; 13. blow; 19 lied; 25. life; 26. sage; 27. hose; 21. arch; 22. toga; 16. huts; 10. slat; 4. dawn; 5. vast; 6. abet; 12. flit; 18. bran; 24. laps; 30. same; 36. moor.

BLOCK PARTY (Week 23)

CIRCLE MATH (Week 23)

A = 4, B = 5, C = 2, D = 1, E = 6, F = 7, G = 3, H = 9, and I = 8.

STATE LIMITS (Week 23)

1. Colorado; 2. New Jersey; 3. Hawaii; 4. Michigan; 5. Kentucky; 6. Tennessee; 7. Maryland.

RING LOGIC (Week 23)

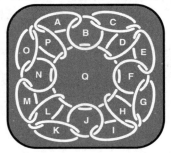

WHAT'S YOUR NUMBER? (Week 23)

25. The difference between the upper-left and lower-right numbers times the difference between the upper-right and lower-left numbers is equal to the middle square.

CIRCLE SEARCH (Week 23)

also, code, core, deal, decode, duet, encode, encore, endure, meet, mere, real, recode, some.

CROSS-UPS (Week 23)

1. waistband; 2. formalwear; 3. matchstick; 4. schoolchild.

WORD CHARADE (Week 23)

unfold

CALL TO ORDER (Week 23)

6, 2, 8, 5, 4, 1, 7, 3.

GETTING IN SHAPE (Week 24)

Boxes 1 and 6.

STACKED UP (Week 24)

Boxes 1, 4, and 6.

ROUND TRIP (Week 24)

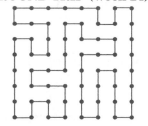

WORD HUNT (Week 24)

boxed, boxer, exact, exalt, excel, exert, exile, exist, exits, expel, extol, extra, exude, index, latex, maxim, relax, sixth, sixty, toxic, toxin.

IN THE ABSTRACT (Week 24)

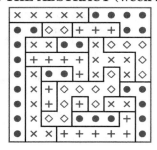

NEXT TO NOTHING (Week 24)

panther

ALPHABET CIRCLE MAZE (Week 24)

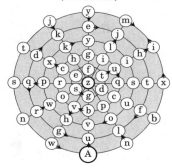

DOVETAILED WORDS (Week 24)

1. paste, adhesive; 2. baton, twirl; 3. doctor, nurse; 4. attic, cellar; 5. jonquil, lilac.

COUNTDOWN (Week 24)

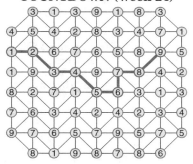

CODE WORD (Week 24)

Code Word: chlorinated. Most lies are uttered with an earnest look and a sincere tone of voice, while truths are often told with a casual shrug and a dismissive laugh.

GOING IN CIRCLES (Week 24)

1. powerful; 2. humorous.

ANIMAL CHARADES (Week 24)

antelope

MAGNIFIND (Week 25)

HEXAGON HUNT (Week 25)

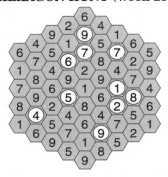

VISION QUEST (Week 25)
Row 2

WORD WHEEL (Week 25)
helm, elm, mite, miter, terror, err, error, orang, orange, ran, rang, range, ranger, anger, germ, germane, man, mane, anew, new, newel, ewe, well, ell, lad, lade, laden, ade, den, dent, entry, try, rye.

COUNT ON IT! (Week 25)
You are truly happy if you don't know why.

WHIRLIGIG (Week 25)
1. outraged; 2. outfield; 3. outburst; 4. outlying; 5. outshine; 6. outdoors; 7. outbreak; 8. outgrown; 9. outclass; 10. outboard; 11. outlines; 12. outright.

SLIDE RULE (Week 25)
fair, flap, flaw, flip, flop, flow, from, glop, glow, glum, gram, grim, grip, grow, pair, plop, plow, plum, pram, prim, prom, prop, prow, wham, whim, whip, whir, whom, wrap.

ASSOCIATIONS (Week 25)
grapefruit, lemon, orange; hot, torrid, sweltering; Manitoba, Ontario, Quebec; lance, spear, harpoon; petroleum, gas, oil; lunch, dinner, breakfast; mule, donkey, burro; plunge, dive, drop. Nothing, it just waved.

QUOTATION MARKS (Week 25)
"The Scarlet Letter" by Nathaniel Hawthorne is considered the first Great American Novel, followed by "Moby-Dick" and "The Adventures of Huckleberry Finn."

SQUARE LINKS (Week 25)
eggplant, argument, attorney, accurate, artistic.

OVERLAY (Week 25)
Diagram A.

QUICK FILL (Week 25)
cultivated

DEDUCTION PROBLEM (Week 25)
By clue 1, the one who ordered pepperoni fourth did not get peppers. The friend who requested pepperoni fourth did not get mushrooms (clue 2) or spinach (clue 3), so that person got onions. By clue 4, Nathan ordered second. Mushrooms were ordered third and Marsha got onions and pepperoni (clue 2). Since two people requested pepperoni and one of them requested peppers (clue 1), the person who got mushrooms asked for sausage. By clue 3, William got pepperoni on his slice first. By elimination, Raquel got mushrooms and sausage and Nathan asked for sausage. William got peppers (clue 1). By elimination, Nathan requested spinach. In summary:
Marsha, onions, pepperoni, fourth
Nathan, spinach, sausage, second
Raquel, mushrooms, sausage, third
William, peppers, pepperoni, first

CARD SENSE (Week 26)

The bottom card isn't the five of hearts (clue 1), the six of diamonds (clue 2), the eight of clubs (clue 3), or the ten of clubs (clue 4), so it is the four of spades. The top card isn't the six of diamonds (clue 1), the eight of clubs (clue 3), or the ten of clubs (clue 4); it is the five of hearts. Since the clubs aren't adjacent (clue 5), the eight of clubs and the ten of clubs are second and fourth from the top in some order. By elimination, the six of diamonds is in the third position. The ten of clubs is second (clue 4) and the eight of clubs is fourth. In summary, from top to bottom: five of hearts, ten of clubs, six of diamonds, eight of clubs, four of spades.

FUN WITH FACTS AND FIGURES (Week 26)

1. $2014 - 2000 = 14$; 2. $14 \times 6 = 84$; 3. $84 - 32 = 52$; 4. $52 \div 13 = 4$; 5. $4 + 1 = 5$ (who, what, where, when, why).

GRAND TOUR (Week 26)

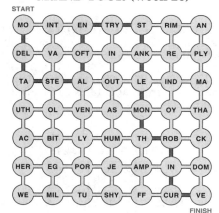

model, delta, taste, steal, aloft, often, entry, tryst, stank, ankle, lemon, month, throb, robin, incur, curve.

COMPOUND IT (Week 26)

1. corner; 2. stone; 3. wall; 4. flower; 5. pot; 6. shot; 7. gun; 8. boat; 9. yard; 10. work (cornerstone, stonewall, wallflower, flowerpot, potshot, shotgun, gunboat, boatyard, yardwork).

ANAGRAM MAZE (Week 26)

1	2	3	4	5	
7					
13		15	16	17	18
19	20	21			24
			28	29	30
	32	33	34		

The path through the maze, with just one anagram given for each, is: 5. gape; 4. star; 3. dues; 2. lone; 1. veto; 7. ante; 13. stab; 19. orbs; 20. egos; 21. wake; 15. ring; 16. dial; 17. rule; 18. diva; 24. meet; 30. mean; 29. maid; 28. ruby; 34. apes; 33. irks; 32. flea.

WAYWORDS (Week 26)

Where the light glows brightest, the shadows are darkest.

CROSS EXAMINATION (Week 26)

1. incorporate; 2. controversial; 3. accommodate; 4. infinitive; 5. petroleum; 6. expedition; 7. perpetual; 8. rhododendron.

BULL'S-EYE LETTER (Week 26)

The Bull's-Eye Letter is N: nick, envy, junk, born, lawn, numb.

WORD LINK (Week 26)

P	E	S	T	E	R		P	E	T
A	L	L			O	T	H	E	R
S	M	I	L	E	D		A	L	E
T		G		E		S			N
E	T	H	E	R		H	E	L	D
S	A	T		E		A		A	
	M			S		R	O	B	E
	P	O	L	I	T	E		E	
	E			S	I	M	P	L	E
C	R	E	A	T	E				

389

ELIMINATION (Week 26)

1. mine, oath, vain (Hanoi, Vietnam); 2. staring (starling); 3. inlet, gulf, lagoon, creek; 4. taxi, cheers, friends, lost; 5. white, oval, house, office (White House, Oval Office); 6. presort (rose); 7. money, doesn't, grow, on, trees (money doesn't grow on trees). Never worry about action, only inaction.

BLOCK PARTY (Week 26)

MISSING DOMINOES (Week 26)

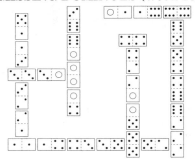

TARGET SHOOT (Week 27)

1. HO: behold, school, cohort; 2. US: trusty, cousin, amused.

IN THE ABSTRACT (Week 27)

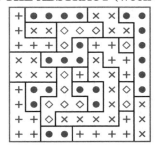

LOOSE TILE (Week 27)

The 2-3 is the Loose Tile.

SEVEN WORD ZINGER (Week 27)

ado, all, dig, eel, hum, icy, sew.

FILLING STATION (Week 27)

1. Steven Spielberg; 2. "Close Encounters of the Third Kind"; 3. "Indiana Jones and the Temple of Doom"; 4. "The Color Purple"; 5. "Jurassic Park"

ALL IN A ROW (Week 27)

Row B. Row A contains six groups: 5553, 369, 333333, 3339, 99, and 981. Row B contains eight groups: 495, 5913, 21555, 5517, 51732, 17325, 594, and 3384. Row C contains four groups: 13815, 1566, 9621, and 621234.

SUDOKU (Week 27)

8	4	5	2	7	1	6	3	9
2	7	6	5	9	3	4	8	1
3	1	9	6	4	8	7	5	2
4	6	3	1	5	7	9	2	8
5	2	8	9	6	4	3	1	7
7	9	1	3	8	2	5	6	4
1	5	4	8	3	9	2	7	6
9	3	2	7	1	6	8	4	5
6	8	7	4	2	5	1	9	3

EASY PICKINGS (Week 27)

If you believe everything you read, you had better not read.

MAGNIFIND (Week 27)

SUDOKU (Week 27)

5	8	4	2	6	9	7	3	1
3	1	6	7	8	4	5	2	9
7	9	2	5	3	1	6	8	4
9	2	7	4	1	6	3	5	8
1	6	5	8	2	3	4	9	7
4	3	8	9	7	5	1	6	2
8	5	3	1	9	7	2	4	6
6	7	9	3	4	2	8	1	5
2	4	1	6	5	8	9	7	3

VISION QUEST (Week 27)
Column E.

ALL IN A ROW (Week 27)
Row A. Row A contains five groups: 351, 2142, 261, 18, and 5121. Row B contains three groups: 45, 27, and 3213. Row C contains four groups: 4131, 3123, 252, and 36.

IN THE ABSTRACT (Week 27)

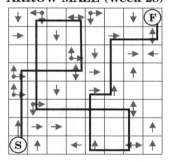

ALPHABET SOUP (Week 27)
boa

TIPS OF THE ICEBERG (Week 28)
1. Flora ($8.80); 2. Greta ($5.60); 3. Al and Charlie ($5.80).

GRAND TOUR (Week 28)

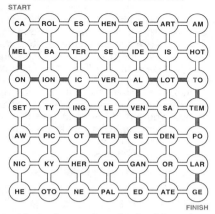

camel, melon, onion, ionic, icing, ingot, otter, terse, seven, venal, allot, lotto, totem, tempo, polar, large.

EASY PICKINGS (Week 28)
Abraham Lincoln was the sixteenth President.

ARROW MAZE (Week 28)

WORD HUNT (Week 28)
jade, jail, jamb, jazz, jean, jeer, jerk, jest, jets, jilt, jinx, join, joke, jolt, judo, junk, jury.

SEVEN WORD ZINGER (Week 28)
egg, fox, hut, ion, rye, sea, sin.

QUICK FILL (Week 28)
woodpecker

391

CARD SENSE (Week 28)

By clue 4, the eight of hearts is not on top. Since the eight of hearts is above both tens (clue 3) and the queen of diamonds and ten of diamonds are adjacent (clue 1), the eight of hearts is second from the top. The king of clubs, then, is on top. The queen of diamonds is between the ten of diamonds and the ten of spades (clue 2), so it is fourth. By clue 5, the ten of spades is not fifth; it is third and the ten of diamonds is fifth. In summary from top to bottom: king of clubs, eight of hearts, ten of spades, queen of diamonds, ten of diamonds.

COUNT ON IT! (Week 28)

Hunger is the best cook.

HEXAGON HUNT (Week 28)

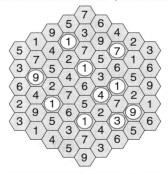

SYMBOL-ISM (Week 28)

Conscience is much like a pencil; it must be sharpened in order to be useful.

COUNT TO TEN (Week 28)

1. row 6; 2. row 10; 3. row 7.

CODE WORD (Week 28)

Code Word: switchboard. With a snorkel and mask, we can watch rainbow-colored fish swimming among brilliant coral reefs.

LOOSE TILE (Week 29)

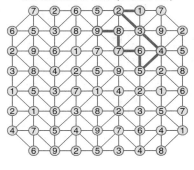

The 1-6 is the Loose Tile.

COMPOUND IT (Week 29)

1. pony; 2. tail; 3. spin; 4. out; 5. law; 6. suit; 7. case; 8. work; 9. book; 10. stall (ponytail, tailspin, spinout, outlaw, lawsuit, suitcase, casework, workbook, bookstall).

ONLINE NETWORK (Week 29)

eccentric, odd, strange; lemon, lime, grapefruit.

COUNTDOWN (Week 29)

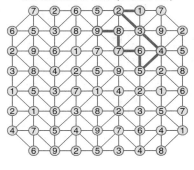

WORD EQUATIONS (Week 29)

1. pro + file = profile; 2. bet + ray = betray; 3. mess + age = message; 4. sect + ion = section; 5. deter + mine = determine.

CIRCLE SEARCH (Week 29)

adhere, advance, bead, beat, bet, head, heat, here, reheat, van, vat.

ELIMINATION (Week 29)

1. cut, sighted, circuit (shortcut, short-sighted, short circuit); 2. whole (wholly), gentle (gently), due (duly); 3. building, fireplace, oven; 4. can, of, worms (can of worms); 5. curriculum (curriculums, curricula), appendix (appendixes, appendices); 6. harm, tray, run (Harry Truman); 7. sweet, peanut, drawn (sweet butter, peanut butter, drawn butter). Facts do not cease to exist when ignored.

WORD CHARADE (Week 29)

```
M (T) P (E) J  F  X  A
J (E) U  Y  I  C  R  G
L  X  R  W  D  O  U  P
S (C) V (C) M (E)(J)(C)
O  B  I  Q  H  Z  W  X
G  R  N  L  R (A) Y  H
Y  F  W  A  Z  H  N  S
B  Q  J (E) G  D  V (T)
```

jacket

COUNT THE TRAPEZOIDS (Week 29)

There are 24 trapezoids: AEQM, AFRM, AGSM, AHTM, BEQN, BFRN, BGSN, BHTN, CEKI, CEQO, CFLI, CFRO, CGSO, CHTO, DEKJ, DEQP, DFLJ, DFRP, DGSP, DHTP, IKQO, ILRO, JKQP, and JLRP.

ANAGRAM MAZE (Week 29)

1		3	4	5	6
7		9			12
13		15		17	18
19		21		23	
25		27		29	30
31	32	33			36

The path through the maze, with just one anagram given for each, is: 1. tend; 7. lied; 13. span; 19. gust; 25. riot; 31. gear; 32. bear; 33. cork; 27. serf; 21. atom; 15. pets; 9. bury; 3. mare; 4. bean; 5. foal; 6. bake; 12. earl; 18. dire; 17. abet; 23. neon; 29. cask; 30. take; 36. scar.

WHAT'S YOUR NUMBER? (Week 29)

19. The top number is the sum of the digits in the bottom number.

LICENSE PLATES (Week 29)

1. Terry Bradshaw; 2. Emmitt Smith; 3. Troy Aikman; 4. John Elway; 5. Jerry Rice; 6. Peyton Manning.

RELATIONSHIPS QUIZ (Week 29)

1. a; 2. d; 3. b; 4. a; 5. c.

MISSING LINKS (Week 30)

BULL'S-EYE LETTER (Week 30)

The Bull's-Eye Letter is R: dark, drug, pour, ruin, wren, peer.

THE LINEUP (Week 30)

1. H; 2. judgment; 3. A; 4. qualify; 5. three (axed, male, zone).

WORD WHEEL (Week 30)

par, part, partridge, art, rid, ridge, gel, gelid, elide, lid, deplane, plan, plane, planet, lane, net, nether, ether, the, there, thereafter, her, here, hereafter, aft, after, aftermath, term, mat, math.

WAYWORDS (Week 30)

Offer hope to those who are losing hope.

STACKED UP (Week 30)

Boxes 3, 4, and 6.

CIRCLE MATH (Week 30)

A = 1, B = 3, C = 7, D = 4, E = 9, F = 8, G = 5, H = 6, and I = 2.

CHANGELINGS (Week 30)

1. SOOT, sort, fort, fore, FIRE.
2. TOLL, tell, fell, feel, FEES.
3. LONG, lone, line, lime, LIMB.
(Using the same number of changes, other answers may be possible.)

SQUARE LINKS (Week 30)
peephole, anecdote, stickpin, downplay, enduring.

ANIMAL CHARADES (Week 30)
pelican

TARGET SHOOT (Week 30)
1. UM: alumni, thumbs, clumsy; 2. CI: facial, recipe, pacify.

MISSING DOMINOES (Week 30)

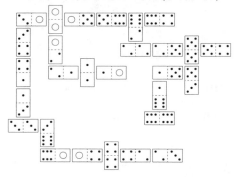

SLIDE RULE (Week 31)
air, are, ark, ask, asp, nap, nip, nor, tan, tap, tar, tie, tin, tip, toe, ton, top, urn, use, yak, yap, yin, yip, yon.

FILLING STATION (Week 31)
1. Philippines; 2. Charles Barkley; 3. Niagara Falls; 4. "The Phantom of the Opera"; 5. roller coaster.

SWITCHEROO (Week 31)
1. b; 2. d; 3. a; 4. b; 5. d; 6. c.

TRI, TRI AGAIN (Week 31)

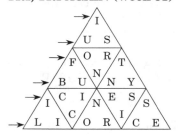

SUDOKU (Week 31)

8	7	6	3	5	2	1	9	4
5	1	9	8	4	6	7	2	3
2	4	3	7	9	1	6	5	8
1	8	5	2	3	7	9	4	6
4	9	7	6	1	5	3	8	2
6	3	2	9	8	4	5	1	7
3	2	8	1	6	9	4	7	5
9	6	4	5	7	8	2	3	1
7	5	1	4	2	3	8	6	9

WORD VISIBILITY (Week 31)
1. visor; 2. blush; 3. climb; 4. stern; 5. gloat; 6. drape.

ASSOCIATIONS (Week 31)
rat, squirrel, mouse; bound, jump, leap; flannel, linen, burlap; bravery, courage, valor; marigold, daisy, lilac; screwdriver, hammer, pliers; diamond, emerald, ruby; pecan, cashew, almond. A nervous wreck.

CROSS-UPS (Week 31)
1. marketplace; 2. moonshine.

RINGERS (Week 31)
1. girth, adorn, bugle, squat; 2. yield, farce, vowel, thorn.

CODED STATES (Week 31)
1. New York; 2. Maine; 3. Ohio; 4. Pennsylvania; 5. Wyoming; 6. Nevada; 7. Vermont; 8. South Dakota.

PRESIDENTIAL GOULASH (Week 31)
1. Reagan; 2. Pierce; 3. Taylor; 4. Monroe; 5. Hoover; 6. Arthur; 7. Wilson; 8. Truman; 9. Carter.

ALPHABET CIRCLE MAZE (Week 31)

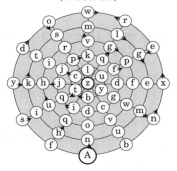

394

STAR WORDS (Week 32)

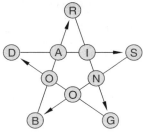

Your sequence of words may begin in any outer circle.

O COUNT (Week 32)
There are 31 O's.

GOING IN CIRCLES (Week 32)
1. horrible; 2. acquaint.

WHO'S WHO? (Week 32)
Lou, who doesn't smoke, is #2, #4, or #5. Since Dan's pants are the same shade as Lou's, Lou isn't #5, and Dan is either #6 or #1. Alf, who is speaking aloud, is #2 or #4. If Alf were #2, Charles would be #1, Bert would be #3, and Martin would be #6. However, this would leave no room for Lou and Dan. Alf, therefore, is #4 and the order of the men is as follows: #1 Martin, #2 Lou, #3 Charles, #4 Alf, #5 Bert, #6 Dan.

IN THE ABSTRACT (Week 32)

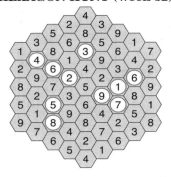

MARCHING ORDERS (Week 32)

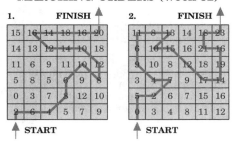

LETTER, PLEASE (Week 32)
Books that are shut are really no more than useless blocks.

HEXAGON HUNT (Week 32)

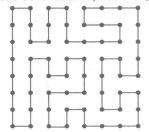

COUNT ON IT! (Week 32)
Many hands make light work.

ROUND TRIP (Week 32)

KEEP ON MOVING (Week 32)
Move 2 squares down, 3 squares left, 4 squares up, 4 squares right, and 1 square down to the asterisk.

CARD SENSE (Week 32)

The bottom card isn't the four of spades (clue 1), the ten of clubs (clue 2), or either diamond (clue 4), so it's the ace of spades. The top card isn't the four of spades (clue 1), the ten of clubs (clue 2), or the five of diamonds (clue 3); it's the six of diamonds. The second card from the top isn't the five of diamonds (clue 1) or the ten of clubs (clue 2), so it's the four of spades. By clue 3, then, the ten of clubs is third from the top and the five of diamonds is fourth from the top. In summary, from top to bottom: six of diamonds, four of spades, ten of clubs, five of diamonds, ace of spades.

ARROW MAZE (Week 32)

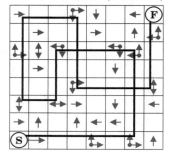

FILLING STATION (Week 32)

1. Mardi Gras; 2. Mississippi River; 3. Diane Sawyer; 4. Pippi Longstocking; 5. birthday cake.

ANAGRAM MAZE (Week 33)

1	2	3	4		6
7			10	11	12
13	14	15			
		21	22	23	
				29	
31	32	33	34	35	

The path through the maze, with just one anagram given for each, is: 6. cafe; 12. tied; 11. dose; 10. prod; 4. chum; 3. lyre; 2. keen; 1. silt; 7. fete; 13. raid; 14. hare; 15. pier; 21. nave; 22. fats; 23. spar; 29. pace; 35. went; 34. stun; 33. thaw; 32. came; 31. file.

ALL IN A ROW (Week 33)

Row B. Row A contains four groups: 931, 4531, 175, and 58. Row B contains five groups: 481, 13621, 634, 17212, and 94. Row C contains four groups: 526, 3424, 724, and 52312.

LOOSE TILE (Week 33)

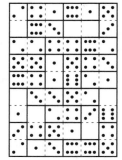

The 0-5 is the Loose Tile.

ALPHABET SOUP (Week 33)

tuna

QUOTATION MARKS (Week 33)

"The New Frontier of which I speak is not a set of promises — it is a set of challenges. It sums up not what I intend to offer the American people, but what I intend to ask of them."

WAYWORDS (Week 33)

Some stand and watch the parade and some others join in.

CIRCLE MATH (Week 33)

A = 6, B = 1, C = 7, D = 3, E = 2, F = 8, G = 4, H = 9, and I = 5.

ANTONYMS QUIZ (Week 33)

1. c; 2. a; 3. a; 4. b; 5. c; 6. b; 7. a; 8. c.

QUICK FILL (Week 33)

deployment

396

ELIMINATION (Week 33)

1. mad, is, on (Madison); 2. well (we'll), shell (she'll), wed (we'd), cant (can't); 3. questionaire (questionnaire), daquiri (daiquiri), bellweather (bellwether); 4. joyful, elated, thrilled; 5. blessing, in, disguise (blessing in disguise); 6. electrical, chemical, civil (electrical engineering, chemical engineering, civil engineering); 7. roles, shock, helm (Sherlock Holmes). If at first you do succeed, hide your surprise.

WORD HUNT (Week 33)

back, balk, bark, bask, beak, buck, bulk, bunk, cask, cook, cork, dusk, fork, junk, lack, lark, leak, luck, mask, mink, nick, pack, park, peak, peck, perk, pick, pink, pork, puck, punk, rack, risk, sack, sick, silk, sink, work.

COUNTDOWN (Week 33)

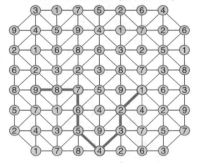

TRI, TRI AGAIN (Week 33)

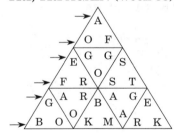

ANIMAL CHARADES (Week 34)
greyhound

COMPOUND IT (Week 34)

1. free; 2. way; 3. side; 4. show; 5. boat; 6. house; 7. mother; 8. land; 9. mark; 10. down (freeway, wayside, sideshow, showboat, boathouse, housemother, motherland, landmark, markdown).

GRAND TOUR (Week 34)

offer, feral, album, bumpy, pylon, loner, erred, redid, idled, ledge, genie, niece, cedar, darts, tsars, arson.

WHAT'S YOUR NUMBER? (Week 34)

17. The middle number equals the top number times the bottom number plus the left number times the right number.

SLIDE RULE (Week 34)

cane, clam, claw, clay, cloy, clue, cone, cram, craw, crow, glow, glue, glum, gone, gram, gray, grow, sane, slam, slaw, slay, sloe, slow, slue, slum, zany, zone, zoom.

CODE WORD (Week 34)

Code Word: demographics. Keeping up with the neighbors can be much harder on them — they always have to find ways to keep ahead.

THE LINEUP (Week 34)

1. H; 2. fragrant; 3. N; 4. receiving; 5. five (skip, rant, ante, mind, flew).

EASY PICKINGS (Week 34)
To take first place, take care.

SUDOKU (Week 34)

7	9	3	2	4	5	8	6	1
1	6	4	9	3	8	7	5	2
8	5	2	1	6	7	9	3	4
9	8	7	5	2	3	1	4	6
2	1	6	7	9	4	5	8	3
3	4	5	8	1	6	2	9	7
5	3	1	6	7	9	4	2	8
6	7	9	4	8	2	3	1	5
4	2	8	3	5	1	6	7	9

BULL'S-EYE LETTER (Week 34)

The Bull's-Eye Letter is W: flew, bawl, twin, week, chow, fawn.

CIRCLE SEARCH (Week 34)

ate, boat, boater, bond, bore, borer, eat, eater, feat, flat, flit, late, later, lit, pat, pate, pit, ref, refer.

OVERLAY (Week 34)

Diagram C.

MISSING DOMINOES (Week 34)

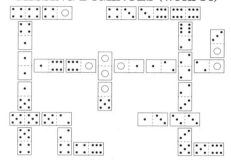

STACKED UP (Week 35)

Boxes 2, 3, and 6.

DEDUCTION PROBLEM (Week 35)

By clue 4, one husband is Sam O'Neill. His wife does not teach science (clue 3) or art (clue 5), so she is Stephanie and teaches history (clue 1). Since Mrs. Jackson teaches art (clue 5), she is not married to Tom (clue 3); she is married to Mike. By elimination, Tom is Peters. Tom teaches music (clue 2) and his wife teaches science (clue 3). By clue 6, Betty is Mrs. Jackson and Mike teaches math. By elimination, Sam teaches social studies and Tom is married to Kate. In summary: Mike (math) and Betty (art) Jackson; Sam (social studies) and Stephanie (history) O'Neill; Tom (music) and Kate (science) Peters.

ASSOCIATIONS (Week 35)

deer, moose, elk; scare, frighten, startle; drop, dive, plunge; waterless, dry, arid; magenta, scarlet, crimson; oregano, rosemary, tarragon; ton, pound, ounce; grapefruit, lemon, lime. To get to the other slide.

TARGET SHOOT (Week 35)

1. LO: saloon, unlock, felony; 2. DD: hidden, cuddly, bidder.

WORD CHARADE (Week 35)

L	G	S	P	B	V	F	N
K	L	C	U	O	E	R	A
Q	P	O	N	M	Ⓛ	K	J
Z	Q	L	G	D	T	Ⓟ	H
Ⓑ	R	F	V	S	H	N	Q
O	Z	Ⓒ	Ⓘ	E	L	M	G
P	K	A	O	J	Ⓤ	T	C
R	O	N	A	D	A	K	Ⓘ

public

SKILLS TEST (Week 35)

Figure 2, because it doesn't have a triangle.

WORD LINK (Week 35)

A	P	R	I	C	O	T		C	
J	O	Y		A			T	O	T
A	T	E		L			R	O	E
R			P	I	N	B	A	L	L
	C	A	P			N		E	
B	R	O	T	H	E	R	S		S
R	Y		X		A	R	C		
A	R	O	M	A	T	I	C		O
C	A	T		O		T	A	P	
E	M	E	R	A	L	D	S		E

ANAGRAM MAZE (Week 35)

		3	4	5	6
					12
13	14	15	16		18
19			22	23	24
25	26				
	32	33	34		

The path through the maze, with just one anagram given for each, is: 3. sing; 4. nest; 5. mope; 6. owls; 12. lacy; 18. scat; 24. blow; 23. ecru; 22. huts; 16. jest; 15. bush; 14. neat; 13. vets; 19. clam; 25. gape; 26. code; 32. grab; 33. feel; 34. skin.

GOING IN CIRCLES (Week 35)

1. pedestal; 2. smallest.

ARROW MAZE (Week 35)

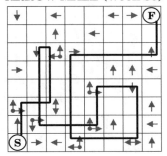

COUNT ON IT! (Week 35)

There's no such thing as a free lunch.

Y COUNT (Week 35)

There are 31 Y's.

SUDOKU (Week 35)

1	4	6	8	2	7	9	5	3
8	5	2	4	3	9	7	6	1
7	9	3	5	6	1	4	8	2
9	6	5	1	7	4	3	2	8
2	7	1	3	8	6	5	9	4
4	3	8	9	5	2	1	7	6
3	2	9	7	4	8	6	1	5
5	8	7	6	1	3	2	4	9
6	1	4	2	9	5	8	3	7

COUNTDOWN (Week 36)

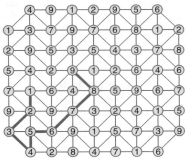

DOVETAILED WORDS (Week 36)

1. guide, follow; 2. penguin, walrus; 3. thriller, horror; 4. absorb, sponge; 5. hobby, pastime.

VISION QUEST (Week 36)

Column D.

WORD HUNT (Week 36)

alert, apart, avert, blurt, chart, court, exert, overt, quart, skirt, smart, spurt, start.

HEXAGON HUNT (Week 36)

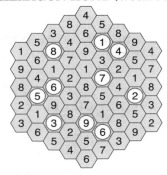

CODE WORD (Week 36)

Code Word: pathfinders. Parents should raise kids on these four F's: fondness, frankness, fairness, and firmness.

TIPS OF THE ICEBERG (Week 36)

1. Hank ($8.40); 2. Laura ($4.40); 3. Inez and Marty ($7.10).

GRAND TOUR (Week 36)

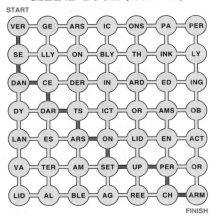

verse, sedan, dance, cedar, darts, tsars, arson, onset, setup, upper, perch, charm.

ALL IN A ROW (Week 36)

Row C. Row A contains three groups: 2214, 531, and 72. Row B contains four groups: 1152, 522, 261, and 711. Row C contains six groups: 4131, 18, 2232, 414, 45, and 513.

ANIMAL CHARADES (Week 36)
tortoise

STACKED UP (Week 36)
Boxes 2, 3, and 4.

EASY PICKINGS (Week 37)
Tom Hanks starred in the movie "Forrest Gump."

ALPHABET CIRCLE MAZE
(Week 37)

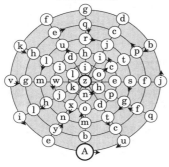

RINGERS (Week 37)
1. sandy, aorta, guide, witch; 2. preen, flaky, debit, rough.

QUICK FILL (Week 37)
subsequent

LICENSE PLATES (Week 37)
1. banana split; 2. oatmeal cookie; 3. chocolate brownie; 4. carrot cake; 5. apple tart; 6. rice pudding.

GOING IN CIRCLES (Week 37)
1. carnival; 2. billfold.

QUOTATION MARKS (Week 37)
To the ancients, the appearance of a swan, with its effortless glide on the mirror of a lake and lovely, unfurling flight, signaled evanescence and evoked immortal longings.

ANAGRAM MAZE (Week 37)

2	3	4	5	6
8				
	14	15	16	
			22	23
25	26	27		29
31		33	34	35

The path through the maze, with just one anagram given for each, is: 6. grin; 5. thaw; 4. peas; 3. snow; 2. blow; 8. rams; 14. vote; 15. bake; 16. ream; 22. kids; 23. coin; 29. neon; 35. fate; 34. stab; 33. ripe; 27. loin; 26. cusp; 25. feel; 31. note.

WHAT'S YOUR NUMBER?
(Week 37)
6. The sum of the upper left and lower right numbers minus the sum of the upper right and lower left numbers equals the center number.

CARD SENSE (Week 37)
By clue 1, the three of diamonds is immediately above the jack of clubs. The five of diamonds, then, is immediately above the three of diamonds (clue 2) and the six of spades is immediately below the jack of clubs (clue 3). By clue 4, the four of hearts is on the bottom of the pile. In summary, from top to bottom: five of diamonds, three of diamonds, jack of clubs, six of spades, four of hearts.

COMPOUND IT (Week 37)
1. horse; 2. power; 3. house; 4. hold; 5. out; 6. line; 7. up; 8. lift; 9. off; 10. shoot (horsepower, powerhouse, household, holdout, outline, lineup, uplift, liftoff, offshoot).

COUNT THE TRIANGLES
(Week 37)
There are 30 triangles: ABC, ABD, ABE, ABF, ACD, ACE, ACF, ADE, ADF, AEF, AGH, AGI, AGJ, AGK, AHI, AHJ, AHK, AIJ, AIK, AJK, ALM, ALN, ALO, ALP, AMN, AMO, AMP, ANO, ANP, and AOP.

THE LINEUP (Week 37)
1. D; 2. margarine; 3. U; 4. trouble; 5. three (just, zoom, quip).

CIRCLE SEARCH (Week 38)
ale, band, base, bask, bat, dial, disband, disk, peal, pep, seal.

ELIMINATION (Week 38)
1. Energy, Labor, Defense, Treasury; 2. crime, doesn't, pay (crime doesn't pay); 3. clan (clean), chat (cheat), crate (create); 4. everybody, standstill, pinpoint; 5. alley (Kirstie Alley), watts (Naomi Watts), weaver (Sigourney Weaver); 6. "True Grit," "Rain Man," "Paper Moon"; 7. problem. You are truly happy if you don't know why.

COUNT TO TEN (Week 38)
1. row 7; 2. row 4; 3. row 6.

SYMBOL-ISM (Week 38)
Here's something that costs more in the end than a good education — the absence of it.

BULL'S-EYE LETTER (Week 38)
The Bull's-Eye Letter is F: wife, calf, fact, gift, hoof, fish.

ASSOCIATIONS (Week 38)
simple, easy, effortless; conceal, hide, disguise; north, south, west; strict, severe, harsh; Dallas, Austin, Houston; jail, prison, brig; write, scribble, doodle; talk, say, utter. Answer: they tide.

SUDOKU (Week 38)

4	9	8	7	5	3	6	1	2
5	6	2	1	8	4	7	3	9
1	3	7	2	9	6	8	5	4
9	7	6	5	4	8	1	2	3
3	4	5	6	1	2	9	8	7
2	8	1	3	7	9	4	6	5
6	1	4	9	3	5	2	7	8
7	5	9	8	2	1	3	4	6
8	2	3	4	6	7	5	9	1

TRI, TRI AGAIN (Week 38)

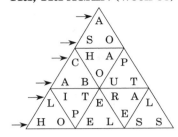

WORD CHARADE (Week 38)

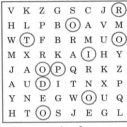

tripod

TARGET SHOOT (Week 38)
1. RV: survey, carved, marvel; 2. EE: sleeve, breezy, cheese.

SLIDE RULE (Week 38)
cab, can, caw, cay, cob, con, coo, cow, coy, cry, cub, fan, fib, fin, fob, fro, fry, fun, gab, gay, gin, gob, goo, gun, guy, man, maw, may, mob, moo, mow, tab, tan, tin, ton, too, tow, toy, try, tub.

CIRCLE MATH (Week 38)
A = 7, B = 8, C = 6, D = 9, E = 4, F = 1, G = 2, H = 3, and I = 5.

FILLING STATION (Week 38)
1. hyacinth; 2. pepperoni pizza; 3. "Bonnie and Clyde"; 4. Mongolia; 5. Alexander Graham Bell.

ORDERLY STATES (Week 38)
1. Ohio; 2. Illinois; 3. Wisconsin; 4. California; 5. Oregon; 6. Alabama; 7. Tennessee; 8. New Jersey.

IN THE ABSTRACT (Week 39)

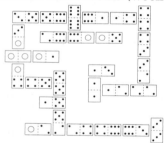

SWITCHEROO (Week 39)
1. b; 2. c; 3. d; 4. c; 5. a; 6. d.

WORD WHEEL (Week 39)
abs, absolve, absolvent, sol, solve, solvent, vent, entry, try, tryst, star, starch, tar, arc, arch, archway, way, wayward, war, ward, wardrobe, rob, robe, before, for, fore, ore.

CROSS-UPS (Week 39)
1. airstrip; 2. horsepower.

MISSING DOMINOES (Week 39)

MAGNIFIND (Week 39)

RELATIONSHIPS QUIZ (Week 39)
1. b; 2. c; 3. b; 4. c; 5. b.

WHIRLIGIG (Week 39)
1. allergy; 2. altered; 3. alumnus; 4. alfalfa; 5. almonds; 6. already; 7. alludes; 8. alarmed; 9. alcohol; 10. algebra; 11. almanac; 12. alleged.

FLOWER IN FLUX (Week 39)
Flower 4.

ALPHABET SOUP (Week 39)
seal, cow.

PRESIDENTIAL FINALES (Week 39)
1. Barack Obama; 2. Herbert Hoover; 3. Grover Cleveland; 4. Thomas Jefferson; 5. Calvin Coolidge; 6. Franklin Roosevelt; 7. James Monroe; 8. Bill Clinton; 9. Ronald Reagan; 10. Ulysses Grant; 11. Zachary Taylor; 12. Abraham Lincoln.

LETTER, PLEASE (Week 39)
"It is with books as with men: A very small number play a great part."

CARD SENSE (Week 39)
By clue 1, the seven of spades is immediately between the three of diamonds and the three of clubs, in some order. Since the king of hearts is immediately between the three of clubs and the four of clubs, in some order (clue 2), the three of clubs is third from the top. By clue 3, the four of clubs is on top, the king of hearts is second, the seven of spades is fourth, and the three of diamonds is fifth. In summary, from top to bottom: four of clubs, king of hearts, three of clubs, seven of spades, and three of diamonds.

ARROW MAZE (Week 40)

ANTONYMS QUIZ (Week 40)
1. b; 2. a; 3. a; 4. c; 5. c; 6. b; 7. a; 8. c.

MARCHING ORDERS (Week 40)

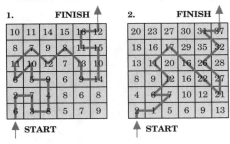

1. **FINISH** ... 2. **FINISH**

START ... **START**

STAR WORDS (Week 40)

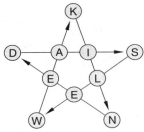

Your sequence of words may begin in any outer circle.

WAYWORDS (Week 40)
Friends raise your standard of living.

WORD EQUATIONS (Week 40)
1. gal + lop = gallop; 2. arm + or = armor; 3. con + serve = conserve; 4. mill + ion = million; 5. hone + sty = honesty.

ANAGRAM MAZE (Week 40)

1	2			
7			10	11	12
13	14		16		18
	20	21	22		24
				29	30
			35		

The path through the maze, with just one anagram given for each, is: 2. tarp; 1. pole; 7. fare; 13. bean; 14. boss; 20. sued; 21. hoes; 22. cask; 16. nets; 10. inch; 11. cola; 12. taco; 18. awry; 24. diet; 30. alms; 29. plié; 35. emit.

BLOCK PARTY (Week 40)

ONLINE NETWORK (Week 40)
combine, unite, incorporate; classify, categorize, group.

ELIMINATION (Week 40)
1. auras, tail (Australia); 2. pray and prey, beet and beat, grate and great; 3. mushrooms, pepperoni, sausage; 4. don't, cry, over, spilt, milk (don't cry over spilt milk); 5. strung (r, s, t, u), fight (f, g, h, i); 6. finger (Finland, Germany); 7. slander, lasso, salary, asleep. Honest criticism is worth more than flattery.

ALL IN A ROW (Week 40)
Row B. Row A contains five groups: 381, 42312, 714, 822, and 2253. Row B contains six groups: 21351, 822, 291, 6411, 57, and 4215. Row C contains five groups: 3153, 5232, 84, 723, and 237.

RING LOGIC (Week 40)

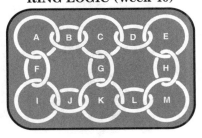

WORD WHEEL (Week 40)
boa, boar, oar, arc, arch, archer, cherub, her, rub, bat, bath, bathe, the, them, hem, emigrate, migrate, grate, rat, rate, ate, tea, tear, ear, earmuff, arm, muff, muffin, fin, final, finale, ale.

FUN WITH FACTS AND FIGURES (Week 41)
1. 7 x 8 = 56; 2. 56 + 24 = 80; 3. 80 − 32 = 48; 4. 48 ÷ 8 = 6; 5. 6 + 26 = 32.

SUDOKU (Week 41)

6	1	8	9	7	4	3	2	5
5	7	9	3	6	2	4	1	8
3	4	2	8	5	1	7	6	9
9	6	1	2	3	7	8	5	4
8	3	5	4	1	9	6	7	2
7	2	4	6	8	5	1	9	3
2	5	6	7	4	3	9	8	1
4	9	7	1	2	8	5	3	6
1	8	3	5	9	6	2	4	7

ALPHABET SOUP (Week 41)
tea, milk.

BOX STARS (Week 41)
Box 4.

HEXAGON HUNT (Week 41)

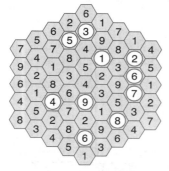

MAGNIFIND (Week 41)

ANIMAL CHARADES (Week 41)
crocodile

GOING IN CIRCLES (Week 41)
1. emotions; 2. knapsack.

KEEP ON MOVING (Week 41)
Move 2 squares right, 3 squares up, 4 squares left, 1 square down, and 3 squares right to the asterisk.

SQUARE LINKS (Week 41)
elephant, behavior, sabotage, feminine, equation.

MISSING LINKS (Week 41)

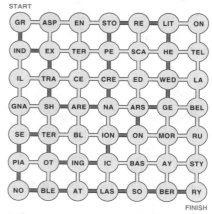

GRAND TOUR (Week 42)

grind, index, extra, trash, share, arena, nacre, crepe, pesto, store, relit, lithe, hewed, wedge, gears, arson, onion, ionic, icing, ingot, otter, terse, sepia, piano, noble, bleat, atlas, lasso, sober, berry.

COMPOUND IT (Week 42)
1. second; 2. hand; 3. book; 4. mark; 5. down; 6. town; 7. ship; 8. board; 9. room; 10. mate (secondhand, handbook, bookmark, markdown, downtown, township, shipboard, boardroom, roommate).

VISION QUEST (Week 42)
Row 4.

DEDUCTION PROBLEM (Week 42)

If Betty were right, she would be the doctor and Cindy would also be a doctor, so Betty isn't right and neither she nor Cindy became a doctor. Cindy's guess, then, is also wrong; Dora became the professor. By elimination, Alice became the doctor and, because her statement is true, Cindy became a politician. Betty, then, became a lawyer. In summary: Alice is the doctor; Betty is the lawyer; Cindy is the politician; Dora is the professor.

COUNTDOWN (Week 42)

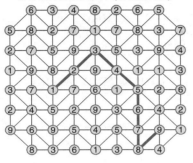

SEVEN WORD ZINGER (Week 42)

asp, keg, mud, oak, pay, win, zoo.

BULL'S-EYE LETTER (Week 42)

The Bull's-Eye Letter is S: sick, wisp, soap, pups, jabs, cash.

THE LINEUP (Week 42)

1. F; 2. clarity; 3. S; 4. labyrinth; 5. three (kiss, mute, exit).

STACKED UP (Week 42)

Boxes 1, 2, and 6.

WORD CHARADE (Week 42)

S	T	F	Ⓔ	S	N	H	T
A	Ⓖ	O	G	B	V	Ⓔ	I
C	Ⓔ	R	Ⓛ	N	R	V	U
Ⓔ	X	U	C	T	A	N	T
K	Q	S	Ⓔ	D	U	T	H
F	B	Ⓐ	K	Ⓔ	C	I	F
C	O	L	J	P	S	A	Ⓤ
L	R	Ⓔ	A	M	O	F	L

league

ASSOCIATIONS (Week 42)

promise, pledge, vow; ax, tomahawk, hatchet; own, possess, have; Ecuador, Peru, Colombia; price, worth, value; bandit, burglar, thief; prohibit, forbid, ban; dime, penny, quarter. Answer: traffic jam.

SLIDE RULE (Week 42)

gear, glad, goad, good, grad, gray, near, nope, nose, nosy, pear, play, plod, ploy, poor, pope, pose, pray, prod, read, rear, road, roar, rood, rope, ropy, rose, rosy.

IN THE ABSTRACT (Week 42)

CIRCLE MATH (Week 42)

A = 2, B = 4, C = 6, D = 3, E = 1, F = 9, G = 8, H = 5, and I = 7.

ORDERLY STATES (Week 43)

1. Pennsylvania; 2. North Dakota; 3. Alaska; 4. Virginia; 5. Kansas; 6. Connecticut; 7. Rhode Island; 8. Indiana.

FILLING STATION (Week 43)

1. Paul McCartney; 2. French Revolution; 3. George Orwell; 4. carrier pigeon; 5. "Charlotte's Web."

WHAT'S YOUR NUMBER? (Week 43)

16. The first number multiplied by the second number equals the third number multiplied by the fourth number.

405

QUICK FILL (Week 43)
indelicate

WORD HUNT (Week 43)
made, maid, mail, maim, main, male, malt, mama, mare, mart, meal, meat, meld, melt, memo, mere, mesh, mete, mild, mile, milk, mime, mind, mink, mint, mire, moan, moat, mode, mold, mole, molt, monk, mote, much, muck, muse, mush, must.

OVERLAY (Week 43)
Diagram A

BLOCK PARTY (Week 43)

DEDUCTION PROBLEM (Week 43)
All the time the old woman will stay with each child — one, two, or three months — will take place in one visit of consecutive months. She'll spend June, July, and August with her daughter Maria and four consecutive months will be spent with sons Roger and Jay in some order (three with one and then one with the other). Since the one month visit isn't in May, those four months aren't February through May, and since she'll be at Flo's in November, those four months aren't September through December either. By elimination, the four months with Roger and Jay are January through April. She isn't at Jay's in March, so she's with Roger January through March, and with Jay in April. The son she'll see in September when she leaves Maria's, then, is Joe, with whom she'll spend two months, from September through October. This leaves May and December, so the daughter with whom she'll spend two months is Flo, for November and December. By elimination, she'll spend May with Karen. In summary: January through March with Roger; April with Jay; May with Karen; June through August with Maria; September and October with Joe; November and December with Flo.

MISSING DOMINOES (Week 43)

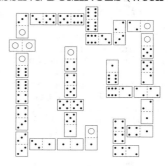

EASY PICKINGS (Week 43)
Looking good is less important than looking friendly.

ROUND TRIP (Week 43)

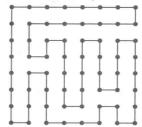

COUNT ON IT! (Week 43)
The best things in life are free.

WORD VISIBILITY (Week 43)
1. joker; 2. glaze; 3. chart; 4. brisk; 5. enemy; 6. meter; 7. twist; 8. drill.

CARD SENSE (Week 44)
By clue 2, the bottom card is red. It isn't the ace of hearts (clue 4), so it is the three of diamonds. The top card isn't the ace of hearts (clue 1), six of clubs (clue 3), or jack of spades (clue 4); it is the ace of spades. Since the six of clubs is somewhere above the ace of hearts (clue 1) and the ace of hearts is somewhere above the jack of spades (clue 4), the six of clubs is second from the top, the ace of hearts is third, and the jack of spades is fourth. In summary, from top to bottom: ace of spades, six of clubs, ace of hearts, jack of spades, and three of diamonds.

WAYWORDS (Week 44)
Experience is learning what not to do.

WORD LINK (Week 44)

P	R	O	T	E	C	T	I	O	N
L	O	B	E			E		C	
E	D	I	C	T		N		T	
N			H	A	M	S	T	E	R
T	R	E	N	D		E	A	T	
Y			I		O		B		M
	C		C	A	M	E	L		E
S	O	D	A		E		E	A	R
A	P	O	L	O	G	E	T	I	C
T	E	E		A		S	L	Y	

CODE WORD (Week 44)
Code Word: subordinately. All that the American West once was, Alaska still is. Abounding with natural marvels and largely untouched by human ambition, it strikes the newcomer as a land of endless prospect.

TRI, TRI AGAIN (Week 44)

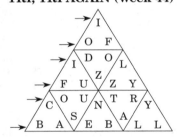

LOOSE TILE (Week 44)

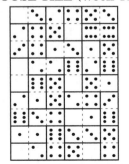

The 1-4 is the Loose Tile.

CIRCLE SEARCH (Week 44)
all, allow, fin, fish, fit, low, now, opt, owl, own, shall, shallow, shop, snow, stop, top.

ANAGRAM MAZE (Week 44)

		3	4	5	6
					12
13	14	15	16		18
19			22	23	24
25	26				
	32	33	34		

The path through the maze, with just one anagram given for each, is: 3. teak; 4. best; 5. prod; 6. deaf; 12. rife; 18. meat; 24. acme; 23. soil; 22. veer; 16. last; 15. pets; 14. gape; 13. ecru; 19. cone; 25. glue; 26. jest; 32. idle; 33. goat; 34. acre.

ALL IN A ROW (Week 44)
Row A. Row A contains six groups: 454, 4216, 913, 1363, 373, and 85. Row B contains four groups: 49, 715, 652, and 2713. Row C contains three groups: 3514, 42214, and 2443.

SUDOKU (Week 44)

5	8	4	9	7	2	3	6	1
7	1	6	3	5	4	9	8	2
9	2	3	8	6	1	5	4	7
4	5	1	6	2	7	8	3	9
8	6	2	5	9	3	7	1	4
3	7	9	1	4	8	6	2	5
6	3	7	4	1	5	2	9	8
1	9	5	2	8	6	4	7	3
2	4	8	7	3	9	1	5	6

TARGET SHOOT (Week 44)
1. WI: mowing, unwise, rewind; 2. YO: joyous, anyone, coyote.

SUDOKU (Week 44)

5	4	6	3	2	7	1	8	9
2	7	3	1	9	8	4	5	6
9	8	1	6	4	5	2	7	3
7	6	9	5	1	2	8	3	4
4	2	8	9	3	6	7	1	5
1	3	5	7	8	4	6	9	2
6	1	7	4	5	9	3	2	8
8	9	4	2	7	3	5	6	1
3	5	2	8	6	1	9	4	7

L COUNT (Week 44)

There are 43 L's in the sentence.

HEXAGON HUNT (Week 45)

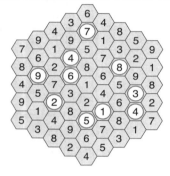

GOING IN CIRCLES (Week 45)

1. swimming; 2. zucchini.

ELIMINATION (Week 45)

1. garden, gradual, ragamuffin, argument; 2. edifice, debacle, iambic, died, call; 3. charity, begins, at, home (charity begins at home); 4. seen (seven), noel (novel); 5. Oliver, twist, little, women ("Oliver Twist" and "Little Women"); 6. broken, plant, guest; 7. sauerkraut, lager, pretzel, schnapps. "Slang is language in its play clothes."

ALL IN A ROW (Week 45)

Row B. Row A contains five groups: 551, 164, 3332, 29, and 812. Row B contains six groups: 74, 821, 56, 641, 173, and 38. Row C contains three groups: 236, 3611, and 6212.

ONLINE NETWORK (Week 45)

canasta, bridge, pinochle; astonish, amaze, surprise.

CODE WORD (Week 45)

Code Word: grandiosely. Our galaxy is far larger, brighter, and more massive than most other galaxies. The Milky Way's starry disk spans one hundred twenty thousand light-years.

ASSOCIATIONS (Week 45)

Tuesday, Wednesday, Thursday; steal, rob, pilfer; stout, plump, fat; avoid, shun, evade; desire, wish, want; Perth, Sydney, Canberra; cry, bawl, sob; pursue, chase, hunt. "I'm feline fine!"

COUNT TO TEN (Week 45)

1. row 7; 2. row 4; 3. row 8.

COUNT THE RECTANGLES (Week 45)

There are 32 rectangles: ABHG, ACIG, ACML, ACQP, ACSR, ADKG, ADOL, ADTR, BCIH, BDKH, CDFE, CDKI, CDOM, CDTS, EFKI, EFOM, EFTS, GIML, GIQP, GISR, GJNL, GKOL, GKTR, IJNM, IKOM, IKTS, JKON, LMQP, LMSR, LOTR, MOTS, and PQSR.

IN THE ABSTRACT (Week 45)

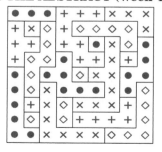

THE LINEUP (Week 45)

1. F; 2. liniment; 3. E; 4. croquet; 5. gaze, book, jump.

ARROW MAZE (Week 45)

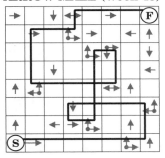

ANIMAL CHARADES (Week 45)
octopus.

ANAGRAM MAZE (Week 46)

	2	3	4	5	6
8					
	14	15	16		
			22	23	24
25	26	27			30
31		33	34	35	36

The path through the maze, with just one anagram given for each, is: 6. lame; 5. cars; 4. owns; 3. does; 2. news; 8. newt; 14. knee; 15. nuts; 16. coal; 22. diet; 23. fast; 24. vane; 30. raps; 36. cape; 35. ripe; 34. arid; 33. rely; 27. much; 26. mace; 25. what; 31. emit.

EASY PICKINGS (Week 46)
The four seasons of the year are spring, summer, autumn, and winter.

MAGNIFIND (Week 46)

CARD SENSE (Week 46)
The seven of spades is directly above the nine of hearts (clue 1). By clue 2, since the spades are adjacent, the ace of spades is directly above the seven of spades. The queen of diamonds is somewhere below the ace of spades (clue 3), but not directly below the nine of hearts (clue 4). The jack of clubs, then, is directly below the nine of hearts and the queen of diamonds is on the bottom. In summary, from top to bottom: ace of spades, seven of spades, nine of hearts, jack of clubs, queen of diamonds.

SEVEN WORD ZINGER (Week 46)
arc, due, emu, hat, mow, wee, win.

FUN WITH FACTS AND FIGURES (Week 46)
1. 60 x 3 (January, June, July) = 180; 2. 180 ÷ 12 = 15; 3. 15 + 13 (Massachusetts) = 28; 4. 28 − 20 = 8; 5. 8 + 4 (for) = 12.

GRAND TOUR (Week 46)

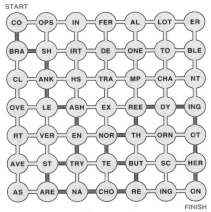

cobra, brash, shank, ankle, leash, ashen, entry, tryst, stare, arena, nacho, chore, rebut, butte, tenor, north, three, reedy, dying, ingot, other, heron.

COMPOUND IT (Week 46)
1. wheel; 2. chair; 3. lift; 4. off; 5. shore; 6. bird; 7. brain; 8. child; 9. proof; 10. read. (wheelchair, chairlift, liftoff, offshore, shorebird, birdbrain, brainchild, childproof, proofread).

FILLING STATION (Week 46)
1. armadillo; 2. "Criminal Minds"; 3. Sacramento; 4. Bette Midler; 5. chocolate chip cookie.

TARGET SHOOT (Week 46)
1. RR: barrel, carrot, mirror; 2. EA: bleach, creamy, grease.

COUNTDOWN (Week 46)

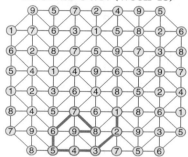

COUNT ON IT! (Week 46)
There wasn't a dry eye in the house.

LICENSE PLATES (Week 47)
1. table tennis; 2. field hockey; 3. figure skating; 4. water polo; 5. synchronized swimming; 6. downhill skiing.

SUDOKU (Week 47)

4	8	1	3	9	5	2	6	7
6	5	7	4	2	8	1	9	3
2	3	9	6	7	1	8	4	5
9	2	4	5	8	6	7	3	1
5	6	3	1	4	7	9	8	2
1	7	8	2	3	9	6	5	4
3	4	6	8	1	2	5	7	9
7	1	5	9	6	3	4	2	8
8	9	2	7	5	4	3	1	6

MISSING DOMINOES (Week 47)

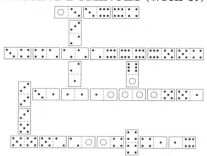

ALPHABET SOUP (Week 47)
lady, bug (ladybug).

BLOCK PARTY (Week 47)

MARCHING ORDERS (Week 47)

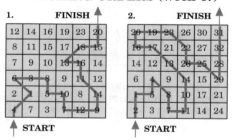

CHANGELINGS (Week 47)
1. RIPE, rope, cope, core, CORN.
2. PINK, pins, pans, cans, CARS.
3. FIND, mind, mine, mane, MATE.
(Using the same number of changes, other answers may be possible for each Changeling.)

VISION QUEST (Week 47)
Row 4.

SYMBOL-ISM (Week 47)
For both the emperor and the pauper, the rules should be the same.

RELATIONSHIPS QUIZ (Week 47)
1. c; 2. c; 3. a; 4. d; 5. a.

SQUARE LINKS (Week 47)
activate, chewable, glossary, notation, listener.

WORD VISIBILITY (Week 47)

1. knead; 2. audio; 3. lithe; 4. bylaw; 5. manor; 6. brace.

OVERLAY (Week 47)

Diagram B.

ANTONYMS QUIZ (Week 48)

1. a; 2. b; 3. b; 4. c; 5. c; 6. a; 7. b; 8. a.

QUICK FILL (Week 48)

microphone.

ORDERLY STATES (Week 48)

1. Arizona; 2. Oklahoma; 3. Washington; 4. New Mexico; 5. Montana; 6. Louisiana; 7. Georgia; 8. South Dakota.

CROSS EXAMINATION (Week 48)

1. language; 2. sightseeing; 3. destitution; 4. metabolism; 5. tenacious; 6. vegetable; 7. whippoorwill; 8. handkerchief.

LOOSE TILE (Week 48)

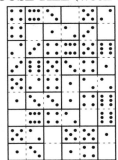

The 5-6 is the Loose Tile.

WAYWORDS (Week 48)

Few things are harder to put up with than a good example.

KEEP ON MOVING (Week 48)

Move one square right, three squares up, three squares right, two squares down, one square right, and two squares up to the asterisk.

DOVETAILED WORDS (Week 48)

1. baby, child; 2. dairy, cattle; 3. panda, bamboo; 4. courage, nerve; 5. decal, sticker.

TIPS OF THE ICEBERG (Week 48)

1. Noel ($11.50); 2. Hank ($5.20); 3. Jack and Ken ($9.90).

CIRCLE SEARCH (Week 48)

bee, bran, brie, brow, brown, brownie, nip, now, own, pan, pie, pin, pip, tee, ten.

WORD CHARADE (Week 48)

A	V	H	K	A	M	X	U
J	Z	R	G	T	W	Z	C
(T)	O	C	(I)	R	P	A	O
W	P	A	E	(I)	M	O	H
N	X	K	P	J	A	V	(I)
J	(R)	(U)	Z	(N)	X	W	N
N	W	S	V	U	G	H	L
(P)	H	R	N	Z	E	P	O

turnip.

MISSING LINKS (Week 48)

F	R	A	N	T	I	C		F			C	L	I	M	B
O		O		L		F	I	N	I	S	H		A		R
R	E	A	R		O			S		A		R	A	D	I	O
T		T		O		D	I	S	T	I	N	C	T		M
U		H		B				N		E		E			E
A	L	U	M	I	N	U	M		R	E	A	C	T		E
T		I		R			F								R
E		N		R		P	R	O	P	E	L	L	E	R	
			C	O	U	N	T		E				E		
							R		R				A		
P		S		S	U	N	S	H	I	N	E		P		
A	C	T	O	R		T		I				Q	U	I	L	T
I		A		R		R		S				I			W
N		D		C	A	F	E	T	E	R	I	A	G		E
T	H	I	N			N		E				T			N
E		U			G			N			O	R	B	I	T
R	O	M	A	N	C	E		T	E	N	O	R			Y

WORD WHEEL (Week 49)

mess, message, ess, sag, sage, age, gem, map, phone, hone, honey, one, eye, yea, year, ear, arrange, ran, rang, range, angel, gel, eleven, eve, even, event, vent, entry, try, rye.

TRI, TRI AGAIN (Week 49)

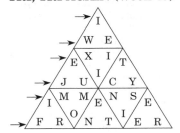

LOOSE TILE (Week 49)

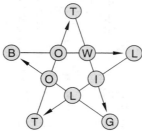

The 0-3 is the Loose Tile.

COUNT ON IT! (Week 49)
A bad penny always shows up.

CIRCLE MATH (Week 49)
A = 6, B = 5, C = 1, D = 2, E = 9, F = 4, G = 3, H = 8, and I = 7.

RINGERS (Week 49)
1. misty, gavel, beech, proud; 2. cruet, fable, livid, polar.

WAYWORDS (Week 49)
The difference between fiction and reality is that the former has to make sense.

CARD SENSE (Week 49)
The card on the bottom isn't a heart or the diamond (clue 3) or the club (clue 4), so it's the two of spades. The fourth card from the top isn't the ten of diamonds (clue 1) or the five of clubs (clue 4); it's either the five of hearts or the ten of hearts. By clue 4, then, the third card from the top is the five of clubs and the second card from the top is either the five of hearts or the ten of hearts. By elimination, the top card is the ten of diamonds. Since the second card from the top isn't the ten of hearts (clue 2), it's the five of hearts. By elimination, the ten of hearts is fourth from the top. In summary, from top to bottom: ten of diamonds, five of hearts, five of clubs, ten of hearts, two of spades.

GRAND TOUR (Week 49)

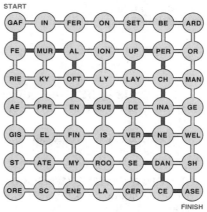

gaffe, femur, mural, aloft, often, ensue, suede, delay, layup, upper, perch, china, inane, never, verse, sedan, dance, cease.

ALL IN A ROW (Week 49)
Row A. Row A contains six groups: 75, 192, 2352, 2811, 1146, and 5241. Row B contains three groups: 3261, 4242, and 3711. Row C contains five groups: 24132, 39, 13611, 1155, and 552.

STAR WORDS (Week 49)

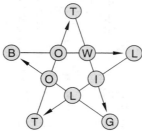

Your sequence of words may begin in any outer circle.

HEXAGON HUNT (Week 49)

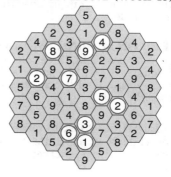

ROUND TRIP (Week 49)

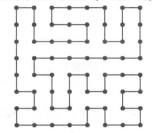

TRI, TRI AGAIN (Week 49)

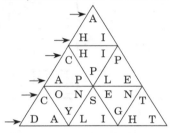

QUOTATION MARKS (Week 50)

Although an estimated four thousand fans saw them off from Heathrow Airport, they were still nervous about their reception in the United States. Two days later, however, about seventy-three million people watched The Beatles on "The Ed Sullivan Show."

STACKED UP (Week 50)
Boxes 1, 2, and 5.

ASSOCIATIONS (Week 50)

clam, oyster, mussel; provide, supply, furnish; sparse, meager, scarce; deer, elk, moose; emphasize, stress, accent; harm, hurt, injure; clean, wash, launder; crimson, scarlet, red. The bridle suite.

SUDOKU (Week 50)

3	8	6	7	5	9	4	2	1
7	4	9	2	1	8	5	3	6
1	5	2	3	6	4	7	9	8
9	6	8	5	7	3	2	1	4
5	2	3	4	9	1	6	8	7
4	1	7	6	8	2	3	5	9
2	9	4	1	3	6	8	7	5
6	7	1	8	2	5	9	4	3
8	3	5	9	4	7	1	6	2

SLIDE RULE (Week 50)
bad, bam, ban, bed, bib, bid, bin, bob, bow, bud, bum, bun, had, ham, hem, hen, hew, hid, him, how, hub, hum, lab, lad, law, led, lid, lob, low, nab, new, nib, nod, now, nub, nun, wad, wan, web, wed, win, won, wow.

IN THE ABSTRACT (Week 50)

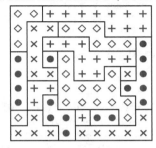

NEXT TO NOTHING (Week 50)
brewing.

MAGIC NUMBER SQUARES (Week 50)

1.

37	9	11	31
15	27	25	21
23	19	17	29
13	33	35	7

2.

47	5	8	38
14	32	29	23
26	20	17	35
11	41	44	2

DEDUCTION PROBLEM (Week 50)
Only one person made a truthful statement. Al said the day in question was Tuesday. Bill said that the day was Friday, Saturday, Sunday, Monday, Tuesday, or Wednesday. Cora said the day was Sunday. Dan said the day was Monday, Tuesday, Wednesday, Thursday, or Friday. Ed said the day was either Saturday or Sunday. If the day were Sunday, then Bill, Cora, and Ed would have been correct, so the day was not Sunday. If the day were Monday, Wednesday, or Friday, then Bill and Dan would have been correct, so the day was not any of those. If the day were Tuesday, then Al, Bill, and Dan would have been correct, so the day was not Tuesday. If the day were Saturday, then Bill and Ed would have been correct, so the day was not Saturday. The day, then, was Thursday and Dan made the only true statement.

413

TARGET SHOOT (Week 50)

1. IM: climax, grimly, animal; 2. UG: cougar, frugal, bought.

CODE WORD (Week 50)

Code Word: housewarming. At a place where the year is split between whole days of light and dark and where the world's twenty-four time zones converge, time itself is another unusual phenomenon of the South Pole.

ELIMINATION (Week 50)

1. tunic, sweater, jodhpurs, petticoat; 2. Superior, Erie, Ontario, Huron, Michigan; 3. rural, molar, aroma, aloof; 4. bistro, raptor, transport, carrot; 5. beauty, is, only, skin, deep (beauty is only skin deep); 6. reminisence (reminiscence), quarentine (quarantine), pilgrimmage (pilgrimage), murmer (murmur); 7. rein (resin), bail (basil), pate (paste); 8. French, ginger, daily, spoon. Speak the truth then leave immediately.

BLOCK PARTY (Week 50)

FUN WITH FACTS AND FIGURES (Week 51)

1. 7 − 3 = 4; 2. 4 x 300 = 1,200; 3. 1,200 ÷ 100 = 12; 4. 12 + 5 = 17; 5. 17 − 1 = 16.

WORD VISBILITY (Week 51)

1. pouch; 2. mango; 3. issue; 4. floor; 5. drama; 6. focus.

WHAT'S YOUR NUMBER? (Week 51)

11. The sum of the top numbers divided by the center number equals the bottom number.

FILLING STATION (Week 51)

1. paperback book; 2. "Pirates of the Caribbean"; 3. Netherlands; 4. flower vase; 5. Wisconsin.

CROSS-UPS (Week 51)

1. seesaw; 2. stopwatch; 3. snapdragon.

ARROW MAZE (Week 51)

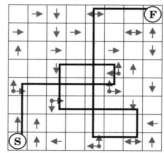

COMPOUND IT (Week 51)

1. rain; 2. coat; 3. tail; 4. bone; 5. head; 6. strong; 7. hold; 8. over; 9. lord; 10. ship. (raincoat, coattail, tailbone, bonehead, headstrong, stronghold, holdover, overlord, lordship).

WORD HUNT (Week 51)

grace, grade, grain, grand, grant, grape, grate, greed, green, grief, grime, grind, gripe, group, growl, grown.

ORDERLY STATES (Week 51)

1. Massachusetts; 2. Michigan; 3. Nebraska; 4. South Carolina; 5. West Virginia; 6. Delaware; 7. Colorado; 8. Arkansas.

COUNTDOWN (Week 51)

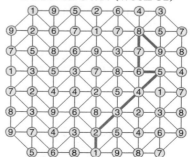

LETTER, PLEASE (Week 51)

"Everything is possible for him who believes." Mark 9:23

GOING IN CIRCLES (Week 51)

1. potatoes; 2. junkyard.

VISION QUEST (Week 52)

Column C.

WORD WHEEL (Week 52)

wit, with, wither, the, her, hero, heroic, icon, con, conform, for, form, formal, formally, mall, all, ally, lye, yea, year, ear, earth, art, that, hat, hatband, ban, band, bandit, and.

ANAGRAM MAZE (Week 52)

		3	4	5	
7	8	9			
13			16	17	18
19	20	21	22		24
					30
	32	33	34	35	36

The path through the maze, with just one anagram given for each, is: 5. skin; 4. drab; 3. cork; 9. nail; 8. fuel; 7. barn; 13. bowl; 19. file; 20. ages; 21. vats; 22. shoe; 16. wand; 17. salt; 18. beat; 24. lift; 30. idle; 36. goat; 35. slap; 34. seam; 33. room; 32. sire.

SKILLS TEST (Week 52)

internally, legislate, potato, subtraction, weather.

WORD CHARADE (Week 52)

A	U	L	X	P	K	(E)	A
Z	J	C	O	B	S	D	O
M	Q	I	Y	J	N	F	W
(G)	K	(G)	B	(G)	V	(G)	H
F	H	J	W	H	X	L	P
R	D	(N)	S	Z	(M)	U	M
I	D	F	B	C	V	I	J
Y	K	A	V	N	C	R	Q

magnet.

ALL IN A ROW (Week 52)

Row B. Row A contains five groups: 392, 7232, 4126, 2615, and 6152. Row B contains six groups: 545, 1427, 73121, 2165, 59, and 275. Row C contains four groups: 3236, 491, 8123, and 761.

MISSING DOMINOES (Week 52)

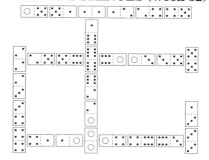

DOVETAILED WORDS (Week 52)

1. yacht, sail; 2. delete, erase; 3. flame, blaze; 4. jacket, garment; 5. knife, blade.

ANIMAL CHARADES (Week 52)

polar bear.

ROUND TRIP (Week 52)

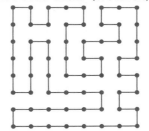

SEVEN WORD ZINGER (Week 52)

ink, lox, may, nun, oat, pea, two.

ALPHABET SOUP (Week 52)

drag, net (dragnet).

CIRCLE MATH (Week 52)

A = 5, B = 7, C = 1, D = 3, E = 8, F = 4, G = 6, H = 9, and I = 2.

415